TECHNICAL OPTICS

VOL. I

Published by

CAMERA LENSES
By A. W. LOCKETT
Revised by H. W. LEE. **5s.** net.

LENS WORK FOR
AMATEURS
By H. ORFORD
Revised by A. W. LOCKETT. **6s.** net.

TELEVISION OPTICS
An Introduction
By L. M. MYERS. **30s.** net.

PHOTOGRAPHIC OPTICS
By ARTHUR COX, B.A., B.Sc. **15s.** net.

INDUSTRIAL MICROSCOPY
By WALTER GARNER, M.Sc. **21s.** net.

MEDICAL PHOTOGRAPHY
Radiographic and Clinical
By T. A. LONGMORE, A.R.P.S. **25s.** net.

PITMAN

535 : 535·8

401'

us/e

TECHNICAL OPTICS

A REVISED AND ENLARGED EDITION OF
"AN INTRODUCTION TO APPLIED OPTICS"

BY

L. C. MARTIN
D.Sc., A.R.C.S., D.I.C.

*Professor of Technical Optics, Imperial College of Science
and Technology, London*

VOLUME I

LONDON
SIR ISAAC PITMAN & SONS, LTD.
1948

First published 1948

SIR ISAAC PITMAN & SONS, Ltd.
PITMAN HOUSE, PARKER STREET, KINGSWAY, LONDON, W.C.2
THE PITMAN PRESS, BATH
PITMAN HOUSE, LITTLE COLLINS STREET, MELBOURNE
27 BECKETTS BUILDINGS, PRESIDENT STREET, JOHANNESBURG

ASSOCIATED COMPANIES
PITMAN PUBLISHING CORPORATION
2 WEST 45TH STREET, NEW YORK
205 WEST MONROE STREET, CHICAGO

SIR ISAAC PITMAN & SONS (CANADA), Ltd.
(INCORPORATING THE COMMERCIAL TEXT BOOK COMPANY)
PITMAN HOUSE, 381–383 CHURCH STREET, TORONTO

BOOK
PRODUCTION
WAR ECONOMY
STANDARD

MADE IN GREAT BRITAIN AT THE PITMAN PRESS, BATH
D8—(T.5494/5)

PREFACE

THE Author's *Introduction to Applied Optics* was out of print during the war, and the opportunity has been taken to prepare a revised and enlarged edition under the shorter title *Technical Optics*, which will be less liable to confusion with several other books on "Applied Optics."

The prefaces to the earlier volumes contained acknowledgments of the kind help of friends and industrial firms, and similar kindness has been shown from many quarters in connection with the new edition. I must now add my thanks to Dr. M. Blackman and other colleagues for discussions and constructive criticism; to Mr. E. F. Fincham for the loan of blocks of his excellent photomicrographs of the retina; to Mr. J. G. Holmes and other members of the staff of Messrs. Chance Bros., Ltd., for information and helpful suggestions; likewise to Dr. H. J. Starkie of Messrs. Imperial Chemical Industries, Ltd. (Plastics Division). Messrs. Ross, Ltd. have supplied particulars of their own measurements of refractive indices of certain special materials, and other information. Numerous other friends have placed me in their debt for information and help.

The book represents, in its projected two volumes, the topics of a lecture course in Technical Optics given to post-graduate students at the Imperial College. This is complementary to the specific instruction in Optical Designing.

This first volume deals with general matters, including a short introduction to the theory of spectacles. The second volume will deal mainly with specific instruments, but I hope to include a chapter on "Aspheric Surfaces."

My aim has been to awaken a living interest in the scientific aspects of the subject rather than special elegance or completeness. If, in this attempt, the treatment is found lacking in detail, the reader will find at least that suitable sources of further information are indicated.

L. C. MARTIN

IMPERIAL COLLEGE OF SCIENCE
   AND TECHNOLOGY

CONTENTS

TECHNICAL OPTICS

CHAPTER I

ELEMENTARY THEORY

The Rectilinear Propagation of Light. "Optics" was the Greek science of *vision*; the word is given a wider meaning to-day, since it includes the study of optical instruments, or the means whereby vision is aided or supplemented. The most superficial observation indicates the eye as the organ of vision, but many philosophers, from Epicurus (342–270 B.C.) to Damianus (sixth century), conceived that the eye emanates something which affects the objects thus rendered visible. This view had appeared inadequate to Plato (427–347 B.C.) and his followers, who recognized that the presence of a self-luminous body plays a great part in the visual process, and who argued therefore that rays from a source of light like the sun unite with rays from the eye to meet rays emanating from the object seen.

Plato's sometime pupil, Aristotle (384–322 B.C.), who had a greater regard for the observation of phenomena than many of his predecessors or successors, doubted the emission of rays from the eye as a factor in vision. In considering the relation between the object and the eye, he argued that the activity of some intervening medium, which he termed the *pellucid*, was necessary; a theory of the greatest interest which was not, however, developed till two thousand years afterwards, and was generally not accepted by the contemporary Platonists. These latter, following the Pythagoreans, considered the "radiations" to consist of a stream of particles moving in straight lines, a natural way of explaining the early observed fact of the "rectilinear propagation of light."

The sizes and shapes of shadows, the familiar sight of a "shaft of sunlight" descending from a distant gap in the clouds, are a sufficient guide to the establishment of this very fundamental idea, that light in such a medium as air travels in straight lines. Damianus asserted that "light" moves in straight lines which are the tracks of "rays."

Euclid (300 B.C.) spoke of the emanation of rays of light radiating out in straight lines from the eye as centre; it is not clear whether we are to regard this as consenting to the theory of emission from the eye, but in any case Euclid really laid the first foundations of "perspective" with the idea of the "centre of perspective" from which the actual directions of objects in space are determined by the directions in which they are seen from this centre. The apparent size of an object may be estimated partly by the rotation of the eye in passing from one extreme of the object to the other, partly by the apparent size of the retinal image. Thus, in any case the estimate depends upon the angular subtense of the object at the eye.

Perspective. Leonardo da Vinci (A.D. 1452–1519) first actually formulated the rule of perspective, indicating that a true picture of an object could be made by holding a transparent plate between object and eye, and marking on the plate the projection of the object (Fig. 1A). Supreme artist and scientist, Leonardo wrote

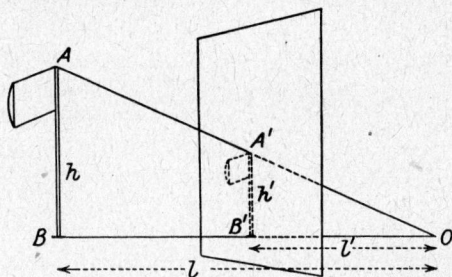

FIG. 1A

down only a part of his scientific discoveries, but it is practically certain that he knew of the principle of the "camera obscura" described a few years later (1558) by Giambattista della Porta in his *Magia naturalis*.

In the demonstration of the "camera," a room is provided with a dark shutter for the window, which is pierced by a small hole. On the white wall opposite the opening, an inverted image of exterior objects now appears in its natural colours. If a white screen is moved between the aperture and the wall (keeping it parallel to the wall) it will receive an image of an exterior object, the size of the image being proportional to the distance of the screen from the hole. In a later section the "definition" or sharpness of detail in the image will receive consideration.

There are a few simple geometrical ideas of some importance in applied optics which arise directly owing to the effects of our experience in connection with the rectilinear propagation of light and the accompanying laws of perspective. In Fig. 1A, h and h' are the vertical dimensions of the object AB and the projection A'B'; imagine this projection drawn on glass.

When AB and A′B′ are both perpendicular to the line BB′O, a natural measure of the visual angle under which the object appears from the perspective centre is the tangent of the angle, i.e. $\dfrac{h}{l}$; clearly the projection as actually drawn on the glass subtends the same angle when held as shown in the figure, so that

$$\frac{h'}{l'} = \frac{h}{l}$$

but the picture when drawn can be made to subtend a greater or less angle at the perspective centre by varying the distance or inclination of the plate relatively to the eye.

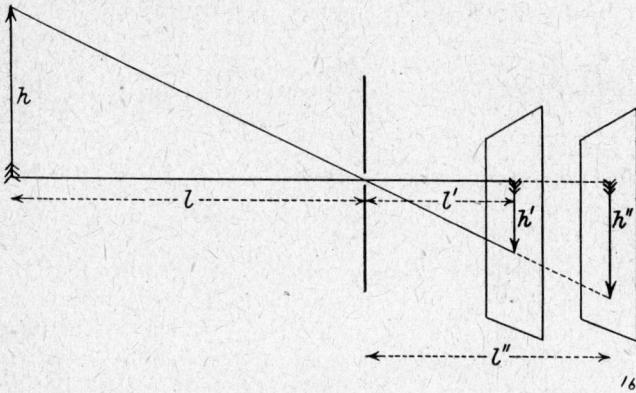

FIG. 1B

Similarly, in the camera obscura, when we deal for simplicity with the projection of images on screens parallel to the object, of which the perpendicular distances from the "pinhole" are l', l'', while the respective sizes of the images are h', h''

$$\frac{h}{l} = \frac{h'}{l'} = \frac{h''}{l''}.$$

Whatever the position or inclination of the image planes, we may (if we please) reproduce the pictures by drawing, or by receiving them on photographic plates, and these reproductions *when put back into the original image positions* will subtend the same angle at the "pinhole" as the original object; or again, by altering the distance or inclination of the picture, it can be viewed under varying angular subtenses. Of course, the picture can be turned "right way up," while still retaining the correct visual angles. There are special reasons for viewing such a reproduction, or any picture made truly in the laws of perspective projection, under the proper visual angle.

Distortion through False Perspective. Fig. 2 (*a*) illustrates the production of a projection LMN of a square framework viewed (edge-on) from O; in Fig. 2 (*b*) the reproduction is shown as viewed from a point O' too close to L; O' thus acts as a perspective centre. The lines O'L, O'M, O'N now determine the directions in which the corners of the framework are seen, but their distances are indeterminate unless our experience of the original object furnishes a rough guide. If we knew the framework were rectangular, so that the front and back parts must appear of equal height (allowing mentally for the requisite distance interval), the shortness of the distance O'L in relation to OL will produce an apparent foreshortening of the

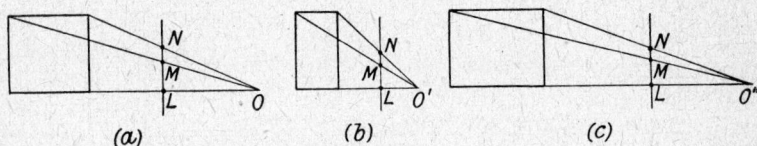

(a)   *(b)*   *(c)*

FIG. 2

image; conversely, the case shown in Fig. 2 (*c*) exhibits the apparent lengthening due to a view-point at too great a distance.

Such distortion of the apparent space relations in the image as interpreted through the projections often arises in the viewing of photographs, especially of buildings, galleries, and the like, where experience makes us see what the relative proportions of the original object must have been. We shall return to this subject when dealing with photographic optics, but students should select a suitable photograph and study the apparent space distortion produced by viewing the picture at different distances. Similar space distortion effects are often encountered in the images presented by various optical instruments; we shall deal with these in later sections.

The conception of the "ray" of light proved a fruitful principle in the development of optics; the properties of shadows found a ready explanation, and the development of photometry (the measurement of quantities of light) was begun on right lines, but it must be remembered that while this idea is a most useful servant, it must in the end be subordinated to the wider physical conceptions of the wave nature of light and its properties of periodicity.

The Law of Reflection. In Fig. 3, SS' is the trace of a plane reflecting surface perpendicular to the plane of the diagram. A ray starts from the point O, is reflected at P, and passes through the

point K. The normal to the surface at P is PN ; $\widehat{OPN}$ is the "angle
of incidence" ; $\widehat{NPK}$ is the "angle of reflection." The law of
reflection states that—

"*The angle of reflection is equal to the angle of incidence. Both
incident and reflected rays lie in one plane together with the normal
at the point of incidence.*" This statement of the law applies to
reflection at curved as well as plane surfaces. The Greeks were
aware of the equality of the angles of incidence and reflection, but
the complete statement of the law of reflection was first given by
the Arab Alhazen (or El Hassan) (A.D. 1100), who added that the
incident and reflected rays both lie in one plane perpendicular to
the mirror surface at the point of reflection. However, Hero of

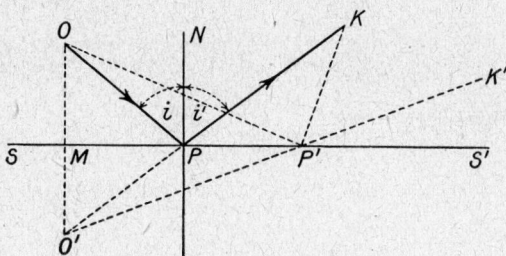

FIG. 3

Alexandria (second century A.D.) had discovered a useful property
of the ray path, which is a finger-post pointing to a most important
and general principle. It is easily seen that the path OPK taken
by the deflected ray is the shortest possible for the reflected light.
Dropping a perpendicular OM on SS' and producing to O', so that
OM is equal to MO', we can then draw the line O'P which is equal
to OP, and, moreover, the line O'PK is evidently straight.

Any other route from O to K involving one point in the surface,
OP' + P'K, for example, is now seen to be longer than OPK, for

$$OP' + P'K = O'P' + P'K$$

and, since two sides of a triangle are greater than the third, it is
clear that the route involving equal angles of incidence and reflection
is the shortest of all.

A ray OP' reflected at P' will evidently be reflected in the direction
P'K', i.e. in continuation of the line O'P', if it is to satisfy the law
of reflection. Hence, all the rays such as OP, which before reflection
diverge from the point O, appear after reflection to be diverging
from a point O', which we term the *image* of the object point O.
It is a *virtual image*, because the rays do not actually intersect in the

image; however, if the surface is perfectly plane, the image looks perfect also; every ray from O in any colour will, after reflection, appear to diverge from the same image point O'. The image is free from *aberration*.

Corollaries of the Law of Reflection. There are two simple corollaries of the law of reflection which it is worth while to recall at the present stage. The first shows that if the mirror is rotated about an axis perpendicular to the plane of incidence, the deflection of the reflected ray is double that of the mirror. In Fig. 4 (*a*), PN, PN' show

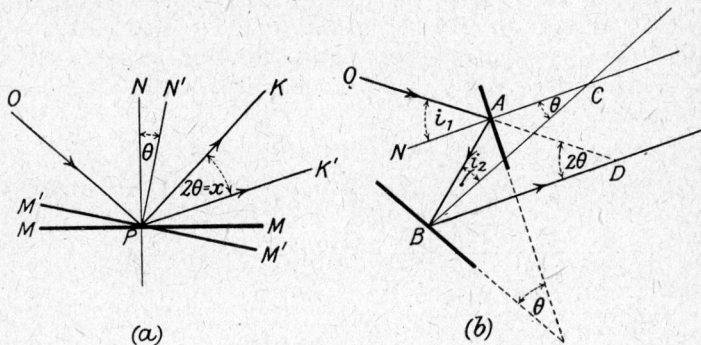

(*a*)   (*b*)

Fig. 4

the two positions of the normal to the mirror which rotates about P. PK, PK' are the two positions of the reflected ray.

Then
$$\widehat{OPN} = \widehat{NPK}$$

and
$$\widehat{OPN'} = \widehat{N'PK'}.$$

From the second equation
$$\widehat{OPN} + \theta = \widehat{NPK} - \theta + x,$$

whence
$$x = 2\theta.$$

The second corollary concerns the case when a ray is reflected in turn from two mirrors, the normal of the second lying in the plane of incidence of the first reflection; the three parts of the ray path then all lie in one plane.

In Fig. 4 (*b*), the ray is shown reflected at A and B, the angles of incidence at these points being i_1 and i_2 respectively; the normals intersect at C, including the angle θ. If the incident ray is produced it meets the final path BD in the point D; the angle $\widehat{ADB}$ is thus the *deflection* of the ray. Since NA is the normal at A,

$$\widehat{NAB} = i_1 = i_2 + \theta \text{ (from the triangle BAC)} \qquad . \qquad (a)$$

also $\qquad \widehat{OAB} = 2i_1 = \widehat{ABD} + \widehat{ADB}$ (from the triangle ABD),

$$= 2i_2 + \widehat{ADB}$$

but $\qquad\qquad 2i_1 = 2i_2 + 2\theta$ (from (a) above).

Therefore $\widehat{ADB}$, the angle of deflection, is twice the angle between the mirrors. Hence, for example, if θ is 45°, the ray will be deflected

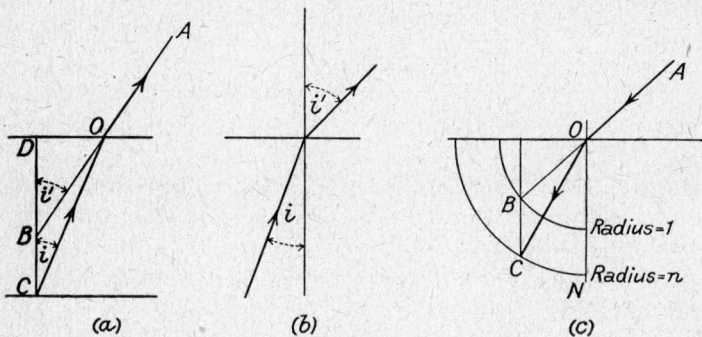

(a)   (b)   (c)

Fig. 5

through 90°, quite independently of the particular values of i_1 and i_2; if θ is 90°, the ray will be returned in an opposite direction but parallel to its first path.

The Law of Refraction. The qualitative effects of refraction were known to the Greeks, and quantitative measurements of angles of incidence and refraction at a water surface were made by Ptolemy (A.D. 127). He found that for small angles the ratio of the angle of refraction to that of incidence was approximately constant, and considered this constancy to be the *law* of refraction, even though his own observations show that it is not fulfilled for large angles.

Alhazen pointed out that the incident and refracted rays lie in one plane with the normal to the surface at the point of refraction, but neither he nor later workers such as Kepler succeeded in formulating the true quantitative relation; Kepler sought, in fact, for some relation between the *deflection* and the angle of incidence. It was left for Willebrord Snell (1591–1626) to find the first exact form of the law; this he put in a useful geometrical relation which still has its value in graphical methods of ray-tracing used in the design of optical systems. In Fig. 5 (a), OD shows a plane refracting surface (say of water), and C is an object beneath it; CD is perpendicular to the surface. A ray from C refracted at O will travel in the direction OA. This gives a means of locating the point B where AO (produced in a direction opposite to the light) meets CD. Snell found that for a given pair of media such as air and water, the ratio OC : OB is constant.

The angle of refraction is the angle between the refracted ray and the normal at the point of incidence. If the angles of incidence and refraction between the ray and the normal are i and i' respectively (Fig. 5 (b)), then clearly $\widehat{OCD} = i$, and $\widehat{OBD} = i'$, so that

$$\frac{OC}{OB} = \frac{\dfrac{OD}{OB}}{\dfrac{OD}{OC}} = \frac{\sin i'}{\sin i} = \text{constant}$$

The formal statement of the law of refraction is—

The sine of the angle of refraction bears a constant ratio to the sine of the angle of incidence. Both incident and refracted rays lie in one plane, together with the normal to the surface at the point of incidence.

This form of the law applies to refraction at both plane and curved surfaces, and was first given by Descartes (A.D. 1637).

Graphical Ray-tracing. The following are practical examples of the use of a graphical method of ray-tracing based on Snell's construction. Fig. 5 (c) shows a simple method of finding the path of a ray AO after refraction at a surface separating two different homogeneous media. If the law of refraction is given in the form

$$\sin i = n \sin i'$$

then n is called the refractive index of the medium (containing the refracted ray) with respect to the first medium. Take O as centre, and draw two circles with radii of "unity" and "n" respectively, using any convenient units. For example, the radii in a case of refraction from air into water might be 1 in. and 1·333 in., as n for water = 1·333. Produce AO to meet the unit circle in B; then draw through B a line BC parallel to the normal ON at the point of refraction. The line BC cuts the second circle in C; then OC is the path of the refracted ray.

This method of ray tracing is often used by optical designers in company with an exact trigonometrical trace; the graphical control is a useful check when forming a new design, and helps to avoid subtle but dangerous errors in numerical work, such as giving too small a thickness to a lens; see below.

The important fact that a ray when reversed retraces the forward path was known to Alhazen; it is easily inferred that a ray traversing a plane parallel slab of one medium, which is immersed in another medium, emerges in a direction parallel to the original path. This will also be the case after traversing *two* plane parallel slabs A and B, of different material as in Fig. 6. Under these circumstances, the

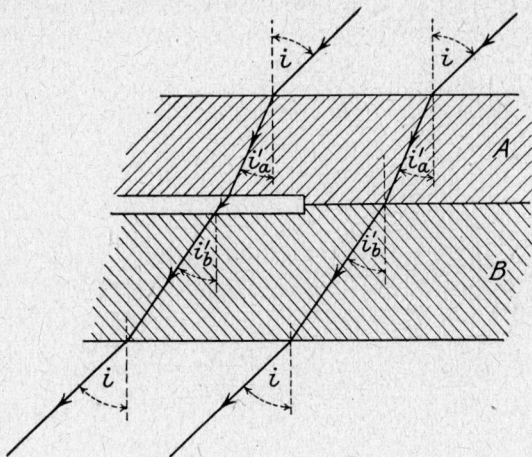

FIG. 6

initial angle of incidence on A is equal to the final angle of emergence from B. If the law of refraction from "air" to slab A is

$$\sin i = n_a \sin i'_a$$

and that from air to slab B is

$$\sin i = n_b \sin i'_b$$

these, and the principle of reversibility, make it clear that refraction from block A to block B fulfils the equation

$$n_a \sin i'_a = n_b \sin i'_b$$

In accordance with the usual practice of designating the quantities of the image space by a dash, the generalized law of refraction can be written

$$n \sin i = n' \sin i'$$

where n and n' are the "refractive indices" of the media of incidence and refraction respectively, with respect to air.

Imagining that the two slabs are situated in a vacuum, while slab A is of air, the law of refraction shows that the apparent refractive index of medium B with respect to air would be n_{bv}/n_{av}, where n_{bv} and n_{av} are *absolute* refractive indices measured with respect to a vacuum. The refractive index of air under ordinary conditions is about 1·00029, so that if the actual physical measurement is made in air the result must be corrected by multiplying by the proper factor, taking account of temperature, pressure, etc., if the absolute refractive index is required. Ordinary "refractive indices," such as are given in glass lists and tables, are usually measured with respect to air at normal temperature and pressure.

Fig. 7 shows all the construction required in tracing an incident ray through the three lenses A, B, and C; the centres of the curved

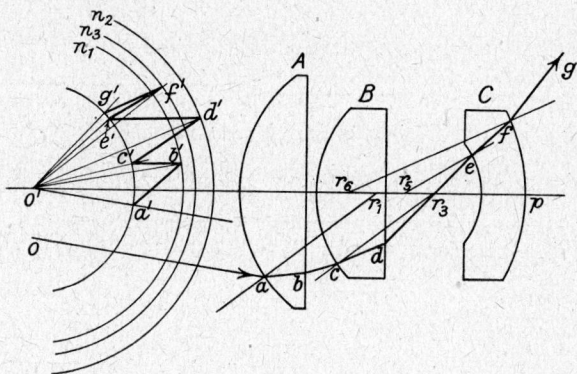

FIG. 7

surfaces are shown in the drawing, which is, of course, drawn accurately to scale. This system of the application of Snell's construction is due to Dowell, and is taken from a paper contributed to the Optical Convention in 1926.

The laws of refraction for the three lenses are of the form

$$\sin i = n_a \sin i' \text{ (air to glass)}$$

and

$$\sin i' = \frac{1}{n_a} \sin i \text{ (glass to air)}$$

A suitable point o' is taken, and circles are drawn with radii of unity, and n_1, n_2, n_3, for the three lenses A, B, and C, as shown.

The line oa is the incident ray, and ar_1 gives the normal at the point of incidence. Draw $o'a'$ parallel to oa, intersecting the unit circle in a'; then draw $a'b'$ parallel to the normal ar_1, cutting the n, circle in b'; $o'b'$ represents the direction of the refracted ray ab, which can itself conveniently be drawn by the aid of a parallel ruler.

When tracking a glass to air refraction, the n circle and the unit circle can be considered as having radii proportional to 1 and $1/n$ respectively, so the procedure in tracking the ray will be understood; $b'c'$ is drawn parallel to the normal at b; $o'c'$ then represents the *direction* of the ray from b to c.

Total Reflection and the Critical Angle. The law of refraction

$$n \sin i = n' \sin i'$$

whence

$$\sin i' = (n/n') \sin i$$

applied to a passage from a rarer to a denser medium, so that n/n' is less than unity, shows that i' has a real value for all possible values of i from $0°$ to $90°$. If we consider the reversed ray direction for which the same law is valid, the relation

$$\sin i = (n'/n) \sin i'$$

in which n'/n is greater than unity, shows that i can only have a real value provided that the right-hand side of the last equation is not greater than unity. If such were the case, the equation would cease to be valid, the refracted ray would no longer be found in the rarer medium. Experience shows that a certain proportion of the light energy, about 5 per cent in the case of a "glass to air" transmission, is reflected at the surface when the incidence is normal. As the angle of incidence increases the proportion of energy reflected rises, slowly at first, but more quickly later, until the angle of the refracted ray in the rarer medium would be $90°$, which occurs at the so-called "critical angle" of incidence in the denser medium, when

$$(\sin i') \, n'/n = 1, \text{ or } \sin i' = n/n'$$

There is then a comparatively sudden increase in the intensity of the reflected light; *total reflection* occurs and persists for all greater angles of incidence. This matter will be considered more closely in the discussion of polarization.

The phenomena of the critical angle are of great importance in practical methods of measuring refractive index.

Dispersion. The effects of colour associated with the refraction of light were the subject of much discussion from the earliest times. A German monk, Theodoricus de Saxonia (about A.D. 1305), showed that the rainbow was formed by the refraction and internal reflection of sunlight in spherical raindrops, and the discussion was amplified later by Descartes (A.D. 1637). The general idea up to the time of Newton was that "colour" was a modification of light varying with the degree of refraction. About 1666 Newton began the series of experiments which showed that sunlight, subjected to two refractions in passing through a prism, gave rise to "rays" of differing colour, which, if reunited by suitable optical means, would again produce white light. Light of one colour, when isolated, was shown to possess a particular degree of refrangibility (relative degree of refraction) associated with the colour, and it was further shown that such more or less "homogeneous" light suffered no change of colour by reflection, refraction, or absorption. Newton also showed that the sine law of refraction was obeyed by each coloured light separately, but no very exact determination of any physical property of light associated with a change of colour was possible until the time of Fraunhofer, who described the *dark* lines of the solar "spectrum."

The light from certain sources when dispersed by refraction through a prism is found to be resolved into a limited number of very homogeneous components, giving corresponding sharp bright lines in the spectrum. It is possible to measure a *precise* refractive index for the prism, corresponding to each line, and consequently we can first discuss the action of optical systems in homogeneous light on the basis of a *precise* law of refraction. The question of the dispersion of light, the properties of materials in this respect, and the production of a "spectrum" will receive fuller discussion in a later section.

Image Formation by Refraction at a Plane Surface. Referring to Fig. 8A, rays from a point B are refracted at a plane surface OY, the initial and final media having refractive indices n and n' respectively. The ray BO is refracted normally, while BD takes the path DD'. Producing D'D backwards, this line cuts BO in B', and Snell's law gives

$$n'\text{BD} = n\text{B'D}$$

When the points O and D are very close together, the apparent point of origin of the refracted rays leaving the surface at all such points near O is the point B' on BO, where

$$n'\text{BO} = n\text{B'O}$$

If it is desired to measure the refractive index (with respect to air) of some medium with a plane surface, a useful approximate method is to measure, first, the real depth, second, the apparent depth of some object situated a short distance (1 or 2 centimetres) below the surface. These measurements are conveniently made with a microscope carrying a 2-in. or 3-in. objective and possessing a scale to register the displacement of the microscope parallel to its axis. The surface may be located by focussing some fine dust upon it.

Then refractive index $= \dfrac{\text{BO}}{\text{B'O}} = \dfrac{\text{real depth of B}}{\text{apparent depth}}$

With regard to rays refracted at more oblique angles, calculation or graphical construction will show that they intersect BO at points further from B, while the mutual intersecting points (e.g. B″ in the diagram) do not lie on BO at all. If a great number of refracted rays are drawn they touch a curve, Fig. 8B (the caustic), which can be regarded as the locus of the mutual intersecting points of infinitely close rays. This variation of the points of intersection of the rays is called *aberration*.

It can be shown that the equation to the caustic, referred to the point O as origin, and taking OB as the x axis direction, is

$$\left(\frac{N}{h}x\right)^{\frac{2}{3}} + \left\{\frac{\sqrt{(N^2-1)}}{h}y\right\}^{\frac{2}{3}} = 1.$$

where $N = n'/n$, and $h = OB$.

Only one branch of this curve is shown in the figure. The caustic meets the line $y = o$ in the object point $x = h/N$, and meets the surface

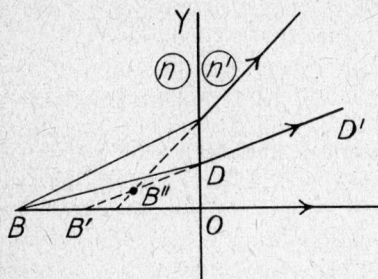

FIG. 8A

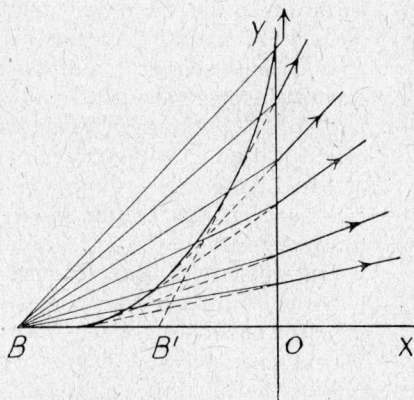

FIG. 8B. THE CAUSTIC CURVE FOR REFRACTION AT A PLANE SURFACE

$x = o$ in the points $y = \pm h\sqrt{(N^2-1)}$ where the incident ray falls at the critical angle. The top branches of the whole curve represented by the equation are not included in the caustic proper.

The above discussion of the apparent points of divergence of pairs of rays relate only to rays in the plane of the diagram. If we imagine Fig. 8A to be rotated around the normal (OB) it will indicate that the cone of rays defined by the locus BD will be refracted into a cone with apex B'. Hence close rays in the plane of the diagram may appear to come from a point such as B″, *not* on the normal, while close pairs of rays on the above refracted cone would appear to diverge from B' on the normal. This differentiation is called *astigmatism*. It occurs thus in refraction at plane surfaces, but not in reflection.

Spherical Surfaces and their Importance in Applied Optics.

A convex spherical surface formed on a stable material will exactly fit into a concave spherical surface of the same radius formed in another piece, in *any* relative positions. In the process of grinding two such surfaces together, it will be understood that any excrescence remaining on either surface will have to bear a great proportion of the pressure which may be exerted to hold the pieces in contact, and therefore will be subject to proportionately great wear if the surfaces are moved relatively to each other; such wear can be greatly increased by the use of a suitable grinding material or abrasive. Hence the production of spherical surfaces of great accuracy of form is possible by more or less automatic working, although a high degree of skill is called for in managing the relative movement of the grinding surfaces, since these only consist, usually, of *segments* of spheres.

In view of this comparative ease of production, the spherical surface is by far the most important of all forms of refracting surfaces. The majority of exact instruments are fitted with lenses having only spherical and plane surfaces. In some few cases, accurate aspherical surfaces are employed in instruments, but the largest use of non-spherical surfaces is in connection with the cylindrical and toric surfaces of spectacles in which the accuracy of figure is generally subject to a much greater tolerance, and, in fact, such surfaces usually show considerable errors when subjected to exact tests.

Trigonometrical Ray Tracing—Spherical Surfaces. The great majority of optical instruments are composed of lenses which are mounted co-axially, so that all the centres of curvature fall on the optical axis. Suitable choice of the components (i.e. proper selection of the refractive indices, radii of curvature, thicknesses, and separations) is required in order to obtain freedom from aberration in the final image.

In early days an approximation to the required construction was often arrived at by empirical trials, but when the alteration of radii was involved (requiring re-grinding and polishing), this was naturally an expensive and lengthy affair. By the beginning of the eighteenth century, however, astronomers like Flamsteed tested their designs by the trigonometrical tracing of rays starting from some object point and passing through the system; in this way the union of the rays in the image point can be investigated and the defects of the system discovered. A design need not then be constructed in glass till it had been perfected by trials on paper. These trigonometrical trials are still of the greatest importance for all classes of optical instruments, including some types of spectacles, although methods have been developed whereby the approximate data for many types of optical systems may be calculated apart from empirical trials of any kind.

In the majority of cases the rays selected for tracing through a system of centred spherical surfaces lie in a plane containing the optical axis. In Fig. 9 the incident ray DP is defined by the point P (in which it intersects the trace of the spherical interface AP between media of refractive indices n and n') and the point B in which it cuts the optical axis ACB passing through the centre of curvature C.

Similarly, the refracted ray will be determined by the point P and the point B' in which it intersects the optical axis; since the incident ray lies in an axial plane, the refracted ray must also lie in the same plane, and therefore intersects the axis.

Distances measured to the right are counted positive; those to the left are negative. Similarly, those measured upwards perpendicular to the axis are positive and those measured downwards are

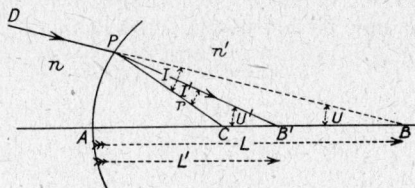

Fig. 9

negative. The "height" of an object or image point is measured *from* the axis *to* the point.

The angles at which the ray directions meet the axis are counted positive if a clockwise turn will bring a line from the axis direction to the ray direction by the lesser angular movement. We adopt the following symbols for trigonometrical work—

AC $= r$ (the radius of curvature is positive when the centre lies to the right of the vertex, and negative when lying to the left of the vertex)

AB $= L$ $\qquad$ $\widehat{PBA} = U$ $\qquad$ $\widehat{CPB} = I$

AB' $= L'$ $\qquad$ $\widehat{PB'A} = U'$ $\qquad$ $\widehat{CPB'} = I'$

The triangle PCB then gives $\qquad \sin I = \dfrac{(L - r)}{r} \sin U$ $\qquad$. $\quad$ (1) m

Also the law of refraction gives $\sin I' = \dfrac{n}{n'} \sin I$ $\qquad$. $\qquad$ (2) m

It is also easily seen from the diagram that $\widehat{PCA} = U + I = U' + I'$ whence
$$U' = U + I - I' \quad . \qquad . \qquad . \qquad . \qquad (3)\, m$$

The triangle PCB' then gives

$$L' - r = \frac{r \sin I'}{\sin U'} \quad . \qquad . \qquad . \qquad . \qquad . \qquad \text{(4) } m$$

Lastly $\qquad\qquad L' = (L' - r) + r \quad . \qquad . \qquad . \qquad . \qquad \text{(5) } m$

These formulae are sufficient to calculate the final intersection distance of the refracted ray, and are of general utility.

Paraxial Rays. Imagine that the ray DP continues to pass through the point B when produced, but that the point P is brought so close to the axis that the inclination of the ray to the axis becomes very small; these conditions are characteristic of a "paraxial" ray. The angles U, U', I, and I' then becomes so small that their sines may be replaced by the angular values of the angles themselves. Smaller type will be employed in formulae dealing with paraxial rays, so that we now have a new set of formulae corresponding to those above—

$$i = \frac{l - r}{r} u \quad . \qquad . \qquad . \qquad . \qquad \text{(1) } p$$

$$i' = \frac{i \cdot n}{n'} \qquad . \qquad . \qquad . \qquad . \qquad \text{(2) } p$$

$$u' = u + i - i' \quad . \qquad . \qquad . \qquad . \qquad \text{(3) } p$$

$$l' - r = \frac{r \cdot i'}{u'} \qquad . \qquad . \qquad . \qquad . \qquad \text{(4) } p$$

$$l' = (l' - r) + r \quad . \qquad . \qquad . \qquad . \qquad \text{(5) } p$$

In using the above paraxial formulae for calculation, it will be noticed that the units in which the paraxial angles are measured have no significance in determining the final result. Hence it is possible to assume any numerical value for u in commencing a calculation. An example of the use of a logarithmic trace for two rays, of which one is a paraxial ray, will be given on page 17.

Five-figure tables, giving logarithms of trigonometrical functions for each hundredth part of a degree, are often suitable. (See references at end of chapter.) Note that the numerical values of the angles are entered in the lower section as their logarithms are obtained during the course of the standard schedule. Hence, U' and u' are found, which are needed to complete the calculation.

Note also that the initial log u in the paraxial work is taken as equal to log sin U in accordance with the freedom of choice of units mentioned above. In this way comparable figures are obtained in the paraxial and "marginal" schedules; in fact, the figures obtained when commencing a calculation with the same L and l in this way are the same (down to line 12) at first in both columns; but if it were desired to continue tracing the rays through another surface, say at a distance of $+$ 1 cm., we should then have for the two rays

L (new surface) $= 28\cdot088 - 1\cdot0 = 27\cdot088$ U $= 1°\cdot7896$

l (,,   ,,) $= 28\cdot701 - 1\cdot0 = 27\cdot701$ $u = 0\cdot03040$

and we would carry through the calculation just as before with these new data. The figures in the columns would no longer be identical.

DATA. $n = 1$ L $= l = -25$ cm.

$n' = 1\cdot5207$ $r = 5\cdot6$ cm.

Calculate l' and L' for U $= -2°$.

				Paraxial
L	$-25\cdot0$		l	$-25\cdot0$
subtract r	$5\cdot6$			$5\cdot6$
L $- r$	$-30\cdot6$			$-30\cdot6$
log sin U	$8\cdot54282\ n$ *		log u	$8\cdot54282\ n$
add log (L $- r$)	$1\cdot48572\ n$			$1\cdot48572\ n$
Sum $=$	$\cdot02854$			$\cdot02854$
subtract log r	$\cdot74819$			$\cdot74819$
log sin I	$9\cdot28035$		log i	$9\cdot28035$
subtract log $\dfrac{n'}{n}$	$\cdot18204$			$\cdot18204$
log sin I'	$9\cdot09831$		log i'	$9\cdot09831$
add log r	$\cdot74819$			$\cdot74819$
Sum $=$	$9\cdot84650$			$9\cdot84650$
subtract log sin U'	$8\cdot49455$		log u'	$8\cdot48287$
log (L' $- r$)	$1\cdot35195$			$1\cdot36363$
(L' $- r$) $=$	$22\cdot488$			$23\cdot101$
add r	$5\cdot6$			$5\cdot6$
L'	$28\cdot088$		l'	$28\cdot701$
U	$-2°\cdot0000$		u	$-\cdot03490$
add I	$10\cdot9936$		i	$\cdot19070$
U $+$ I	$8\cdot9936$		$u + i$	$\cdot15580$
subtract I'	$7\cdot2040$		i'	$\cdot12540$
U'	$1\cdot7896$		u'	$\cdot03040$

* The n shows that the log is of a negative natural number. Also it is usual, in the place of $\bar{2}$, to write 8 (i.e. $10 - 2$), thus saving the use of a negative characteristic.

Calculating machines are often used rather than employing logarithmic methods, but trigonometrical calculation should be used by beginners, as a record of each step in the calculation is thus obtained; in certain cases, checks and additions are needed to the standard schedule above; the whole art of computing, even as far as it goes in the testing of optical systems by trigonometrical ray tracing, is a large subject, while the analytical design of new systems is yet another. Professor Conrady's book on *Applied Optics and Optical Design* may be recommended to those who wish to go more deeply into these subjects.

Formulae for Use with Calculating Machine. An alternative set of formulae, useful in machine tracing, is derived by dropping perpendiculars AD, AD' (Fig. 10), from the apex to the incident and

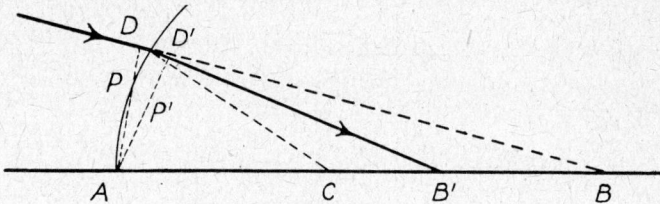

FIG. 10

refracted rays. Their lengths are P and P' respectively. Then writing $R = 1/r$, the reciprocal of the radius, we have, since

$$P = r(\sin I + \sin U),$$

the following set of equations—

	Marginal	*Paraxial*	
	$\sin I = PR - \sin U$	$i = pR - u$	(a)
	$\sin I' = (\sin I)N/N'$	$i' = iN/N'$	(b)
	$U' = U + I - I'$	$u' = u + i - i'$	(c)
	$P' = r(\sin U' + \sin I')$	$p' = r(u' + i')$	(d)
Typical transfer:	$P_2 = P_1' - t_1' \sin U_1'$	$p_2' = p_1' - t_1' u_1'$	(e)

where t_1' is the axial distance between surfaces 1 and 2. If the intersection distances are to be used in opening and closing the calculation, we have

$$P_1 = L_1 \sin U_1$$
$$L' = P'/\sin U'.$$

In machine tracing it is advantageous to record the angles U, U', I, I' encountered at each of the successive surfaces, but the recording of the P values can often be omitted; thus, eliminating P' algebraically, we get as a result (in progressing from surface 1 to surface 2)

$$\sin I_2 = \frac{\sin U_1'(r_1 - t_1' - r_2) + r_1 \sin I_1'}{r_2},$$

together with the paraxial equivalent.

This equation lends itself to machine computation. Having obtained $\sin I_2$, we obtain $\sin I_2'$ from the law of refraction (*b*); and the numerical values of I_2 and I_2' are obtained from tables of natural trigonometrical functions, such as Chrétien's[1] (using radian arguments), or the seven-figure[2] or six-figure tables of Peters. The seven-figure table gives values for every thousandth part of a degree, and combines well with "Bremiker's" five-figure logarithmic table,[3] in which logs of trigonometrical functions are listed for every hundredth part of a degree. Having thus obtained U_2, I_2, and I_2', the value of U_2' follows, see equations (*c*); and the calculation of $\sin I_3$ then proceeds. Opinions differ as to the necessity of checks; they should always be used by inexperienced workers; some of them are discussed in Conrady's book.

T. Smith[4] describes a ray-tracing method suitable for machine work, in which the only table needed is a single-page four-figure sheet giving cosines from sines, though the formulae are somewhat more complex.

Note on Symbols employed in Optical Formulae. The symbols employed in the foregoing computing formulae have been given as used in the usual computing practice; it is important to maintain clear distinctions between paraxial lengths and angles, and the others. Small letters indicate the paraxial quantities, and capitals show those which are not so restricted.

The present book is not, however, concerned largely with computing, and, indeed, the number of students who require a detailed knowledge of that subject will be small in comparison with those who will find it sufficient to use the elementary theory and equations. (It should be, however, within the power of any student to test his approximations by exact calculations, and it should be the aim always to understand how far the approximations actually depart from the truth.)

Particularly in the theory of ophthalmic lenses it has been usual to reserve the use of capital letters to denote the reciprocal of a length symbolized by the small letter. Thus, if r represents a radius of curvature, the symbol R may often be used to denote the curvature $\frac{1}{r}$.

However, in order to save confusion as far as possible, the reciprocal quantities will be written in thicker type, thus

$$\mathbf{R} = \frac{1}{r} = \text{curvature.}$$

$$\mathbf{L} = \frac{1}{l}, \text{ and so on.}$$

The computing equations above are given in the form used at the Imperial College, but it has been found that many elementary students have been accustomed to writing u and v for object and image distances in the manner used by Coddington. It is the general experience that it is more convenient to use the same letter for corresponding quantities in object and image spaces, distinguishing the latter by a "dash" (thus, l'), and we shall adhere to this usage adopted in the computing formulae, with the exception that the angle between ray and axis in the object and image space will be denoted by α and α'. The standard equations then become

$$\sin I = \frac{(L - r)}{r} \sin \alpha \quad . \qquad . \qquad . \qquad . \quad (\text{101})$$

$$\sin I' = \frac{n}{n'} \sin I \quad . \qquad . \qquad . \qquad . \quad (\text{102})$$

$$\alpha' = \alpha + I - I' \quad . \qquad . \qquad . \qquad . \quad (\text{103})$$

$$L' - r = \frac{r \sin I'}{\sin \alpha'} \cdot \qquad . \qquad . \qquad . \quad (\text{104})$$

$$L' = (L' - r) + r \quad . \qquad . \qquad . \quad (\text{105})$$

in which the Roman capitals still stand for exact lengths.

Refraction of a Ray in the Axial Plane at a Spherical Surface.
Formulae 101 and 104 of the section above give

$$\sin I = \frac{L - r}{r} \sin \alpha$$

$$\sin I' = \frac{L' - r}{r} \sin \alpha'$$

Dividing, we obtain

$$\frac{\sin I}{\sin I'} = \frac{n'}{n} = \frac{L - r}{L' - r} \cdot \frac{\sin \alpha}{\sin \alpha'}$$

whence (see Fig. 9)

$$\frac{n'}{n} = \frac{L - r}{L' - r} \cdot \frac{PB'}{PB}$$

When we restrict the rays concerned to the paraxial region so that AP is very small, then

$$PB = l, \text{ and } PB' = l', \text{ sufficiently nearly.}$$

Hence, in the paraxial form, the exact equation becomes reduced to

$$\frac{n'}{n} = \frac{(l - r)l'}{(l' - r)l} \cdot \qquad . \qquad . \qquad . \quad (\text{106})$$

and thus

$$\frac{n'}{l'} - \frac{n}{l} = \frac{n' - n}{r} \qquad . \qquad . \qquad . \quad (\text{107})$$

It seems at first sight as if the calculation of l', given the other quantities, by means of this formula would be considerably shorter than the logarithmic computation previously given; it is true that approximate results using tables of reciprocals can be obtained quickly, but if the calculation is to be performed to the same degree of accuracy as before, the process will not be found to be shortened. The paraxial formula itself indicates that while AP (Fig. 9) is sufficiently small, any ray thus directed towards one point B at a distance l will be refracted towards a point B' at a distance l' along the axis containing the centre C. The whole of the rays in a narrow cone with its apex at B will thus be refracted so as to form a fresh cone still narrow with its apex at B'. The formula holds also for rays diverging from one object point on the axis, and shows that they will after refraction pass through one image point or appear to diverge from it.

In the computing exercise, however, the exact paths of rays not confined to the paraxial region were found, and further inquiry on these lines will show that the paraxial formula (exact for paraxial rays) generally gives a useful approximation also for the distances at which those rays cross the axis, which make appreciable angles with it, and so enable us quickly to calculate the results obtained with beams of larger apertures, such as are dealt with by optical instruments in practice. Further experience will teach the restrictions under which these approximations are of use.

The Focal Lengths of a Single Refracting Surface. Imagine an axial object point or source of light at an infinite distance away to the left from a spherical refracting surface. Such a source gives rays which are parallel to the axis when reaching the refracting surface (Fig. 11a). If $l = -\infty$, equation (107) gives

$$l' = \frac{n'r}{(n' - n)} = f'$$

and this distance is called f', the *second focal length* of the refracting surface. On the other hand, if the rays are to be rendered parallel after refraction at the surface (Fig. 11b), $l' = +\infty$, and this requires $l = -\dfrac{nr}{(n' - n)} = f$. This distance is called f, the first focal length of the refracting surface. This notation distinguishes points relating to the image space by a "dash."

In cases where, as in Fig. 11, the incident light proceeding from left to right encounters a convex refracting surface of a medium of greater refractive index, the first focal point, F, is situated at a distance f, which will be numerically negative, from the surface, so that it lies to the left; the second focal point F′ at a distance f' (positive in this case) will lie to the right. Note especially that $\frac{f}{f'} = -\frac{n}{n'}$.

Students should draw the diagram showing the positions of the focal points for a case of a concave surface, and a selected pair of

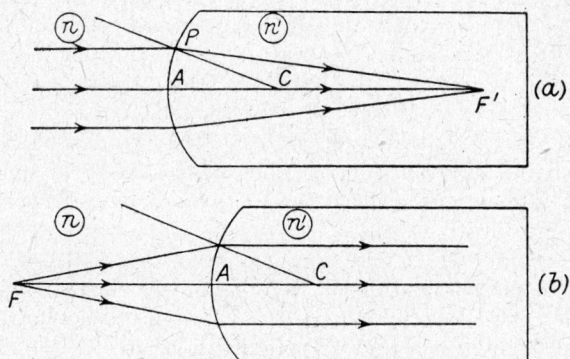

FIG. 11

refractive indices. For the sake of clearness in the diagrams, rays are shown in Fig. 11 which are far outside the paraxial region.

Object of Finite Size. In Fig. 12 the points B and B′ represent an axial object and image respectively, the image being produced by refraction of a paraxial bundle of rays from B at the spherical surface shown with centre C and apex A. Let the line BCB′ rotate

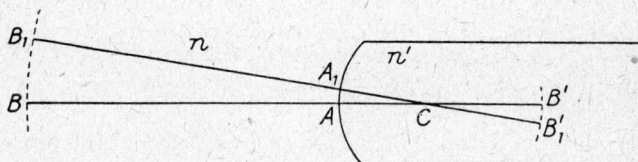

FIG. 12

about the centre C, then the points B_1 and B_1', at the extremities of the line in a new position at a small angle with the first, must equally well represent object and image points, i.e. conjugate foci with respect to the same surface.

Therefore, while BB_1 and $B'B_1'$ are very small, they represent a small linear object and image, both perpendicular to BCB′. If the line BCB′ be taken as the optical axis, it is to be noticed that rays are concerned in the "imaging" of B_1 which do not lie in a plane containing BCB', as they may have all directions making small angles with $B_1 A_1 B_1'$.

The above reasoning applies satisfactorily only to objects and images which are not close to the centre of curvature of a surface. Therefore, in order to make the reasoning more general, it is necessary to show that a small linear object situated at the centre of curvature and perpendicular to the axis has also an image perpendicular to the axis.

In Fig. 13, C is the centre of curvature of the spherical refracting surface shown by its trace APS. The rays OPC and MAC are evidently radial, and suffer no change of direction at the surface. The rays NA and LP are, however, directed towards B_1, where B_1 is close to C, and

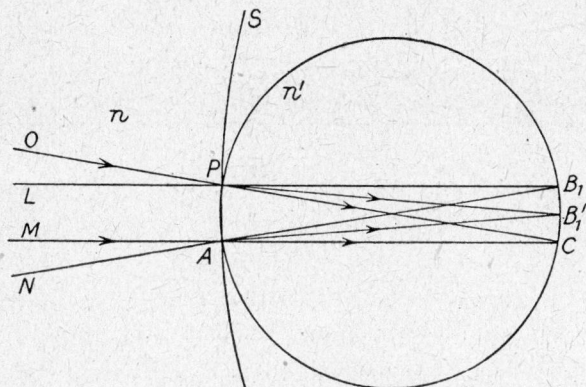

FIG. 13

lies on a circle laid through A, P, and C. We may consider CB_1 as a small virtual object perpendicular to the axis. The arc is also small, so that the discussion is confined to paraxial rays.

The angles $\widehat{OPL}$ and $\widehat{MAN}$ are clearly equal, and these are the angles of incidence of the rays LP and NA. Therefore the angles of refraction will be equal, and the refracted rays will be directed towards the point B_1' on the arc of the same circle; also it is easily seen that $n'(CB_1')$ $= n(CB_1)$ very nearly. CB_1' is evidently to be regarded as the image.

In this important special case (image formation at the centre of curvature of the refracting surface) the curvatures of object and image are identical.

The object and image in both instances are situated on spherical surfaces, and it will be shown in a later section that, in general, the curvature of the image surface corresponding to a plane object surface may be calculated from the properties of the optical system. Nevertheless, it is a useful conception that, bearing in mind the paraxial restrictions and dealing with small objects and images, we may conceive the planes of the object space in the neighbourhood of the axis to be represented by corresponding planes in the image space.

In corrected optical systems such as those of photographic lenses this correspondence may take on a much wider significance, and release itself from the restrictions of the paraxial region.

Magnification. In Fig. 14, B' and B are the axial points of two "conjugate planes" in which an image of height h' and a virtual object of height h are found. As in previous cases, the perpendicular dimensions in the diagram are exaggerated for the sake of clarity.

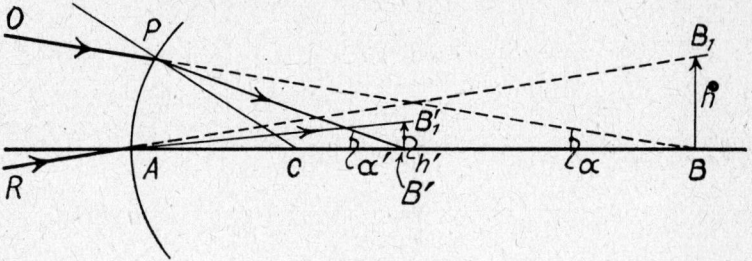

FIG. 14

The points B and B' are determined, as in Fig. 9, by the axial crossing points of the incident and refracted rays, and we have

$$PB \sin \alpha = PB' \sin \alpha'$$

which under restriction to the paraxial limitations will give

$$l\alpha = l'\alpha'$$

with sufficiently close approximation.

The conjugate points B_1 and B_1' are determined, on the theory of conjugate planes, by the points in which these planes are intersected by the incident ray AB_1, and the refracted ray AB_1' respectively. The law of refraction gives—

$$\frac{nh}{AB_1} = \frac{n'h'}{AB_1'}$$

and again under the paraxial restriction this becomes, sufficiently nearly,

$$\frac{nh}{l} = \frac{n'h'}{l'} \qquad . \qquad . \qquad . \qquad (108)$$

Multiplying equation (108) by the second equation of this section, we obtain the important relation

$$nh\alpha = n'h'\alpha' . \qquad . \qquad . \qquad . \qquad (109)$$

This relation, first used by R. Smith, has also been credited to Helmholtz and Lagrange. Huygens used it in a modified form. A form sometimes useful is

$$\frac{l' - r}{h'} = \frac{l - r}{h}$$

This is easily obtained by combining equation (108) with equation (106).

An Optical Invariant. The equation (109) is one of great importance. Imagining a system of centred co-axial refracting surfaces, the equation asserts that the product of the refractive index, the image height, and the angle of inclination of a ray intersecting the axis in that image plane will be constant throughout the system. (The same ray is naturally to be considered always.) Thus for surfaces 1, 2, 3, etc.,

$$n_1 h_1 \alpha_1 = n_2 h_2 \alpha_2 = n_3 h_3 \alpha_3$$

We now have all the material for building up a theory of the action of optical systems consisting of such a series of centred co-axial spherical refracting surfaces.

There is a rather wider meaning, however, which may be attached to the invariant formula (109), which is illustrated by Fig. 15. As usual, let APQ be the refracting surface, and let P and Q be points on this surface through which rays are directed to the virtual object point B_1, making a small angle $(\widehat{QB_1P} = \beta)$ with each other, which is small in the paraxial sense; both Q and P are supposed close to A, so that the discussion is again confined to paraxial rays. The refracted directions intersect in the image point at an angle β'.

Then under these restrictions

$$\beta l = \beta' l'$$

whence from equation (108)

$$nh\beta = n'h'\beta' \qquad . \qquad . \qquad . \qquad . \qquad (110)$$

so that the invariant relation holds not only for angles α and α' made with the axis by a ray intersecting the axial points of object and image, but also for the angles β and β' between pairs of rays passing through conjugate points in the object and image spaces, that is, within the limitations set forth above.

Variations of Magnification. Taking the case of Fig. 11, a graphical study, or calculations with the aid of equations (107) and (108) should be made, to follow the changes of magnification with the relative conjugate distances. If the object is real and infinitely distant away to the left $(l = -\infty)$, the magnification

h'/h is zero. If now the object draws nearer, moving up towards the system from the left, the image tends to move to the right while increasing in size though remaining inverted. The numerical value of h'/h thus increases though remaining negative till the object arrives at the first principal focus F ($l = f$), when the image distance is infinite ($l' = \pm \infty$) and $h'/h = \mp \infty$. If the object continues to the right the image is virtual and erect; it is at first at a great distance to the left, but moves up to overtake the object in the surface, where the magnification has dropped to $+ 1$. The object can still move to the right as a virtual object (one towards which the incident rays converge), and the image remains erect though diminishing in size as the object distance increases; meanwhile the magnification shrinks towards zero as the image tends

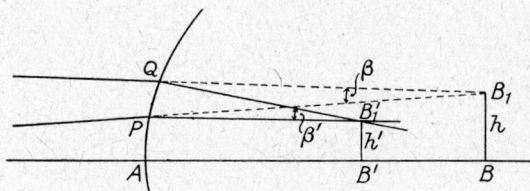

FIG. 15

towards its limiting position in the second principal focus, F'. It is thus seen that for each pair of conjugate distances there is one associated value of the paraxial magnification, and that a pair of conjugates can be found to produce any numerical value of the magnification provided that virtual objects and images are taken into account. Similar conclusions will apply to a lens or, in general, to any system.

The Thin Lens. The originators of the general theory of centred optical systems owed a great deal to the study of the properties of ordinary convex and concave thin lenses, which have been used for spectacles certainly since the thirteenth century. We shall study the paraxial properties of a single thin lens before going on to the general cases.

Consider a lens (Fig. 16) of small aperture constructed of a medium of refractive index n to be bounded by two surfaces of radii r_1 and r_2, and to be situated in a medium of refractive index 1. Assuming an axial object point at a distance l from the vertex of the first surface, equation (107) gives for refraction at that surface

$$\frac{n}{l_1'} - \frac{1}{l_1} = \frac{n-1}{r_1}$$

Note that "n" and "1" are written instead of n' and n in this equation. The "image" formed by refraction at the first surface now acts as the "object" for the second surface, and the general equation gives

$$\frac{1}{l_2'} - \frac{n}{l_2} = \frac{1 - n}{r_2}$$

But if the lens be considered to be of negligible thickness, $l_1' = l_2$, and the two equations when added give

$$\frac{1}{l_2'} - \frac{1}{l_1} = (n - 1)\left(\frac{1}{r_1} - \frac{1}{r_2}\right)$$

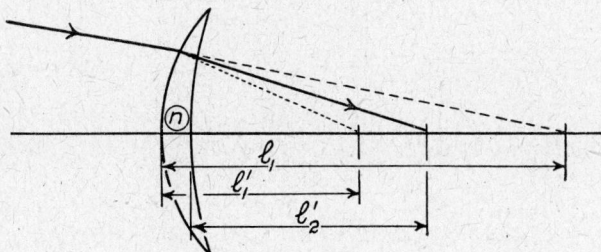

FIG. 16

For the present purpose the equation can be written simply

$$\frac{1}{l'} - \frac{1}{l} = (n - 1)\left(\frac{1}{r_1} - \frac{1}{r_2}\right) \qquad . \qquad . \quad \text{(III)}$$

where l' and l are axial distances of image and object measured "from the lens."

In Fig. 16 r_1 and r_2, as well as the distances of the axial conjugate points, are all positive; but the investigation is quite general for any type of thin lens. The lens of Fig. 16 obviously is not thin, since its thickness is appreciable in comparison with the conjugate distances l_1, etc. In a double convex lens, r_1 will be numerically positive and r_2 numerically negative, so that the operation of forming

$$\left(\frac{1}{r_1} - \frac{1}{r_2}\right)$$

involves the arithmetical addition of the reciprocals.

Fig. 17 represents various familiar forms of lenses. Evidently the lenses which are thicker at the axis than at the edge cannot be made infinitely thin without also reducing the diameter of the lens to zero; therefore it is not surprising that the approximate theory is more generally accurate for those lenses which are thinnest in the middle. However, it is always useful for approximate calculation. Experience will teach the restrictions of use.

Taking an object at an infinite distance to the left (incident parallel light), we find, writing f' in place of l',

$$\frac{1}{f'} = (n - 1)\left(\frac{1}{r_1} - \frac{1}{r_2}\right) \quad . \quad . \quad . \quad (112)$$

When l' is to be infinite, $l = -f'$. In this case, l becomes f, then we have, as in the case of a single refraction, two "focal lengths" of

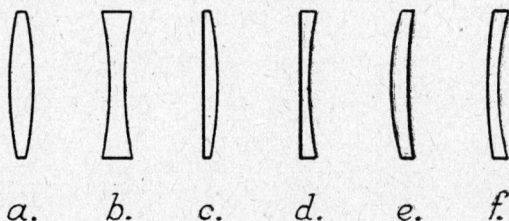

a.   *b.*   *c.*   *d.*   *e.*   *f.*

(a) double-convex.   (d) plano-concave.

(b)   "   " -concave.   (e) meniscus (positive).

(c) plano-convex.   (f)   "   "   (negative)

Fig. 17

opposite sign, but in this case equal numerically. Note that the refractive index of the object space is now identical with that of the final image space.

Since a ray can pass undeviated through the centre of a thin lens it is clear that the magnification is given by

$$m = h'/h = l'/l$$

Geometrical Illustration of the " Thin Lens " Formula. Consider first the thin lens formula above, and refer to Fig. 18 (a), in which we represent a ray passing through the lens at unit distance from the axis, and passing through the object and image points B and B' at angles α and α' respectively with the axis. Then

$$\alpha = \frac{1}{l} \text{ and } \alpha' = \frac{1}{l'}$$

Note that α will be numerically negative in the diagram. But

$$\widehat{QPB'} = \phi = \widehat{PBB'} + \widehat{PB'B};$$

in this equation all the angles are treated as positive, so that

$$\phi = \alpha' + (-\alpha) = \frac{1}{l'} - \frac{1}{l} = \frac{1}{f'}$$

Thus, the equation implies that the numerical sum of the angles α and α' will be constant, and that the ray from the object point incident at unit height will suffer a constant deviation.

A wire bent thus into two straight pieces at an angle $(180° - \phi)$ and pivoted at the junction at unit height from the axis could be

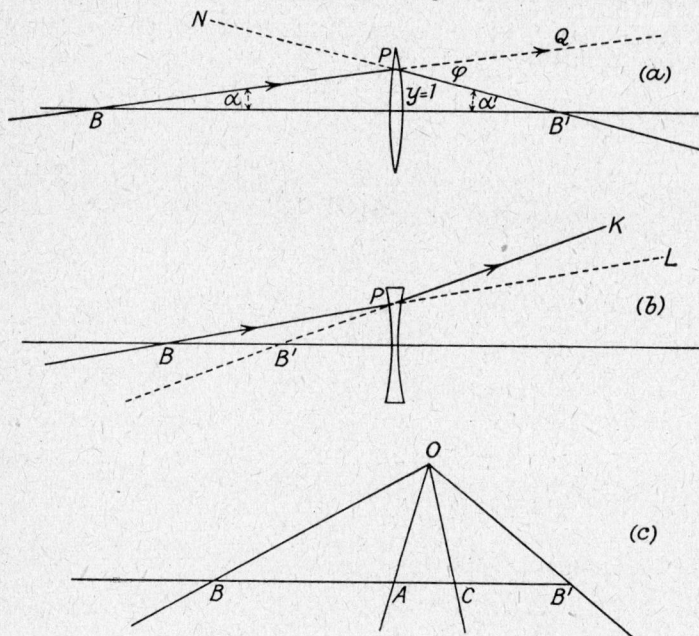

FIG. 18. GEOMETRICAL INTERPRETATION OF PARAXIAL FORMULAE

swung into various positions; the crossing points of the axis with the wires will illustrate the relations of the conjugate points. Fig. 18B illustrates the case of a diverging or negative lens.

It is to be noted that a real wire framework of this kind does not quite correctly represent the paraxial formula, since the relative inclinations of the represented "rays" will be fairly large, but it will be useful for gaining first ideas.

Geometrical Interpretation of the Single Surface Formula. Formula (106) gave

$$\frac{(l - r)l'}{(l' - r)l} = \frac{n'}{n}$$

Applying this relation to the case of Fig. 12, where B and B' represent conjugate points, A the apex of the refracting surface, and C the centre of curvature, we obtain (noting that l in Fig. 12 will be numerically negative, while r is numerically positive, so that $(l - r)$ = CB (numerically negative).)

$$\frac{CB . AB'}{CB' . AB} = \frac{n'}{n}$$

In Fig. 18 (c) set out B, A, C, and B' on a straight line and, taking any point O (for clearness it should be placed approximately as shown), join it to all these points and produce the lines beyond them. Imagine a perpendicular of length p dropped from O on the line BB'; we easily see that

$$p . CB = 2(\text{area of triangle OBC}) = OB . OC . \sin \widehat{COB}$$

$$p . AB' \qquad\qquad = OA . OB' \sin \widehat{AOB'}$$

$$p . CB' \qquad\qquad = OC . OB' \sin \widehat{COB'}$$

$$p . AB \qquad\qquad = OB . OA \sin \widehat{AOB}$$

Hence, $$\frac{CB . AB'}{CB' . AB} = \frac{OB . OC . OA . OB' . \sin \widehat{COB} . \sin \widehat{AOB'}}{OC . OB' . OB . OA . \sin \widehat{COB'} . \sin \widehat{AOB}}$$

$$= \frac{\sin \widehat{COB} . \sin \widehat{AOB'}}{\sin \widehat{COB'} . \sin \widehat{AOB}}$$

If OB, OA, OC, OB' represented a fixed framework of wires at definite angles, then the right-hand side of the above equation would be constant, and the condition of formula (106) would be fulfilled. In order to make the wires OB and OB' mark the object and image points by their axial crossing point, it will be sufficient to drive in two pins at A and C, so that the fixed radius of curvature of the surface is taken into account. Then the framework will move over the pins and the wires OB and OB' (or extensions which may be added to mark virtual points as above) will indicate the true positions of conjugate foci.

In geometry the ratio $\dfrac{CB . AB'}{CB' . AB}$, or $\dfrac{CB}{AB} : \dfrac{CB'}{AB'}$ is called the "cross ratio of the range CBAB'," and may be shown as above to be equal to the "cross ratio of the pencil" given by the ratio of the products of the sines given above. It is a case of a projective relation between the object space and the image space, and was first worked out in the above form by Möbius.[4]

" Powers " of Lenses and Surfaces. In theoretical optics the conception of the "powers" of lenses and the "curvatures" of surfaces have proved very useful. Thus, the power of a lens is the reciprocal of the focal length; the curvature of a surface is the reciprocal of the radius of curvature. Writing F for "power" and R for curvature, the equation

$$\frac{1}{f'} = (n - 1) \left(\frac{1}{r_1} - \frac{1}{r_2} \right)$$

becomes
$$F = (n - 1)\ (R_1 - R_2) \qquad . \qquad . \qquad . \quad (112)*$$

and it is sometimes useful to write $R = R_1 - R_2$, so that

$$F = (n - 1)\ R$$

In dealing with spectacles, it is now usual to take the unit of length as 1 metre; the power of a spectacle lens is then the reciprocal of the focal length measured in metres, and the unit of power is then known as the "Diopter." This name for the unit of power is ascribed to F. Monoyer of Strassburg, and was introduced in the seventies of last century. Nagel made a similar suggestion in 1868. In this system the "curvature" of a surface is the reciprocal of the radius in metres as first suggested by Herschel in 1827.

Lloyd has also introduced the term of "vergence." The "thin lens" formula,

$$\frac{1}{l'} - \frac{1}{l} = \frac{1}{f'}$$

may be re-written

$$L' - L = F \qquad . \qquad . \qquad . \qquad . \quad (113)$$

where L' and L are the "vergencies" to image and object respectively. Note that in dealing with spectacles the focal power will invariably be $\frac{1}{f'}$, so that a "dash" to the F is unnecessary.

The equation

$$\frac{n'}{l'} - \frac{n}{l} = \frac{n' - n}{r_1}$$

can also be written in a simplified form in the notation of "reduced vergencies"; if

$$\bar{l} = l/n \text{ and } \bar{l'} = l'/n'$$

---

* A " dash " to the F is unnecessary; see below.

it then becomes

$$\frac{1}{l'} - \frac{1}{l} = \frac{n' - n}{r_1}$$

or, alternatively, if $n/l = 1/\bar{l} = \bar{L}$ and so on, the equation can then be written

$$\bar{L}' - \bar{L} = (n' - n) \, R_1 = F_1$$

where F_1 is defined as the focal power of the surface.

In the case of a "thin lens," the equation becomes transformed thus—

$$\bar{L}' - \bar{L} = (n - 1) \left(\frac{1}{r_1} - \frac{1}{r_2} \right) = \frac{(n-1)}{r_1} + \frac{(1-n)}{r_2} = F_1 + F_2 = F$$

Hence, the power of the lens is the sum of the powers of the two surfaces. It should be noted that the *power of a surface* is *not* in general the reciprocal of its focal length. Thus, in the general equation (107), when l is infinite,

$$l' = f' = \frac{r_1 n'}{(n' - n)} = \frac{n'}{F_1}$$

It is often the case that expressions can be considerably simplified by introducing such symbols as are used above.

Calculation Through a Series of Surfaces. When the "vergence" relations are used, the paraxial ray may be followed through a system of coaxial refracting surfaces as follows—

First surface: $\bar{L}_1' = \bar{L}_1 + F_1$

For the second surface, at a distance d_1' from the first, we have—

$$l_2 = l_1' - d_1'$$

and

$$L_2 = n_2/l_2$$

Alternatively, on dividing by the refractive index, we obtain

$$\bar{l}_2 = \bar{l}_1' - \bar{d}_1'$$

or

$$\bar{L}_2 = 1/(\bar{l}_1' - \bar{d}_1')$$

Then

$$\bar{L}_2' = \bar{L}_2 + F_2, \text{ and so on.}$$

Such a method may save time if the powers of the successive surfaces are given. A numerical example appears on page 51.

Owing to the reversibility of the path of a ray, such equations as the above can be used for tracing rays from left to right or from right to left; most simply if, *just for this purpose*, the "dash" denotes something measured in the medium lying to the right of a point or surface, and its absence denotes a corresponding value referred to the medium lying to the left. (See the Appendix to this book, on p. 332.)

In the general equations the "dashed" and plain symbols refer to the object and image spaces respectively; the conditions under which they can be used for tracing the paths of rays from right to left without involving a change in the sign of the power of a lens or a surface are also examined in the appendix.

Astigmatism Arising from Oblique Refraction at a Spherical Surface.

We will now investigate the refraction of a narrow fan of rays, such as would lie in the plane of the diagram, Fig. 19, represented by LAB_t and MPB_t directed towards the "object point" B_t. They are refracted at the spherical surface AP separating media of refractive indices n and n'; the centre of curvature is at C. Let the angles of

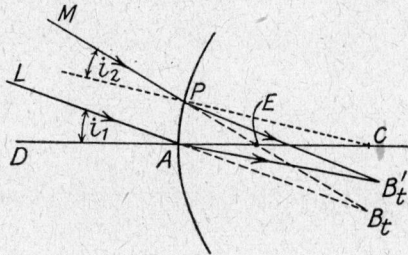

FIG. 19

incidence of the two rays be i_1 and i_2. The lines PB_t and AC cross one another at E.

The law of refraction is

$$n \sin i = n' \sin i'$$

Differentiating, we obtain

$$n \, di \cos i = n' \, di' \cos i' \qquad . \qquad . \qquad . \qquad (114)$$

The two rays considered may be supposed to have angles of incidence which are very nearly equal; if so, we may put in the equation above

$$di = i_1 - i_2 = \widehat{CAB_t} - \widehat{CPB_t}$$

and since from the triangles PEC and AEB_t

$$\widehat{CPB_t} + \widehat{PCA} = \widehat{CAB_t} + \widehat{AB_tP},$$

$$di = \widehat{CAB_t} - \widehat{CPB_t} = \widehat{PCA} - \widehat{AB_tP}$$

The values of the angles on the right of this equation can be represented by their angular measure, expressed sufficiently nearly by

$$\widehat{PCA} = \frac{AP}{r}, \qquad \widehat{AB_tP} = \frac{AP \cos i}{t}, \qquad \text{where } t = AB_t*$$

* Imagine a perpendicular dropped from A to the line PB_t. When di tends towards zero, both i_1 and i_2 tend to the value i.

Thus $$di = AP\left(\frac{1}{r} - \frac{\cos i}{t}\right)$$

Similarly,* $$di' = AP\left(\frac{1}{r} - \frac{\cos i'}{t'}\right), \text{ where } t' = AB'_t$$

Substituting these values in equation (114) and dividing both sides by AP,

$$n \cos i\left(\frac{1}{r} - \frac{\cos i}{t}\right) = n' \cos i'\left(\frac{1}{r} - \frac{\cos i'}{t'}\right)$$

On re-arranging

$$\frac{n' \cos^2 i'}{t'} - \frac{n \cos^2 i}{t} = \frac{n' \cos i' - n \cos i}{r} \qquad . \qquad (115)$$

This equation, then, gives the relation between the distances of the convergence points of a very narrow fan of rays, lying in a plane passing through the centre of curvature of the refracting surface, before and after refraction, the distances being measured from the surface. Such a fan is called a "tangential fan." The rays have the same limitations with respect to each other as the paraxial ray has to the axis in the Gaussian theory. In ordinary cases, the signs of conjugate distances arising in such equations are identical with the signs of their projections on the axis of the system.

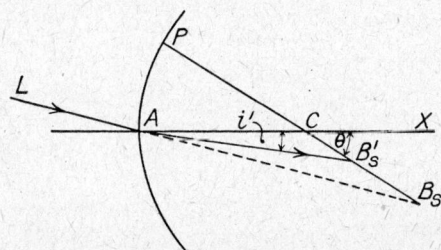

Sagittal Fan. Referring to Fig. 20, imagine a spherical refracting surface represented by the section AP, with its centre of curvature at C. A ray LA in the plane of the diagram is refracted at A into the direction AB_s'. If the object point on the incident ray is at B_s, draw the line $CB_s'B_s$ cutting the final direction of the ray, after refraction, in the point B_s', and the surface in P.

If the diagram were slightly rotated about the axis $PCB_s'B_s$, the points B_s' and B_s would remain in the plane of the paper, and the section of the surface in the diagram would have the same position, but the sections LA and AB_s' of the ray would have new positions slightly above or below the present plane of the diagram, although still directed towards B_s and B_s' respectively. In this manner we

* A similar argument could have been carried out for this case.

have obtained two ray paths of a sagittal fan; the convergence points before and after refraction are B_s and B_s'. They have a projective relation with regard to the centre C.

Let $AB_s = s$, and $AB_s' = s'$. Then, from the triangle ACB_s',

$$\frac{CB_s'}{\sin i'} = \frac{s'}{\sin \widehat{ACB_s}}$$

whence
$$\sin \widehat{ACB_s} = \frac{s' \sin i'}{CB_s'}.$$

Similarly,
$$\frac{CB_s}{\sin i} = \frac{s}{\sin \widehat{ACB_s}}$$

whence
$$\sin \widehat{ACB_s} = \frac{s \sin i}{CB_s}$$

Then
$$\frac{s' \sin i'}{CB_s'} = \frac{s \sin i}{CB_s}$$

but
$$n' \sin i' = n \sin i$$

Dividing, we obtain
$$\frac{CB_s' \cdot n'}{s'} = \frac{CB_s \cdot n}{s}$$

In order to obtain the ratio of CB_s' to CB_s, project these lengths on the line ACX by multiplying by $\cos \widehat{XCB_s} = \cos \theta$. Then $CB_s' \cos \theta = (s' \cos i' - r)$, and similarly. Then

$$\frac{n'(s' \cos i' - r)}{s'} = \frac{n(s \cos i - r)}{s}$$

and on re-arranging

$$\frac{n'}{s'} - \frac{n}{s} = \frac{n' \cos i' - n \cos i}{r} \qquad . \qquad . \qquad (116)$$

It will be noticed in this expression that the quantity appearing on the right of the equation is the same as that which occurs in the rather more complicated "tangential" equation. Moreover, when the angles of incidence are very small, both (115) and (116) reduce to the paraxial equation (107).

Now, referring to Fig. 12, if we imagine a small diaphragm at the centre C of the refracting surface, the image formation for any object point will be effected by a group of rays passing through C, and consequently the paraxial equation (107) is applicable to calculate the conjugate distances measured along the principal rays. If, however, the diaphragm is situated at the apex A of the surface (Fig. 21), the principal ray from any extra-axial object point will suffer deviation at the surface, and consequently a difference arises between the refraction of neighbouring rays lying in that *plane containing the object point and the axis,* and neighbouring rays in a plane perpendicular to the one just mentioned. Such sets

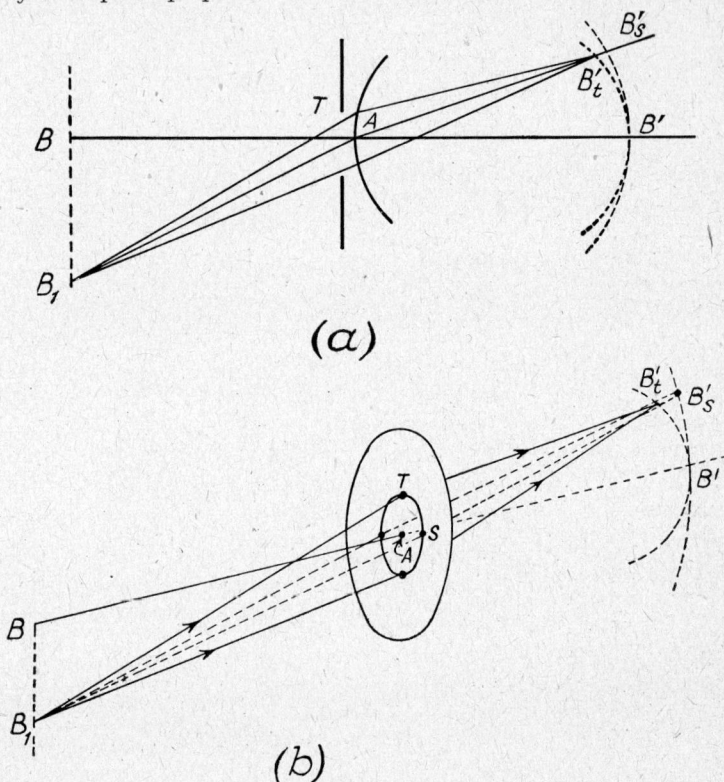

(a)

(b)

Fig. 21

of rays, diverging from the object point, constitute the "tangential" and "sagittal" "fans" respectively. The corresponding conjugate distances along the principal ray have to be calculated by the formulae (115) and (116) respectively.

The axial symmetry ensures that, in general, if the object surface is symmetrical about the axis, the two surfaces containing the tangential and sagittal image points respectively will also be symmetrical about the axis. The parts of all these surfaces close to the axis will be very close to the corresponding planes tangential at the axial points (the image surfaces have a common tangent), and such planes represent the conjugate object and image planes of paraxial theory.

Fig. 21 is intended to suggest the relative positions of the rays. The extra-axial object point is B_1, and the plane containing this point and the axis AB contains also the tangential rays (indicated by arrows), which meet the diaphragm in the diameter indicated by the point T. The sagittal rays (broken lines) meet the diaphragm at the extremities of the diameter indicated by S. The broken curves through B_t' and B_s' are to suggest the loci of the image points corresponding to the line BB_1 of the object surface. Rotation of the diagram around the axis BAB' would transform these lines into conjugate surfaces.

Astigmatic *reflection* at a spherical surface will be discussed in Vol. II.

Astigmatism of a Thin Lens Passed Centrally by an Oblique Pencil. Formulae 115 and 116 may be applied to find the tangential and sagittal powers of a thin lens traversed obliquely through its centre by a bundle of rays from a point not on the axis. The principal ray, which passes through the centre of the lens, will be refracted symmetrically, so that the angle θ of emergence from the second face will be equal to the angle of incidence on the first face. Let the internal angle of refraction be ϕ and the refractive index n. Successive applications of the tangential formula give

$$\frac{n \cos^2\phi}{t_1'} - \frac{\cos^2\theta}{t_1} = \frac{n \cos\phi - \cos\theta}{r_1}$$

$$\frac{\cos^2\theta}{t_2'} - \frac{n \cos^2\phi}{t_2} = \frac{\cos\theta - n \cos\phi}{r_2}$$

If the thickness of the lens is negligible $t_2 = t_1'$, and thus, on adding,

$$\cos^2\theta \left(\frac{1}{t_2'} - \frac{1}{t_1} \right) = (n \cos\phi - \cos\theta) \left(\frac{1}{r_1} - \frac{1}{r_2} \right) = \left(\frac{n \cos\phi - \cos\theta}{n - 1} \right) \frac{1}{f'}$$

and thus the oblique tangential power F_t is

$$F_t = \frac{1}{f_t'} = \left(\frac{1}{t_2'} - \frac{1}{t_1} \right) = \left(\frac{n \cos\phi - \cos\theta}{(n - 1) \cos^2\theta} \right) \frac{1}{f'}$$

Similarly, two successive applications of the sagittal formula give

$$F_s = \frac{1}{f_s'} = \left(\frac{n \cos\phi - \cos\theta}{n - 1} \right) \frac{1}{f'} = \left(\frac{n \cos\phi - \cos\theta}{n - 1} \right) F$$

so that

$$\frac{f_t'}{f_s'} = \cos^2\theta = \frac{F_s}{F_t}.$$

In order to evaluate the expressions for the astigmatic powers, note that $n \sin \phi = \sin \theta$, and write,

$$\frac{n \cos \phi - \cos \theta}{\cos^2\theta} = \left\{ n \left(1 - \frac{\sin^2\theta}{n^2} \right)^{\frac{1}{2}} - (1 - \sin^2\theta)^{\frac{1}{2}} \right\} (1 - \sin^2\theta)^{-1}$$

If θ is so small that powers of $\sin \theta$ above the second may be neglected, we obtain, after expansion by the Binomial theorem,

$$\boldsymbol{F}_t = \left(1 + \frac{2n + 1}{2n} \sin^2\theta \right) \boldsymbol{F}, \quad \text{and} \quad \boldsymbol{F}_s = \left(1 + \frac{\sin^2\theta}{2n} \right) \boldsymbol{F}$$

so that the difference of the oblique powers at an angle θ is (sufficiently nearly)

$$\boldsymbol{F}_t - \boldsymbol{F}_s = \boldsymbol{F} \sin^2\theta$$

In the case of a thin lens of a glass for which $n = 1.5$, both the tangential power and the sagittal power exceed the paraxial power approximately by factors of $1 + (4 \sin^2\theta)/3$ and $1 + (\sin^2\theta)/3$ respectively, and for an object field at infinity both focal surfaces are concave towards the lens, the tangential field having the greater curvature.

The lens action in the direction θ is that of a sphero-cylindrical lens (p. 305) having a spherical power $= \boldsymbol{F}_s$ as given above, combined with a cylinder of $\boldsymbol{F} \sin^2\theta$. This formula is, however, only accurate over small ranges of obliquity, and the cylindrical power increases more rapidly than the $\sin^2$ term allows. The empirical expression, $\boldsymbol{F} \tan^2 \theta$, for the cylindrical power, holds fairly accurately up to about $30°$.

REFERENCES

1. Chrétien: *Nouvelles Tables des Sinus Naturels*, Paris, 1932.

(a) Strömgren: *Optical Sine Tables*. (Seven-figure values of x-sin x, with arguments x and sin x.) Copenhagen, 1945.

2. Peters: *Siebenstellige Werte der Trig. Funktionen*, Berlin, 1918.

3. Five-figure logarithm tables (H.M. Stationery Office), London, 1944.

4. T. Smith: *Dictionary of Applied Physics IV*, 314.

5. *Leipziger Berichte*, *VII*, 8 (1855).

CHAPTER II

PARAXIAL THEORY OF OPTICAL SYSTEMS

THE simple laws which were known to relate the sizes and positions of objects and images in the simple cases of refraction of a paraxial bundle by a spherical surface, or by a thin lens, naturally led to attempts to extend these laws to more complex cases, such as a succession of spherical refracting surfaces with their centres on one axis.

The case of a centred system of thin lenses was discussed by Cotes, who investigated the relation between the angles made with the axis, by a ray in an axial plane, before and after refraction by the system. The treatment was given in R. Smith's *Compleat System of Opticks* (1738); the general case of a succession of refracting surfaces was also dealt with in this book, but not in a manner which has been found very convenient. Amongst other early workers in the field were Euler, and Lagrange, who derived general laws, but the greatest advance must be credited to Gauss.[1] His method was to apply the simple formulae to the case of successive refractions at a number of centred spherical surfaces separating media of different refractive indices; then by making certain substitutions he was able to express the final relation between the dimensions of the object and image spaces in a more general form, of a type which could always be obtained, no matter what the number of refractions.

The work of Möbius (1855) indicated, however, that the projective relationship found between the object and image spaces for a single refraction would entail as a direct consequence a geometrical relationship between the object and image spaces after any number of refractions, again of a type which would be independent of the construction of the optical system. Then, in 1856 and 1858, Clerk Maxwell published a discussion of the properties of a "perfect" optical system, in which the discussion of the "mechanism" of the image formation is not introduced, with the exception of the single provision that the image is formed by the union of rays which are straight lines in the object and image spaces.

The features of a "perfect" imagery in the sense imagined by Maxwell may be shortly stated as follows—

1. Every ray of a pencil passing through a single point of the object space must, after transmission, pass through a single point of the image space. Failure to fulfil this condition may be termed *Astigmatism.**

* The term is here used in a more general sense than in the usual connotation, which will be explained in Chapter IV.

2. To every plane perpendicular to the axis in the object space there corresponds a plane also perpendicular to the axis in the image space. Failure to fulfil this condition may be termed *Curvature of the field*.

3. The image of any figure found in an image plane must be geometrically "similar" to the corresponding figure in the corresponding or "conjugate" object plane. Failure to fulfil this condition may be known as *Distortion*.

From these premises, Maxwell showed by means of simple geometrical considerations that if an instrument can be assumed to give perfect images of plane figures situated in two planes of the object space, perpendicular to the axis, the imagery will be perfect for all other pairs of conjugate planes.

Image formation of this kind is styled "collinear." It is free from restrictions as to angles of rays, sizes of object and image, and separations and radii of surfaces, but the results may only be applied to actual cases of image formation in so far as the system can be shown to fulfil the necessary conditions; thus, in the general case this theory only holds for the paraxial region, but its validity may be extended in special cases such as those of highly-corrected photographic lenses, which may be corrected for rays passing through the margins of the lenses and forming images at a comparatively large distance from the axis.

The method of discussion used by Abbe (1872), and developed independently of Maxwell, was to assume the existence of two pairs of conjugate planes for which the imagery is perfect in the Maxwellian sense. The two planes in the object space are parallel, and perpendicular to the axis of that space; likewise for the image space. The magnification for each pair of conjugate planes is assigned unique values, M_1 and M_2 (say); then it is shown that any other pair of conjugate planes must give perfect imagery and possess a unique value of the magnification.

Parallel rays in the object space are brought to a single focus in the second focal plane; rays from points in the first focal plane (in the object space) are rendered parallel in the image space. When the axial distances of conjugate planes are measured from these focal planes, specially simple relations are found to hold between such distances, and simple equations are also obtained for the magnification. The existence of a pair of planes for which the magnification is unity is evident from the possibility of choosing one, and only one, pair of conjugate planes to give any real value, positive or negative, of magnification.

The Abbe theory of general optical systems is available in

English[2]; in the present book the main results will first be obtained in a more geometrical discussion.

The analytical relations between collinear or homographic spaces have been applied to the general theory of image formation by Czapski. The forms of the expressions giving the correlation of the two spaces lead at once to the equations of two planes of discontinuity which appear in the rôles of the focal planes. When these planes are chosen as reference planes, the equations giving the relations between co-ordinates of the object and image spaces can be put into specially simple forms. The general cases of image formation are comprised by the *obverse* and the *reverse* modes; the first is characterized by the case of the pinhole camera, which gives

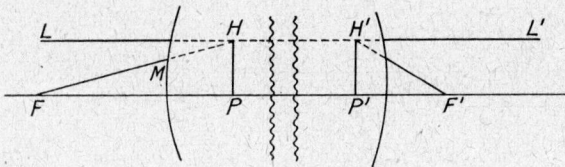

Fig. 22

an "upside down" *and* "right-to-left" reversal; the image formed by a plane mirror is a case of the "reverse" mode, since, for example, images in a vertical mirror exhibit a right-to-left reversal, but no inversion.

The analytical discussions have a considerable academic interest, but so far as applied optics is concerned they are not essential, and the main results can be obtained with facility by the simple geometrical treatment which follows.

A Perfect Optical System. Let us postulate for a beginning an optical system perfect in the Maxwellian sense, having one axis of symmetry. A ray LH (Fig. 22), parallel to the axis, will, in general, after passing through the system, be inclined at an angle to the axis, and will pass through the axial point F'. All rays parallel to the axis in the object space will therefore pass through F', since they may be regarded as derived from one point at an infinite distance. The point F' is the *second principal focus* of the system.

Produce the line LH to L'; let it cut the final direction of the refracted ray in the point H'.

In the object space there must be some axial point F from which the rays, after refraction by the system, are parallel to the axis in the image space; let F represent this point, and let the line FMH represent a ray which, after refraction, takes the final path represented by the same line HL'. These rays must now lie all in one axial plane.

Referring now to Maxwell's first condition, the point H represents the crossing point of two rays in the object space, and the point H' is the corresponding point of the image space. Dropping perpendiculars HP, H'P' to the axis, we obtain the traces of the so-called *principal planes*. **HP and H'P' may be regarded as object and image, and the magnification is evidently unity.**

The distances PF and P'F' are the *focal lengths* of the system; they will be denoted by f and f' respectively.

The most valuable property of the principal planes is that any ray of the object space, passing through a point H of the first plane

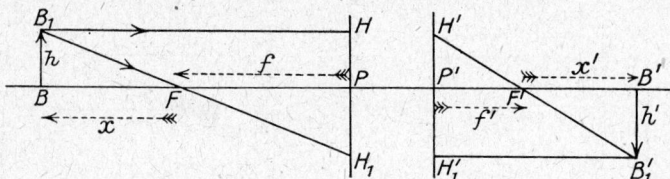

FIG. 23

at a particular distance y from the axis, must pass through the conjugate image point H' in the second principal plane (in the image space); since the magnification is unity, H' will be at the same distance y from the axis.

Construction to Find the Image. The principal planes and focal points are supposed to be given. Referring to Fig. 23, the construction is shown by which the image in the plane through B', corresponding to the object at B, can be found. It is evidently sufficient to trace two rays from the object space into the image space. The first one is parallel to the axis, and intersects the first principal plane in the point H; after refraction it must leave the second principal plane from the point H' (where P'H' = PH) and pass through the second principal focus F'. The other ray passes through the first principal focus F, as shown, and is parallel to the axis after refraction; its distance from the axis in the image space is found from the distance at which it intersects the first principal plane. Note that PH = h and $PH_1 = P'H'_1 = h'$, where h and h' are the heights of object BB_1 and image $B'B_1'$ respectively.

We had $\qquad$ PF $= f$, $\quad$ P'F' $= f'$

Let $\qquad$ FB $= x$, $\quad$ F'B' $= x'$

(Note that "FB" means the distance measured *from* F *to* B, and similarly.) Referring to the sign conventions (p. 15), note that h

and h', as shown in the diagram, are numerically positive and negative respectively; also f and x are both numerically negative in this case, while f' and x' are numerically positive. Then from the similar triangles B_1BF_1 and H_1PF,

$$\frac{h}{h'} = -\frac{x}{f} \qquad . \qquad . \qquad . \qquad (201)$$

Note the necessary negative sign on the right-hand side of the equation. Similarly,

$$\frac{h'}{h} = -\frac{x'}{f'} \qquad . \qquad . \qquad . \qquad (202)$$

and by multiplying corresponding sides of the last two equations we obtain

$$xx' = ff' \qquad . \qquad . \qquad . \qquad (203)$$

This relation was known to Newton, in a special form, and is sometimes called after his name.

It is to be noted that these equations are not dependent upon the particular positions assigned to the principal planes and focal

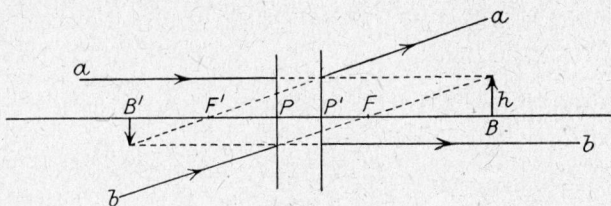

FIG. 24

planes; the form of the equations remains the same if, for example, P is shown to the left of F, although the diagrams then look different.

The student should himself draw the diagram for the case when F and F' interchange the positions they have in Fig. 23; this will correspond in practice to the case typified by a double concave lens which causes a parallel bundle to diverge after transmission. It is recommended that the rays of the image space shall be drawn in red in order to distinguish them. When this is done it will be evident that the object space interpenetrates the image space; an object or a virtual object may be situated in *any* position relative to an optical system. Fig. 24 shows the construction when the object is virtual and is situated to the right of such a "diverging" system; the image is found also to be virtual and situated to the left of the system. The equations are still valid, though f and x are now positive, and f' and x' negative, in the diagram.

To Trace any Ray from the Object Space into the Image Space.
Let P, F, P′, F′ be the axial points of the principal and focal planes
in the object and image spaces. Let (a), Fig. 25, be any ray in the
object space; it is desired to find its direction in the image space.*

Draw the ray (b) in the object space passing through F and parallel
to (a). These parallel rays will meet in one point of the second focal
plane. The distances at which they cross the second principal plane
are known, for these are determined by the distances in the first

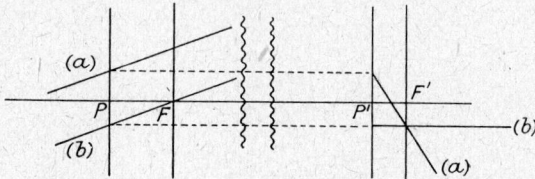

FIG. 25

principal plane. The path of ray (b) is completely known, since it
travels parallel to the axis in the image space; hence the point at
which it cuts the second focal plane is known, and this is the second
of the two required points on the path of ray (a) in the image space.

A similar method is obviously possible for a ray not lying in an
axial plane.

Relation between Positions of Conjugate Planes. Fig. 26 illustrates
a simple graphical method of exhibiting the relations between the

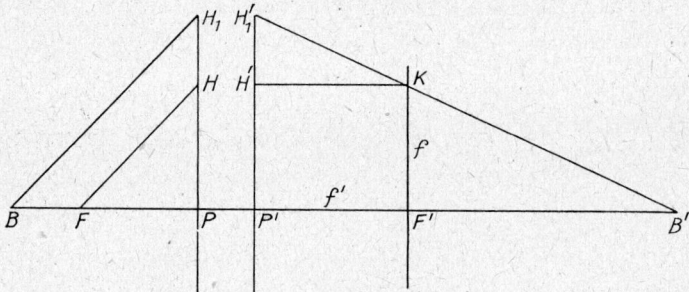

FIG. 26

positions of axial object and image points B and B′ respectively.
PH is made equal to FP, and BH_1 is drawn parallel to FH. The
path of these "rays" in the image space is then determined; both
pass through the point K in the second focal plane, of which the

---

* Fig. 25 may appear unfamiliar, but it is useful to practise changing the
relative positions of principal and focal planes. The student should draw the
figure for the more usual case.

co-ordinates with respect to the axes P'F' and P'H' are numerically equal to f' and f respectively. Hence the construction to find the image point is to make $P'H_1' = BP$, join $H_1'K'$ and produce to meet the axis in B'.

The Nodal Points of an Optical System. The focal points and principal planes of an optical system are shown, as before, in Fig. 27. It is desired to find under what conditions a point on the axis can be found in the object space, so that a ray directed towards it will, after transmission by the system, leave the conjugate point in the image space at an equal angle with the axis.

Start by taking any point K in the second focal plane through which the ray H'K travels parallel to the axis. The path of the

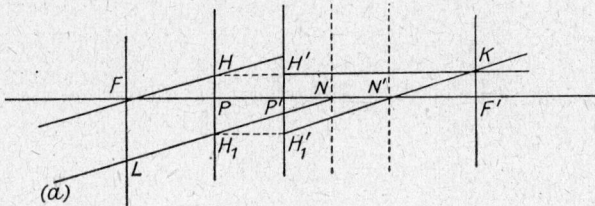

FIG. 27

corresponding ray in the object space is FH; the rays cut the principal planes in the points H and H'. at the same distance from the axis.

Through K draw the line $KN'H_1'$ parallel to FH, cutting the axis in N' and the second principal plane in H_1'; taking H_1 in the first principal plane so that $PH_1 = P'H_1'$, draw the line LH_1N parallel to $H_1'K$, cutting the first focal plane in L, the first principal plane in H_1, and the axis in N. Then FH and LH_1 may represent parallel rays of the object space meeting in K after transmission, and the ray LH_1N is one for which the paths before and after transmission are parallel.

We have thus obtained a system with two points N and N' fulfilling the condition required above; it remains to examine the location of N and N'. They are the *Nodal Points* of the system.

Since the figure $NH_1H_1'N'$ is a parallelogram, $H_1H_1' = PP' = NN'$. Again, since $FL = HH_1 = H'H_1'$, it will be clear from the construction that the triangles FLN and $H'H_1'K$ are equal in all respects, and hence $FN = H'K = P'F'$, showing that N is a fixed point independent of the inclination of the ray LN.

It is also seen from the triangles FPH and N'F'K that $F'N' = PF$, showing that N' is also fixed with regard to the other points of the system.

From the above equations it follows that

$$\frac{FP}{FN} = \frac{F'N'}{F'P'} = -\frac{f}{f'}$$

The Nodal Planes. Since N and N' are axial conjugate points, the planes perpendicular to the axis passing through these points are conjugate planes. An object in the first has an image in the second. The magnification is obtained from equation (202),

$$\frac{h''}{h} = -\frac{x'}{f'} = -\frac{F'N'}{f'} = -\frac{PF}{f'} = -\frac{f}{f'}$$

It follows at once from the equations above that in cases when the two focal lengths are numerically equal, and $f' = -f$, the nodal and principal planes will coincide, and the "magnification" will be unity.

Longitudinal or Axial Magnification. Starting with the formula (203) above, let $\triangle x'$ be the variation in x' caused by a change $\triangle x$ in x. Then

$$(x + \triangle x)(x' + \triangle x') = ff'$$
$$xx' + x'\triangle x + x\triangle x' + \triangle x\triangle x' = ff'$$

and by using (203) again, and re-arranging,

$$\triangle x' = -\frac{x'\triangle x}{x + \triangle x} \quad . \quad . \quad . \quad (204)$$

When $\triangle x'$ and $\triangle x$ are reduced to infinitesimal quantities, their product (occurring in the last equation but one) will be negligible, and we shall have in the usual notation

$$\frac{dx'}{dx} = -\frac{x'}{x} \quad . \quad . \quad . \quad (205)$$

Dividing equation (202) by (201),

$$\frac{x'}{x} = \left(\frac{h'}{h}\right)^2 \cdot \frac{f'}{f}$$

Hence,

$$\frac{dx'}{dx} = -\left(\frac{h'}{h}\right)^2 \cdot \frac{f'}{f} \quad . \quad . \quad (206)*$$

This formula throws light on the relation between the space representation in the axial direction as compared with the representation

---

* It will be proved below that $-\left(\dfrac{f'}{f}\right) = \dfrac{n'}{n}$ where n' and n are the refractive indices of object and image spaces; hence, $\dfrac{dx'}{dx} = \left(\dfrac{h'}{h}\right)^2 \dfrac{n'}{n}$.

of dimensions perpendicular to the axis. In the case of an un-distorted presentation, $\dfrac{dx'}{dx}$ would be directly proportional to the magnification $\left(\dfrac{h'}{h}\right)$ instead of to the square of this ratio.

Combination of Two Systems. The next step is the investigation of the position of the principal and focal planes of a combination of two systems for which the data are known and which are co-axial. It is possible to commence by considering two coaxial *systems* as is done in this section, or to consider the action of two surfaces as the first step and so build up the theory as is done below (p. 55).

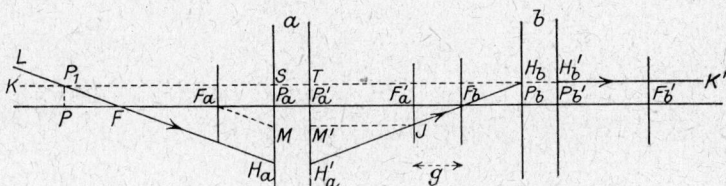

FIG. 28

Fig. 28 represents the focal and principal planes of two co-axial systems, a and b (*met by the light in the order a, b*), of which the "adjacent" focal points are situated so that

$$F_a'F_b = g$$

There is no restriction as to the media in which the systems are placed, but, of course, there must be no change of medium between the two systems. Since it must be granted from the general theory that the principal and focal planes of the combination exist, it is simple to proceed by finding that axial point of the object space, a ray from which is rendered parallel to the axis in the final image space after the double transmission.

Any ray passing through the first focal point F_b of the system (b) must fulfil this condition; such a ray is shown in the diagram by $H_a'F_bH_b'$, and it cuts the second focal plane of system (a) in the point J. What was its course before refraction by (a)?

If the ray M′J, parallel to the axis and cutting the second principal plane of (a) in the point M′ be drawn, its course before transmission by system (a) must pass through both F_a and M, where M lies in the first principal plane so that $P_aM = P_a'M'$. Now, since there are two rays which meet in the point J in the second focal plane of (a), their courses must have been parallel before transmission by (a), and the required path LH_a becomes known; it cuts the axis in the point F, which is recognized as the first focal point of the combination.

If the *final* path $H_b'K'$ of this same ray be produced backwards to K, it will intersect the initial path LH_a in the point P_1. Wherever the second principal plane of the combination is situated, the intersection height of the final path of the ray with this plane must be equal to H_bP_b in the diagram, and this is equal to P_1P, where P is the foot of the perpendicular dropped from P_1 to the axis.

The initial path of a ray entering a system intersects the first principal plane at the same height from the axis as that with which the final path intersects the second principal plane. Hence P_1P must lie in the first principal plane of the combination, since P_1 is (in general) the only point on the incident ray at the required distance from the axis.

From the above construction the following relations are derived—

$$\frac{P_1P}{PF} = \frac{P_aM}{F_aP_a} \quad . \quad (a) \text{ and } \frac{F_bP_b}{H_bP_b} = \frac{F_a'F_b}{F_a'J}$$

From the second of these relations, putting $F_a'J = P_aM$, and $H_bP_b = P_1P$, we obtain

$$\frac{F_bP_b}{P_1P} = \frac{F_a'F_b}{P_aM} \quad . \quad . \quad . \quad . \quad . \quad . \quad (b)$$

Multiplying corresponding sides of (a) and (b), we then obtain

$$\frac{F_bP_b}{PF} = \frac{F_a'F_b}{F_aP_a}, \text{ or } -\frac{f_b}{f} = -\frac{g}{f_a}$$

where f is written for PF, giving

$$f = \frac{f_af_b}{g} \quad . \quad . \quad . \quad . \quad . \quad . \quad (207)$$

Let the separation of "adjacent" principal points, $P_a'P_b = d$. If the line KK' parallel to the axis cuts the first and second principal planes of (a) in the points S and T respectively,

$$\frac{F_a'F_b}{P_a'P_b} = \frac{P_a'M'}{TH_a'} = \frac{P_aM}{SH_a}$$

Also

$$\frac{P_aF_a}{P_aP} = \frac{P_aM}{SH_a}$$

whence

$$\frac{P_aF_a}{P_aP} = \frac{F_a'F_b}{P_a'P_b} \text{ or } \frac{f_a}{P_aP} = \frac{g}{d}, \text{ or } P_aP = \frac{f_ad}{g} \quad . \quad (208)$$

In a similar manner it may be shown that

$$f' = -\frac{f_a' f_b'}{g} \qquad \qquad \qquad (209)$$

and $\qquad$ $P_b' P' = \frac{f_b' d}{g}$. $\qquad \qquad \qquad$ (210)

The student should draw the necessary diagrams and work out the two last formulae for himself.

The above formulae are sufficient for the calculation of the positions of the focal and principal planes of combinations with more

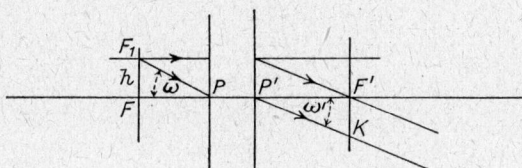

FIG. 29

than two members, since they can be combined in pairs till the constants of the whole system are obtained.

Application of the General Theory. The discussion of cases of refraction at curved surfaces, which led up to the formulae concerning the thin lens, and the general relations between the object and image spaces for a single refraction when narrow pencils are dealt with, indicated that the Maxwellian conditions of perfect imagery are likely to be generally valid only in so far as rays are confined to the paraxial region and images are comparatively small. While this is true, there are many cases in which useful approximations can be obtained by the theory.

The inquiry may first be made under what circumstances the focal lengths of a system will differ numerically. In Fig. 29 the focal and principal planes of a "perfect" system are shown, but the angles of the rays with the axis are large. *The diagram can best be regarded as representing a possible case of the action of a real lens system, if it be assumed that all distances shown perpendicular to the axis are represented on a greatly enlarged scale*; in fact, this applies to the great majority of the cases in which such diagrams are employed.

F_1 represents, then, a point very near the axis in the first focal plane; the ray $F_1 P$ is traced through the system by the usual method. According to our conventions, the geometry of the figure allows us to write for the angles ω and ω' which the ray makes with the axis at P and P',

$$\tan \omega = -\frac{h}{f} \text{ and } \tan \omega' = \frac{h}{f'}$$

where $h = FF_1 = KF'$. Note that these distances are both measured upwards, i.e. from F to F_1, and from K to F'; they are both positive. When ω and ω' are very small, these relations give

$$f\omega = -f'\omega'$$

But the Lagrange relation (109), $nh\alpha = n'h'\alpha'$, applied to the present case, gives $nh\omega = n'h'\omega'$, where the h and h' refer to the sizes of object and image in the conjugate planes represented by the axial crossing points of one ray; in the case above, these points are P and P', the axial points of the unit planes where $h = h'$. Hence, in this case,

$$n\omega = n'\omega'$$

and since

$$f\omega = -f'\omega',$$

we have

$$-\frac{n}{f} = \frac{n'}{f'} \qquad . \qquad . \qquad . \qquad . \qquad (211)$$

The value of n'/f' is the power, **F**, of the system.

A system will have numerically different focal lengths, then, when the initial and final media are not the same; a typical case is the human eye, for which the anterior focal length in air may be taken as -16.8 mm., while the posterior focal length is 22.4 mm., the object space being filled with the "vitreous humour," of refractive index about 1.33.

Power of a System. Numerical Calculation. Fig. 27 shows a pair of parallel rays entering an optical system at an angle ω (say) with the axis. One of them passes through the first focal point. They intersect in the second focal plane at a distance h' from the axis where

$$h' = f \tan \omega$$

In the "reduced" notation, equation (108) becomes

$$h\bar{L} = h'\bar{L}'$$

and this equation can be applied to any series of refracting surfaces or optical systems, so that

$$\frac{h_1'}{h_1} = \frac{\bar{L}_1}{\bar{L}_1'}, \quad \frac{h_2'}{h_2} = \frac{\bar{L}_2}{\bar{L}_2'}, \text{ etc.}$$

and since $h_2 = h_1'$ being identical, we have for k elements

$$m = \frac{h_k'}{h_1} = \frac{\bar{L}_1 \times \bar{L}_2 \times \ldots \bar{L}_k}{\bar{L}_1' \times \bar{L}_2' \times \ldots \bar{L}_k'} = \prod_{1}^{k} \frac{\bar{L}}{\bar{L}'} \qquad (212)$$

If the original object is at an infinite distance, then we can imagine two stars, one on the axis, the other sending a parallel beam into the system at an angle ω with the axis. The images are found in the final focal plane at a distance $h_k' = f \tan \omega$, where f is the first focal length of the whole combination.

For the corresponding image size formed by the first element, we have

$$h_1' = f_1 \tan \omega$$

and hence the final h_k' is given by

$$h_k' = f_1 \tan \omega \prod_{2}^{k} \frac{\bar{L}}{\bar{L}'} = f \tan \omega$$

Hence, if we calculate the values of $\bar{L}$ and $\bar{L}'$ arising in the refraction of a paraxial ray (originally parallel to the axis) through the system, we can find the focal length of the combination by the relations

$$f = f_1 \prod_{2}^{k} \frac{\bar{L}}{\bar{L}'} \qquad (213)$$

By tracing light through the system in the opposite direction in an exactly similar manner we could obtain the second focal length

$$f' = f_k' \prod_{k-1}^{1} \frac{\bar{L}'}{\bar{L}} \qquad (214)$$

but otherwise it is easily calculated by equation (211). The paraxial trace gives also, on a final result, the position of the second focal point. The position of the second principal point is found at a distance of $-f'$ from the second focal point.

Numerical Example. Schematic Eye. Gullstrand has given figures for a simple optical system intended closely to imitate the optical action of the human eye. (A more complex arrangement is detailed in Chapter V.) This "schematic eye" has three refracting surfaces, of which the first is the convexity of the cornea; and the second and third enclose the crystalline lens, imagined as embedded in a single medium. The lengths are given in metres.

$r_1 = 0.0078.$

$r_2 = 0.01.$

$r_3 = -0.0060.$

Humour: $n = 1.336, \ d_1 = 0.0036$

Crystalline: $n = 1.4130; d_2 = 0.0036$

Humour: $n = 1.336$

The calculation for the vergencies and focal lengths is shown below.

From the table $\bar{L}_3' = 78\cdot70$, whence $l_3' = 1\cdot336/78\cdot70$ m. $= 16\cdot97$ mm.

Therefore the distance of the second focal point from the cornea $= 16\cdot97 + d_1 + d_2 = 24\cdot17$ mm. The focal length

$$f = f_1 \prod_2^3 \frac{\bar{L}}{\bar{L}'} = -23\cdot22 \times 0\cdot8634 \times 0\cdot8370 = -16\cdot78 \text{ mm.}$$

$$f' = -\frac{n'}{n}f = 1\cdot336 \times 16\cdot78 = 22\cdot42 \text{ mm.}$$

The second principal point is found at a distance from the cornea

$$= 24\cdot17 - 22\cdot42 = 1\cdot75 \text{ mm.}$$

$$\text{Power of eye} = \frac{1}{\cdot01678} = \frac{1\cdot336}{\cdot02242} = 59\cdot59 \text{ diopters.}$$

FORMULAE AND CALCULATION

$$\bar{L}' = \bar{L} + F \qquad\qquad l_1' = 1/\bar{L}_1', \qquad\qquad \bar{L}_2 = 1/(\bar{l}_1' - \bar{d})$$

	1ST SURFACE		2ND SURFACE		3RD SURFACE	
	Number	Logarithm	Number	Logarithm	Number	Logarithm
n	1·0000		1·3360	·1258	1·4130	0·1501
r	0·0078	$\bar{3}$·8921	0·0100	$\bar{2}$·0000	− 0·0060	$\bar{3}$·7782n
n'	1·3360	0·1258	1·4130	·1501	1·3360	0·1258
d	0·0036	$\bar{3}$·5563	0·0036	$\bar{3}$·5563		
$\bar{d}$	0·002694	$\bar{3}$·4305	0·002548	$\bar{3}$·4062		
$n' - n$	0·3360	$\bar{1}$·5263	0·0770	$\bar{2}$·8865	− 0·0770	$\bar{2}$·8865n
R	128·2	2·1079	100·0	2·0000	− 166·65	2·2218n
F	43·07	1·6342	7·70	0·8865	12·83	1·1083
f (mm.)	− 23·22	1·3658n				
f' (mm.)	31·02	1·4916				
$\bar{L}$	0		48·71	1·6876	65·87	1·8187
$\bar{L}'$	43·07	1·6342	56·41	1·7514	78·70	1·8960
$\bar{l}'$	0·02322	$\bar{2}$·3658	0·01773	$\bar{2}$·2486	0·01271	$\bar{2}$·1040
$\bar{l}' - \bar{d}$	0·02053	$\bar{2}$·3124	0·01518	$\bar{2}$·1813		
$1/(\bar{l}' - d)$	48·71	1·6876	65·87	1·8187		
$\bar{L}/\bar{L}'$			0·8634	$\bar{1}$·9362	0·8370	$\bar{1}$·9227

Reference of Conjugate Distance Equation to Principal Points and Nodal Points.

If l' is the axial distance of the image measured from the principal point P', then

$$l' = x' + f'$$

and, similarly, the distance l of the object from P is

$$l = x + f$$

Hence, writing

$$x' = l' - f'$$

and

$$x = l - f$$

and substituting in (203), we obtain

$$(l' - f')(l - f) = ff'$$

whence

$$ll' - lf' - fl' = 0$$

and dividing by ll'

$$\frac{f'}{l'} + \frac{f}{l} = 1 \qquad . \qquad . \qquad . \qquad . \qquad (215)$$

Again, let z' be the distance of the image measured from the nodal point N', then

$$x' = z' + f$$

and similarly,

$$x = z + f'$$

and, on multiplying as above, we obtain

$$zz' + f'z' + fz = 0$$

or

$$\frac{f'}{z} + \frac{f}{z'} = -1 \qquad . \qquad . \qquad . \qquad (216)$$

These relations may be modified again by using the relation between the focal lengths and the power **F**,

$$\frac{n'}{f'} = -\frac{n}{f} = \textbf{F}$$

obtaining for the principal point equation

$$\frac{n'}{l'} - \frac{n}{l} = \textbf{F} \qquad . \qquad . \qquad . \qquad . \qquad (217)$$

and for the nodal point equation,

$$\frac{1}{n'z'} - \frac{1}{nz} = \frac{\textbf{F}}{nn'} \quad . \; . \; . \; \text{ or } \; \frac{n}{z'} - \frac{n'}{z} = \textbf{F} \; . \qquad . \qquad (218)$$

These forms are instances of the simpler forms of the general Gaussian equation,

$$All' + Bl' - Cl - D = 0$$

which is discussed below.

Two Coaxial Lenses in Air. Let each lens be treated as "thin," then the principal planes of such a thin lens are no longer separated. Let d be the separation of the lenses, then if (as before) $F_a'F_b = g$, we obtain $d = f_a' + g - f_b = f_a' + f_b' + g$, if the lenses are in air.

We obtained $f = \dfrac{f_a f_b}{g}$, and this formula is convenient in some cases; alternatively

$$f' = -\frac{f_a' f_b'}{g} = \frac{f_a' f_b'}{f_a' + f_b' - d}$$

so that

$$\frac{1}{f'} = \frac{1}{f_a'} + \frac{1}{f_b'} - \frac{d}{f_a' f_b'} \qquad . \qquad . \qquad . \qquad (219)$$

The application of equations (208) and (210) to this case give

$$P_a P = \frac{f'd}{f_b'}, \text{ and } P_b P' = -\frac{f'd}{f_a'} \text{ or } = \frac{f'd}{f_a} \qquad . \qquad (220)$$

Refraction at a Single Spherical Surface. Having now discussed the broad properties of collinear systems on the geometrical lines suggested by Maxwell, we will now seek to derive analytical formulae for the optical constants (the focal lengths, etc.) of a system in terms of its given parameters, i.e. the radii and separation of the surfaces, and the refractive indices of the media. It is helpful to study the effect of such a system on the path of a ray, expressed by the angles between the ray and the axis before and after refraction; we will first take the case of a single spherical refracting surface. Referring to Fig. 14, note that the angle of incidence (i) is $\widehat{CPB}$,

so that if the angle

$$\widehat{ACP} = \omega,$$
$$\omega = \alpha + i$$

and, similarly,

$$\omega = \alpha' + i'$$

If the distance (y) of P above A is so small that the angles are of paraxial magnitude, the law of refraction takes the form

$$ni = n'i'$$

and thus from above, $n(\omega - \alpha) = n'(\omega - \alpha')$
or transposing, $\qquad n'\alpha' - n\alpha = (n' - n)\omega$

In the paraxial case, $\omega = y/r$, hence the preceding equation becomes

$$n'\alpha' - n\alpha = y(n' - n)/r$$

or
$$n'\alpha' - n\alpha = y\mathbf{F} \qquad . \qquad . \qquad . \qquad . \qquad (221)$$

where the power $\mathbf{F}$ is
$$\mathbf{F} = \frac{n' - n}{r}$$

Refraction by Two Coaxial Spherical Surfaces. It is convenient now to introduce the so-called "reduced inclinations" typified by

$$\bar{\alpha} = n\alpha$$

when the equation (221) applied to the first surface becomes

$$\bar{\alpha}_1' - \bar{\alpha}_1 = \mathbf{F}_1 y_1 \qquad . \qquad . \qquad . \qquad . \qquad (a)$$

Let the refracted ray as considered above meet a second surface of power $\mathbf{F}_2$ at a "reduced" distance $\bar{d}$ from the first. Let the

points P_1, P_2 where it intersects the surfaces have heights y_1 and y_2 respectively above the axis (Fig. 30).

Let the distance between the feet of the perpendiculars from P_1 and P_2 to the axis be δ; then, strictly,

$$y_2 = y_1 - \delta \tan \alpha_1'$$

Remembering, however, that y_1 and y_2 are both very small, we may neglect the difference between δ and the length $A_1A_2 = d$, the separation of the surfaces, and since α_1' is also very small, the equation may be written with sufficient accuracy

$$y_2 = y_1 - d\alpha_1', \quad \text{or } y_2 = y_1 - \bar{d}\,\bar{\alpha}_1' \,. \qquad . \qquad . \qquad (b)$$

where $\bar{d} = \dfrac{d}{n_a}$, and $\bar{\alpha}_1' = n_a\alpha_1'$.

We can add to equations (a) and (b) above,

$$\bar{\alpha}_2' = \bar{\alpha}_1' + \mathbf{F}_2 y_2$$

giving the final reduced inclination of the ray after refraction at the second surface.

Eliminating y_2 and $\bar{\alpha}_1{}'$, we obtain

$$\bar{\alpha}_2{}' = y_1(\mathbf{F}_1 + \mathbf{F}_2 - \mathbf{F}_1\,\mathbf{F}_2\bar{d}) + \bar{\alpha}_1\,(\mathrm{I} - \mathbf{F}_2\bar{d})$$

Dividing by $\bar{\alpha}_1$

$$\frac{\bar{\alpha}_2{}'}{\bar{\alpha}_1} = \frac{y_1}{\bar{\alpha}_1}\,(\mathbf{F}_1 + \mathbf{F}_2 - \mathbf{F}_1\,\mathbf{F}_2\bar{d}) + (\mathrm{I} - \mathbf{F}_2\bar{d})$$

Remembering the meaning of the "reduced" distances and inclinations now being employed, and the Lagrange relation ($h\bar{\alpha} = h'\bar{\alpha}$, in this notation), we find for the height h' of the image of the object (height h)

$$\frac{h}{h'} = \frac{A_1 B}{n}\,(\mathbf{F}_1 + \mathbf{F}_2 - \mathbf{F}_1\,\mathbf{F}_2\bar{d}) + (\mathrm{I} - \mathbf{F}_2\bar{d})\,;$$

writing

$$\mathbf{F} = \mathbf{F}_1 + \mathbf{F}_2 - \mathbf{F}_1\,\mathbf{F}_2\bar{d} \quad . \qquad . \qquad . \qquad . \qquad . \;\; (222)$$

we have

$$\frac{h}{h'} = \frac{\mathbf{F}}{n}\left(A_1 B + \frac{n(\mathrm{I} - \mathbf{F}_2\bar{d})}{\mathbf{F}} \right)$$

Assuming the validity of the general theory and comparing this equation with the equation (201),

$$\frac{h}{h'} = -\frac{x}{f}$$

we may write $\dfrac{\mathbf{F}}{n} = -\dfrac{\mathrm{I}}{f}$, and $x = \mathrm{FB} = A_1 B + \dfrac{n(\mathrm{I} - \mathbf{F}_2\bar{d})}{\mathbf{F}}$

whence

$$\mathbf{F} = -\frac{n}{f} = \frac{n'}{f'} \qquad . \qquad . \qquad . \qquad . \qquad . \;\; (223)$$

(writing n and n' for the refractive indices of the first and last media).

For the distance ($\mathrm{FA}_1 = \mathrm{FB} - A_1 B$) from the first principal focus to the first surface of the system, we obtain

$$\mathrm{FA}_1 = \frac{n(\mathrm{I} - \mathbf{F}_2\bar{d})}{\mathbf{F}} \qquad . \qquad . \qquad . \;\; (224)$$

In a similar way it can be shown that the distance of the second principal focus from the apex of the second surface is given by

$$A_2 \mathrm{F}' = \frac{n'(\mathrm{I} - \mathbf{F}_1\bar{d})}{\mathbf{F}} \qquad . \qquad . \qquad . \;\; (225)$$

The ordinary case of a thick lens in air is represented by putting $n = n' = \mathrm{I}$.

These results can be used to calculate the positions of the focal and principal planes of lenses of finite thickness, as for the spectacle lenses of Fig. 177, Chapter IX. Thus

$$A_2P' = A_2F' - f' = \frac{n'(1 - F_1\bar{d})}{F} - \frac{n'}{F} = -\frac{n'F_1\bar{d}}{F} . \quad (226)$$

Compare this result with that of equation (210). Also work out an expression for A_1P, i.e. $A_1P = \dfrac{n\bar{F}\bar{d}}{F}$ . . . . . (227)

It must not be forgotten that $\bar{d}$ in the above equations is the reduced thickness, i.e. $\dfrac{d}{n_a}$, where n_a is the refractive index of the lens.

Vertex Powers. The so-called "vertex powers" of a system in air are of some importance in the theory of spectacles. Thus we have for a thick lens in air (see also p. 298),

$$\text{Front vertex power} = \frac{1}{FA_1} = \frac{F}{1 - F_2\bar{d}} . \quad (228)$$

$$\text{Back vertex power} = \frac{1}{A_2F} = \frac{F}{1 - F_1\bar{d}} . \quad (229)$$

It is not usual to make any distinction in sign between the front and back vertex powers. The back vertex power will be written F_v. Note that the form of the expressions for the corresponding powers of a system of two thin lenses will be the same, with the exception that the reduced distance $\bar{d}$ will be replaced by the true distance d.

Analytical Discussion. It may be of some service for those who wish to go more fully into the theory, to read the following simplified discussion, which is on the lines of the Gaussian method.

In Fig. 31, B and B' are paraxial conjugate points for the refracting spherical surface AP.

Let AB $= k$ and AB' $= k'$. These distances are connected, then, by the relation

$$\frac{n'}{k'} - \frac{n}{k} = F_1$$

Let BP be a ray refracted through the surface at a very small distance, AP $= y_1$, from the axis, then multiplying the above equation through by y_1 we have

$$\frac{n'y_1}{k'} - \frac{ny_1}{k} = F_1y_1$$

If α_1' and α_1 are the angles made by the ray with the axis and before refraction, the above equation may be written

$$n'\alpha_1' - n\alpha_1 = F_1y_1$$

Draw a normal plane through the axial point S in the object space, and another through S′ in the image space. Let the ray path intersect these, as shown, in the respective points, T and T′ where $ST = y_o$ and $S'T' = y_2$. Let $AS = b$ and $AS' = d$. Then, remembering the paraxial limitations, and neglecting only small quantities of the second order,

$$y_1 = y_o + b\alpha_1 = y_o + \frac{b}{n} \cdot n\alpha_1$$

$$y_2 = y_1 - d\alpha_1' = y_1 - \frac{d}{n'} \cdot n'\alpha_1'$$

but in order to simplify the appearance of the equations in which the reduced quantities only will appear we shall put $\boldsymbol{b}$ instead of $\bar{b}$; $\boldsymbol{\alpha}$ instead of $\bar{\alpha}$; $\boldsymbol{d}$ instead of $\bar{d}$, merely using thicker type.

Then
$$y_1 = y_o + \boldsymbol{b\alpha}_1$$
$$y_2 = y_1 - \boldsymbol{d\alpha}_1'$$
and (from above)
$$\boldsymbol{\alpha}_1' = \boldsymbol{\alpha}_1 + \boldsymbol{F}_1 y_1$$

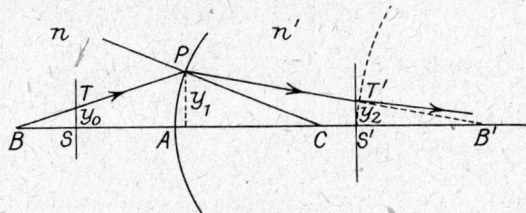

FIG. 31

Eliminating y_1 from these equations, we obtain

$$\boldsymbol{\alpha}_1' = \boldsymbol{F}_1 y_o + \boldsymbol{\alpha}_1(1 + \boldsymbol{F}_1\boldsymbol{b})$$
$$y_2 = (1 - \boldsymbol{d}\,\boldsymbol{F}_1)y_o + \boldsymbol{\alpha}_1(\boldsymbol{b} - \boldsymbol{d} - \boldsymbol{bd}\,\boldsymbol{F}_1)$$

These equations are of the form

$$\left.\begin{array}{l}\boldsymbol{\alpha}_1' = Ay_o + B\boldsymbol{\alpha}_1 \\ y_2 = Cy_o + D\boldsymbol{\alpha}_1\end{array}\right\} (a), \text{ where } \begin{cases}A = \boldsymbol{F}_1, & B = 1 + \boldsymbol{F}_1\boldsymbol{b} \\ C = 1 - \boldsymbol{d}\boldsymbol{F}_1, & D = \boldsymbol{b} - \boldsymbol{d} - \boldsymbol{bd}\boldsymbol{F}_1\end{cases}$$

and by multiplying the co-efficients it is found that $BC - AD = 1$.

As before, let us introduce a second refracting surface with its apex at S', and of power $\boldsymbol{F}_2$; the ray will be refracted at this surface and will intersect a new plane (situated at a reduced distance $\boldsymbol{b}'$ from S') at a height of y_3 (say). Then

$$\boldsymbol{\alpha}_2' = \boldsymbol{\alpha}_1' + \boldsymbol{F}_2 y_2$$
$$y_3 = y_2 - \boldsymbol{b}'\boldsymbol{\alpha}_2'$$

and we may proceed to eliminate y_2 and $\boldsymbol{\alpha}_1'$ from equations (a) and the last two, obtaining

$$\left.\begin{array}{l}\boldsymbol{\alpha}_2' = y_o(A + \boldsymbol{F}_2 C) + \boldsymbol{\alpha}_1(B + \boldsymbol{F}_2 D) \\ y_3 = y_o\{C - \boldsymbol{b}'(A + \boldsymbol{F}_2 C) + \boldsymbol{\alpha}_1\{D - \boldsymbol{b}'(B + \boldsymbol{F}_2 D)\}\end{array}\right\}(b)$$

These equations are of the same form as (a) above, and may be written

$$\alpha_2' = A'y_o + B'\alpha_1$$
$$y_3 = C'y_o + D'\alpha_1$$

If we evaluate $B'C' - A'D'$ we find that $B'C' - A'D' = BC - AD = 1$.

Thus, it appears that the form (a) is a most general one for the effect of refraction of a ray at a series of coaxial spherical surfaces.

Let surface "$n + 1$" be a plane reference surface situated in the medium beyond the nth surface of a system. Then we can find relations of the general form

$$\alpha_n' = Ay_o + B\alpha_1$$
$$y_{n+1} = Cy_o + D\alpha_1$$

where A, B, etc., are new constants.

Now let the two reference surfaces denoted by "o" and "$n + 1$" be brought into coincidence with surfaces "1" and "n." These latter must be *fixed* in relation to the system; for example, they may be the first and last refracting surfaces; then the above equations give

$$\alpha_n' = Ay_1 + B\alpha_1$$
$$y_n = Cy_1 + D\alpha_1$$

and it is evident that equations of the same type as above connect α_n' and y_n with α_1 and y_1. A, B, C, and D are now definite constants of the system.

Take a plane at a *reduced distance* $\boldsymbol{l}$ from the first surface above; then let the entrant ray intersect this plane in B_1 at a height h from the axis.

Take a second plane at a *reduced distance* $\boldsymbol{l'}$ from the last surface, and let the emergent ray intersect this in a point B_1' at a distance h' from the axis.

Then

$$y_1 = h + \boldsymbol{l}\alpha_1$$
$$h' = y_n - \boldsymbol{l'}\alpha_n'$$

Eliminating y_1 and y_n, the following equations are found

$$\alpha_n' = hA + \alpha_1 (A\boldsymbol{l} + B)$$
$$h' = h(C - \boldsymbol{l'}A) - \alpha_1 (A\boldsymbol{l}\boldsymbol{l'} + B\boldsymbol{l'} - C\boldsymbol{l} - D) \qquad (c)$$

The form of these equations can be recognized as the same as before. The conditions for image formation will be clear. If the points B_1, B_1' are object and image, the ratio of h' to h will be independent of α_1, the inclination of the incident ray. Then

$$A\boldsymbol{l}\boldsymbol{l'} + B\boldsymbol{l'} - C\boldsymbol{l} - D = 0 \qquad (d)$$

is a general equation connecting the reduced distances of conjugate planes from two planes fixed in reference to the instrument; the position of the latter planes determines the constants B, C, and D.

The relation

$$A\boldsymbol{l}\boldsymbol{l'} + B\boldsymbol{l'} - C\boldsymbol{l} - D = 0$$

yields when multiplied by A

$$A^2\boldsymbol{l}\boldsymbol{l'} + AB\boldsymbol{l'} - AC\boldsymbol{l} - AD = 0$$

and since $BC - AD = 1$

$$(A\boldsymbol{l} + B)(C - A\boldsymbol{l'}) = 1$$

The magnification of the sharp image is given by

$$\frac{h'}{h} = (C - l'A) = \frac{1}{(Al + B)}$$

The positions of the unit planes are given by putting the magnification equal to unity, obtaining

$$C - l_1'A = 1, \; Al_1 + B = 1 \qquad . \qquad . \qquad . \qquad (e)$$

whence

$$l_1' = \frac{C-1}{A} \text{ and } l_1 = \frac{1-B}{A}$$

The position of the first principal focus is found by putting equation (d) into the form

$$A + \frac{B}{l} - \frac{C}{l'} - \frac{D}{ll'} = 0$$

Then, if $l' = \infty$, $A + \dfrac{B}{l_f} = 0$, or $l_f = -\dfrac{B}{A}$

if $l = \infty$, $A - \dfrac{C}{l_f'} = 0$ $\qquad\qquad l_f' = +\dfrac{C}{A}$

The *reduced* distances f and f' of the focal planes from the principal planes therefore appear as

$$f = l_f - l_1 = -\frac{B}{A} - \frac{(1-B)}{A} = -\frac{1}{A}$$

and

$$f' = l_f' - l_1' = \frac{C}{A} - \frac{(C-1)}{A} = \frac{1}{A}$$

Relations between the Distances of Conjugate Planes. It will appear from the form of equation (d) that the more familiar forms of the optical equations connecting the distances of conjugate foci from certain reference points are merely particular cases of the general relation given by (d).

Reference to Principal Planes. To refer the conjugate distances to the unit planes, introduce into (d) the values of B and C obtained from (e). Then

$$A ll' + (1 - Al_1)l' - (1 + Al_1')l - D = 0$$

This equation must become an identity when $l = l_1$ and $l' = l_1'$, thus giving

$$D = - (Al_1'l_1 - l_1' + l_1)$$

Substituting this into the above form it reduces to

$$\frac{1}{(l' - l_1')} - \frac{1}{(l - l_1)} = A = \frac{1}{f'}$$

Now $(l' - l_1')$ is the reduced distance of the image plane from the second principal plane, while $(l - l_1)$ is the reduced distance of the object plane from the first principal plane.

Thus,

$$\frac{n'}{l'} - \frac{n}{l} = A = \frac{n'}{f'}$$

where l' and l stand for real distances now measured from the principal planes, is the simplified form.

Reference to Focal Planes.

Let
$$l - l_f = \mathbf{x} \text{ and } l' - l_{f'} = \mathbf{x}'$$

or
$$l = \mathbf{x} - \frac{B}{A} \text{ and } l' = \mathbf{x}' + \frac{C}{A}$$

The equations c now assume the form
$$\alpha_n' = hA + \alpha_1 A \mathbf{x}$$
$$h' = h(-A\mathbf{x}') - \alpha_1 \left(A\mathbf{x}\mathbf{x}' + \frac{1}{A}\right)$$

The relation between reduced object and image distances measured from the focal planes is therefore
$$\mathbf{x}\mathbf{x}' = -\frac{1}{A^2} = \mathbf{f}\mathbf{f}'$$

or in ordinary distances
$$\frac{x}{n} \cdot \frac{x'}{n'} = \frac{f}{n} \cdot \frac{f'}{n'}, \text{ or } xx' = ff'$$

Also, the magnification will be
$$\frac{h'}{h} = -A\mathbf{x}' = -\frac{\mathbf{x}'}{\mathbf{f}'}$$

the form being again the same when ordinary distances are denoted.

Relations between the Gaussian Constants and the Composition of the Instrument. (Use of Differential Notation.)

The method adopted is to assume the existence of a group of coaxial spherical refracting surfaces for which the equations
$$\left.\begin{array}{l} \alpha'_{n-1} = Ay_1 + B\alpha_1 \\ y_{n-1} = Cy_1 + D\alpha_1 \end{array}\right\} \quad (f)$$

give the final values of α'_{n-1}, y_{n-1}, in terms of α_1 and y, where y_1 and y_{n-1} are the heights at which the ray crosses the first and last surfaces respectively. Then let a new coaxial surface of power $\mathbf{F}_n$ be placed at a reduced distance $\mathbf{d}'$ from the last refracting surface, and let y_n be the height at which the ray crosses it, and α_n' the reduced inclination after refraction. Then
$$y_n = y_{n-1} - \mathbf{d}'\alpha'_{n-1}$$
$$\alpha_n' = \alpha'_{n-1} + y_n \mathbf{F}_n$$

Eliminating y_{n-1} and α'_{n-1} we obtain
$$\alpha_n' = y_1\{A + \mathbf{F}_n(C - \mathbf{d}'A)\} + \alpha_1\{B + \mathbf{F}_n(D - \mathbf{d}'B)\}$$
$$y_n = y_1(C - \mathbf{d}'A) + \alpha_1(D - \mathbf{d}'B).$$

These equations are of the usual form, and the new constants are
$$A_1 = A + \mathbf{F}_n(C - \mathbf{d}'A)$$
$$B_1 = B + \mathbf{F}_n(D - \mathbf{d}'B)$$
$$C_1 = C - \mathbf{d}'A$$
$$D_1 = D - \mathbf{d}'B$$

Let the power A_1 be written $\mathbf{F}$, then the following relations are found
$$A_1 = \mathbf{F}, \quad C_1 = \frac{\partial \mathbf{F}}{\partial \mathbf{F}_n}, \quad D_1 = \frac{\partial B_1}{\partial \mathbf{F}_n} \qquad (g)$$

Imagining the whole system to be reversed, left to right, the values of the y's will be unchanged, but the inclinations will change sign.

The equations (f) above give (by simple algebra, remembering that $BC - AD = 1$)

$$- \alpha_1 = A y_{n-1} + C(- \alpha'_{n-1})$$
$$y_1 = B y_{n-1} + D(- \alpha'_{n-1})$$

where $- \alpha_1$ and $- \alpha'_{n-1}$ are the reduced inclinations of the reversed ray. Thus it is seen that the functions of B and C are now interchanged and we can obtain

$$B_1 = \frac{\partial F}{\partial F_1}, \text{ and } D_1 = \frac{\partial C_1}{\partial F_1} \qquad . \qquad . \qquad . \qquad (h)$$

from the second of which $D = \dfrac{\partial^2 F}{\partial F_1 \partial F_n}$ . . . . . (i)

Successive applications of the equation $A_1 = A + F_n(C - d'A)$, enable us to find the expressions for the powers of groups of refracting surfaces.

For a single surface $F = F_1$, and $B = C = 1$.

For two surfaces F_1 and F_2 separated by a reduced distance d_1,

$$F = F_1 + F_2(1 - d_1 F_1)$$

whence $B = \dfrac{\partial F}{\partial F_1} = 1 - d_1 F_2$, and $C = \dfrac{\partial F}{\partial F_2} = 1 - d_1 F_1$

For three surfaces,

$$F = F_1 + F_2(1 - d_1 F_1) + F_3[C - d_2\{F_1 + F_2(1 - d_1 F_1)\}]$$
$$= F_1 + F_2 + F_3 - d_1 F_1 F_2 - (d_1 + d_2)F_1 F_3 - d_2 F_2 F_3$$
$$+ d_1 d_2 F_1 F_2 F_3 \qquad . \qquad . \qquad . \qquad (j)$$

Measurement of Gaussian Constants. If we imagine, *first*, an object in the first surface of a system, and its corresponding image formed by the whole system, we obtain (p. 60) $h'/h = 1/B$. Again, if the object is so placed that its image is formed in the last surface of the system we obtain $h'/h = C$, and $D = - Cl$. These formulae give means of finding the constants useful in certain cases, such as when experimental measurements are to be made on an actual system. For example, a scale can be placed in contact with either surface, and the size of its image determined with a measuring microscope.

Case of a Thick Lens. If the object be coincident with the first surface of a thick lens of thickness d, and refractive index N,

$$\bar{L}_2 = - \frac{N}{d}, \text{ and } \bar{L}_2' = - \frac{N}{d} + F_2$$

The magnification is then

$$\frac{\bar{L}_2}{\bar{L}_2'} = \frac{N}{N - F_2 d} = \frac{1}{B}$$

Again, if the image be coincident with the last surface,

$$\bar{L}_1' = N/d, \text{ and } \bar{L}_1 = \bar{L}_1' - F_1 = (N - F_1 d)/d$$

The magnification is then

$$\frac{\bar{L}_1}{\bar{L}_1'} = \frac{N - F_1 d}{N} = C$$

In this case $l = \dfrac{d}{N - F_1 d}$, and $D = -\, lC = -\, d/N$; we see that D is the apparent thickness which a plate of the same thickness would possess. We can now easily recover the formula for the power of a thick lens by putting $A = (BC - 1)/D$.

For example, show that in the case of a meniscus lens with refractive index 1.50, thickness $= 0.05$ m., and surfaces of powers $+\, 6D$ and $-\, 1D$, the conjugate distance equation (for distances in metres measured from the surface of the lens) can be put into the form

$$156 ll' + 31 l' - 24 l + 1 = 0$$

Refraction by a Series of Coaxial Thin Lenses.

The form of the results which have been obtained for refraction at a series of coaxial refracting surfaces is much the same as that of the equations for

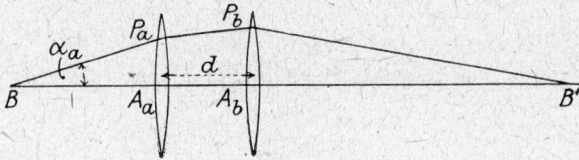

FIG. 32

refraction by a series of thin coaxial lenses; for the ordinary equation

$$\frac{1}{l'} - \frac{1}{l} = F_a$$

when multiplied by $y_a = A_a P_a$ (see Fig. 32), the intersection height of a ray BP_a in the first lens gives

$$\frac{y_a}{l'} - \frac{y_a}{l} = F_a y_a$$

If we write α_a, α_a' for the angles of inclination of the ray before and after refraction by lens a, then

$$\alpha_a' - \alpha_a = F_a y_a, \qquad \text{where } y_a = A_a B \cdot \alpha_a$$

Also
$$y_b = y_a - d \alpha_a',^{*}$$

and
$$\alpha_b' - \alpha_b = F_b y_b.$$

The form of these equations is identical with those which were given in connection with refraction at two spherical surfaces, with the exception that the axial distances now appear as true lengths not as "reduced" lengths.

* Note that α_a' is shown in Fig. 32 as an angle which would numerically be negative.

We thus obtain for a pair of lenses (as in equation (21))

$$F = F_a + F_b - F_a F_b d \qquad . \qquad . \qquad . \qquad (230)$$

also
$$FA_a = \frac{1 - F_b d}{F} \qquad . \qquad . \qquad . \qquad . \qquad (231)$$

and
$$A_b F' = \frac{1 - F_a d}{F} \qquad . \qquad . \qquad . \qquad . \qquad (232)$$

The form of the results for three lenses is the same as that of equation (j).

Spherical Reflecting Surface. Let AP, Fig. 33, be the trace of a spherical reflecting surface with centre C, and let B be an object

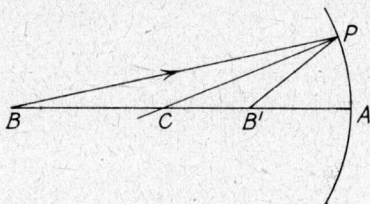

FIG. 33

point on the axial line BCA. An incident ray BP in the axial plane is reflected so as again to intersect the axis at B'. Then

$$\frac{PB}{\sin \widehat{BCP}} = \frac{CB}{\sin \widehat{BPC}} \quad \text{and} \quad \frac{PB'}{\sin \widehat{B'CP}} = \frac{B'C}{\sin \widehat{CPB'}}$$

Since $\widehat{BCP}$ and $\widehat{B'CP}$ are supplementary angles, and the angle of reflection is equal to the angle of incidence, the "sines" disappear when one of the above equations is divided by the other, leaving

$$\frac{PB}{PB'} = \frac{CB}{B'C}$$

When the point P is very close to A, the length BP becomes very nearly equal to BA, and B'P to B'A. Hence, under paraxial restrictions

$$\frac{AB}{AB'} = \frac{CB}{B'C}$$

If lengths are measured from the apex A of the surface, as usual, the last equation may be written

$$\frac{l}{l'} = \frac{l - r}{r - l'}$$

and, by a simple transformation,

$$\frac{1}{l'} + \frac{1}{l} = \frac{2}{r}$$

The mirror has one principal focal distance, given by

$$f = \frac{r}{2}$$

A lens system of positive power gives an inverted image of a real object at infinity; so also does a concave mirror of negative radius.

The "power" of the reflecting surface is therefore given by $F = -\frac{2}{r}$.

Reflection as a Particular Case of Refraction. It is worth noting that if the usual expressions for the laws of reflection and refraction be compared (see Appendix, p. 332, and Fig. 208),

$$i = -i'$$
$$n \sin i = n' \sin i'$$

The second is transformed into the first if we put $n' = -n$. Thus, the law for paraxial refraction at a spherical surface

$$\frac{n'}{l'} - \frac{n}{l} = \frac{n' - n}{r}$$

is at once reduced to the form given above for a reflection. This device is always adopted in the trigonometrical computing of systems involving reflection and involves no change in the form of the standard computing schedule, although it is naturally essential to remember the reversed direction of the light after reflection.

The graphical construction for "object and image" will be obvious; it involves one focal plane and one principal plane, and is illustrated in Fig. 34. The Abbe equations, now becoming

$$\frac{h'}{h} = -\frac{x'}{f} = -\frac{f}{x}, \text{ and } xx' = f^2$$

are valid in this case, and the ordinary forms (p. 43) will further hold for any combination of refractions and reflections.

The conjugate formulae for the case of astigmatic reflection at a spherical surface can also be obtained from equations (115) and (116) by this device. See Vol. II for a further discussion.

Combinations of Refracting and Reflecting Surfaces. Owing to the fact that the paraxial rays have generally to pass back into the same medium after transmission through any system of coaxial refracting surfaces combined with *one* reflecting surface, there can only be one principal focus for such a system, and the same considerations show that there can be only one focal length and therefore one principal plane. The system will therefore be equivalent (so far as paraxial relations are concerned) to a single mirror which must be the image, formed by the refracting system, of the actual reflecting surface. This image clearly acts as the "principal plane"

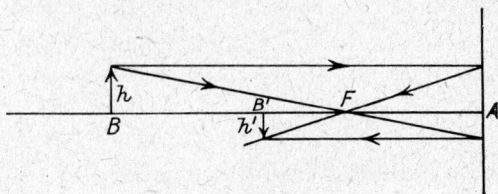

FIG. 34

of the system. Also the apparent centre of curvature and the real centre of curvature will be corresponding conjugate points with regard to the refracting system.

The use of the methods previously outlined for finding the constants of a series of optical surfaces needs some care. It may be imagined for simplicity* that the path of the ray after reflection in such a case is continued onwards in the "left to right" sense, as

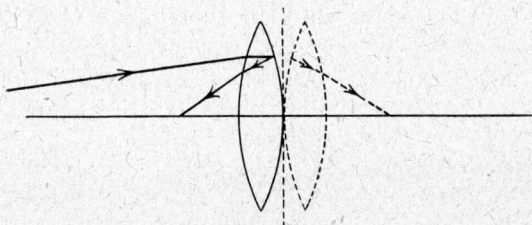

FIG. 35

if a "plane mirror" image of the ray paths were formed, as suggested in Fig. 35, which illustrates the case of one reflecting and one refracting surface. The ray may be considered to be subject to the effect of three surfaces of powers F_1, F_2, F_3, at distances d' and d'', which become equal to the thickness d in the paraxial case. We need not then bother about negative refractive indices.

In applying this method, note that the "power" of the reflecting

---

* A more systematic discussion of the method of dealing with this case on the basis of a reversal of the sign of the refractive index for the right to left direction is given in the Appendix, p. 333, *et seq.*

surface will be of the positive or converging type when the radius is negative. Also in analogy with the general equation

$$\frac{n'}{l'} - \frac{n}{l} = \frac{n' - n}{r} = F$$

where the power is connected with the difference of the *reduced* lengths, the power of the reflecting surface must appear in connection with the reduced lengths also. Thus when $n' = -n$

$$-\frac{n}{l'} - \frac{n}{l} = n\left(-\frac{2}{r}\right) = F$$

It will be realized that a reflecting concave surface will have a power which depends upon the medium in which it is situated if we think of a thin plano-convex lens with a silvered back. The effective power of the system is n times that of the reflecting surface alone, although the power of the plane glass surface is zero.

Case of One Refracting and One Reflecting Surface. Let r_g, r_m be the radii of the refracting and reflecting surfaces respectively. The refractive index is n outside, and n' between the surfaces. A ray in space n, directed towards the apparent centre of curvature of the reflecting surface will be refracted towards the actual centre, which will lie at a distance $r_m + d$ from the refracting surface, where d is the distance between the surfaces. Hence the distance l_c of the apparent centre of curvature from the refracting surface is given by

$$\frac{n'}{r_m + d} - \frac{n}{l_c} = \frac{n' - n}{r_g} = F_1$$

Similarly a ray in space n directed towards the virtual image of the apex of the reflecting surface will be refracted towards the apex itself at a distance d, from the refracting surface, in space n'. Thus the distance l_p of the virtual image of the reflecting surface formed by refraction at the first surface is given by

$$\frac{n'}{d} - \frac{n}{l_p} = \frac{n' - n}{r_g} = F_1$$

Hence, using the relation $r_m = -\dfrac{2n'}{F_2}$ and employing the reduced distances, we obtain by simple algebra

$$\bar{l}_c = \frac{-2 + \bar{d}F_2}{2F_1 + F_2 - \bar{d}F_1F_2}, \quad \bar{l}_p = \frac{\bar{d}}{1 - \bar{d}F_1}$$

The apparent radius of curvature is the distance to the apparent centre from the apparent principal point or surface, i.e. $l_c - l_p$

$$\bar{l}_c - \bar{l}_p = \frac{-2}{2F_1 + F_2 - 2\bar{d}F_1F_2 - 2\bar{d}F_1{}^2 + \bar{d}{}^2F_1{}^2F_2}$$

The quantity in the denominator is therefore the effective power.

The ordinary equations can be applied to this problem (see equation j). For a combination of three surfaces see also Appendix, p. 334.

$$\alpha_3' = y_1\{F_1 + F_2 + F_3 - F_1F_2d_1 - d_1F_1F_3 - d_2F_3(F_1 + F_2 - F_1F_2d_1)\}$$
$$+ \alpha_1(1 - F_2d_1 - d_1F_3 - d_2F_3 + F_2F_3d_2d_1)$$

or
$$\alpha_3' = y_1A + \alpha_1B$$

where
$$B = \frac{\partial A}{\partial F_1}$$

Now when $F_1 = F_3$ and $d_2 = d_1$

$$A = 2F_1 + F_2 - 2F_1F_2d_1 - 2F_1{}^2d_1 + d_1{}^2F_1{}^2F_2$$

which is the power as obtained directly above; and

$$B = 1 - F_2d_1 - 2d_1F_1 + d_1{}^2F_1F_2$$

The distance from the refracting surface to the first focal point will be $l_f = -\dfrac{B}{A}$.

Let the effective powers, in diopters, of the surfaces for refraction and reflection in the above problems be $F_1 = +2$, $F_2 = +4$. If the system is thin, the total power is $(2 \times 2) + 4 = 8D$. (The actual power of a reflecting surface of the same curvature in air would be $\dfrac{4}{n'}$. If $n' = 1\cdot5$, F_2 (air) $= 2\cdot6$ and $r = -0\cdot75$ m.) If the actual thickness $= d = 3$ cm. $= 0\cdot03$ metres, the reduced thickness $\bar{d} = 0\cdot02$ metres.

The power $A = 7\cdot5264$
$$B = 0\cdot8432$$

$$l_f = -\frac{B}{A} = -0\cdot112 \text{ metres.}$$

REFERENCES

[1] *Dioptrische Untersuchungen*, Gottingen, 1841.
[2] Conrady, *Applied Optics and Optical Design* (Oxford University Press, 1929).

CHAPTER III

LIGHT AS WAVE-MOTION

Wave-motion. The first step in the study of wave-motion is the study of "vibration."

Let the point P, Fig. 36, move in a circular path with uniform angular velocity ω.* The centre of the circle is at O, the origin of the co-ordinate axes of X and Y. The co-ordinates of P are x, y.

The point Q found at the foot of the perpendicular dropped from P to the axis of Y will now possess a "Simple Harmonic Motion." If the time t be reckoned as zero when P crosses the axis of X, then

$$y = a \sin \omega t, \text{ or } y = a \sin 2\pi \frac{t}{T}$$

Differentiating† with regard to t,

$$dy/dt = \omega a \cos \omega t, \text{ and again } d^2y/dt^2 = -\omega^2 a \sin \omega t.$$

Thus $\quad dy/dt = \omega x, \qquad$ and $d^2y/dt^2 = -\omega^2 y$

The velocity dy/dt of the point Q is therefore greatest when passing the central position O and is zero when at the extreme points. The acceleration d^2y/dt^2 is greatest at the extreme points, and is always an acceleration towards the centre; it is proportional to the displacement. Evidently it is the type of motion characteristic of a body subject to a restoring force proportional to the displacement, and of which the motion is not otherwise hindered. We shall speak of the angle between

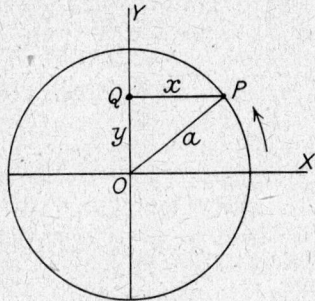

FIG. 36

the radius vector OP and the X axis as the "Phase Angle." The constant "a" is the "amplitude" of the vibration.

Now consider the expression‡

$$y = a \sin 2\pi \left(\frac{t}{T} - \frac{x}{\lambda} \right) \qquad . \qquad . \qquad . \quad (301)$$

* The angular velocity ω (radians per second) is the quotient of $\frac{2\pi}{T}$ where T is the time taken to move through an angle 2π.

† Students not familiar with the calculus should accept these results as a simple expression of the velocity dy/dt and the acceleration d^2y/dt^2 of the point Q.

‡ The corresponding expression $y = a \cos 2\pi \left(\frac{t}{T} - \frac{x}{\lambda} \right)$ equally represents a wave-train; the phase difference as compared with that of equation (301) evidently being $90°$ or $\pi/2$.

as applied to the co-ordinates of a series of points which, when $a = o$, lie in the straight line $y = o$, i.e. the axis of x.

If x is constant while t varies, then the particle at any point x_1 will experience a simple harmonic vibration; on the other hand, if we examine the conditions along the line at any instant by putting $t = t_1$ and allowing x to vary, we obtain a "sine curve," Fig. 37. If t be changed by $\pm T$ while x is constant, or x be changed by λ while t is constant, we shall obtain precisely the same numerical value of y, and also the same velocity and acceleration; we shall

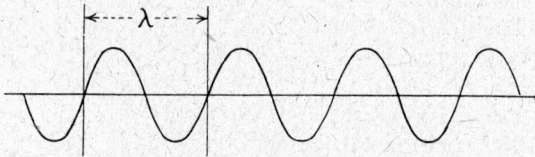

FIG. 37

have vibrations for which the phase angle will be the same or, in other words, the vibrations will be "in the same phase."

The length λ between the normal positions of points vibrating in the same phase is called the "wave-length." The "crests" of such a wave motion represent regions of similar phase.

The appearance of the wave motion is as if a line bent thus into a sine curve were being bodily moved. Actually, each particle is performing a vibration similarly with all the others, but with a difference of phase from those near it. We note that by increasing the time t, we can produce the same variation in y as by diminishing x, for each operation would increase the quantity within the bracket.* Hence, the equation represents a wave-train moving in the positive x direction; while $y = a \sin 2\pi \left(\dfrac{t}{T} + \dfrac{x}{\lambda} \right)$ would represent a wave-train moving in the reversed direction.

In time T a "crest" moves through a distance λ. Hence, in unit time a crest moves through a distance $\dfrac{\lambda}{T}$, and this distance is the velocity V. Hence

$$\lambda = VT \qquad . \qquad . \qquad . \qquad . \qquad . \qquad (302)$$

If N is the "frequency," we shall evidently find N complete wave-lengths in a distance V, since N waves travel out from the source in unit time, and the initial disturbance is propagated to a distance V.

---

* At any one point, after the lapse of a given time, we find the phase characteristic previously of a smaller value of x.

Hence $V = N\lambda$, and $T = \dfrac{1}{N}$; the latter equation is obvious, since T is the time to send out one complete wave, and N are sent out per second.

If the position of a point in space is given by its Cartesian co-ordinates x, y, z, then the equation (301) above can be interpreted as representing a group of plane waves travelling through space in the direction of the x axis; the value of the variable displacement from the normal position (represented by the sine term) is clearly independent of y and z.

In the case of the vibrations of "sound," the motion of the parts of the medium are *not* at right angles to the direction of propagation as in the case we have been considering, but are parallel to it. They are waves of condensation and rarefaction. On the other hand, waves with transverse vibrations can be produced in various elastic media and their properties studied.

It can be proved in the case of all these mechanical vibrations that the energy of a wave motion passing through unit area normal to the direction of propagation is proportional to the square of the amplitude. Suppose, then, that we have a source of wave motion O, of negligible dimensions, at the centre of two spheres of radii "unity" and "r" respectively (see Fig. 38).

Draw a cone of very small solid angle $d\phi$ with its apex at O, marking off areas $d\phi$ and $r^2d\phi$ respectively from the two spheres. *If we may assume that the direction of energy propagation is in straight lines,* all the energy passing through the area $d\phi$ must pass through the other area $r^2d\phi$.

Let I_1 and I_r be the energy per unit area at the two radii, then $I_1 = ka_1^2$ where a_1 is the amplitude at unit radius and $I_r = ka_r^2$ where a_r is the amplitude at radius r.

The conservation of energy is expressed by $I_1d\phi = I_rr^2d\phi$ or $ka_1^2d\phi = ka_r^2r^2d\phi$.

Hence
$$a_r = \frac{a_1}{r} \qquad . \qquad . \qquad . \qquad . \quad (303)$$

Polarization. As mentioned above, the vibrations of sound are in the direction of propagation; but in transverse vibrations such as those which we can set up in a single cord, or as waves in an elastic solid medium, the direction of the motion is important. If we shake the end of the cord in a vertical plane all the other parts will move in a vertical plane also, and so on. In Fig. 38 we may imagine the direction of displacement of the mechanical vibrations of the source in an elastic solid to be in the line OO'. The movement propagated to O' can there have no component parallel to the surface of the sphere, but the maximum tangential displacement in the surface will be in the equator perpendicular to OO'. If a point in the equator, such as A, has the surface component of amplitude a_1/r, the surface amplitude at another point B, where OB makes an angle θ with the equatorial plane, will be a_1/r multiplied by some function of θ which diminishes as θ increases. The direction

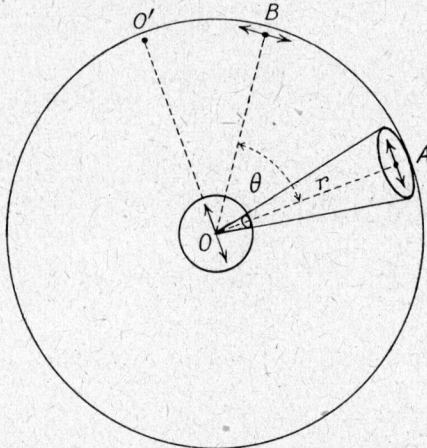

FIG. 38

of the vibrations at any point of the surface will be in a plane containing OO'.

The Nature of Light. The Greek speculations regarding the nature of light have already been referred to, and the "emission" or corpuscular theory was generally accepted until the seventeenth century. In 1637 Descartes published his essay on *Dioptrics* (in which he formulated the law of refraction), expressing the view that light is a pressure which is transmitted by an infinitely elastic medium pervading space. His attempted theoretical explanation of the law of refraction led to the conclusion that light would pass more readily through a more highly refracting medium. This was in opposition to the theory of Fermat (1601–1665) that light would travel from one point to another by such a route that the time is a minimum. In conjunction with the law of refraction, the necessary condition implied in Fermat's idea is that the velocity should vary inversely as the refractive index, as will be seen below.

The principle of the rectilinear propagation of light and the law of reflection at a plane surface have already been shown to agree with

Fermat's principle. For the case of refraction consider Fig. 39. Let the velocities of light above and below the separating surface be V and V'. The points P and Q are on the incident and refracted rays, and PL, QM are perpendicular to the plane of the refracting surface; A is the point of refraction.

The time (t) for the disturbance to travel from P to Q is

$$t = \frac{PA}{V} + \frac{AQ}{V'}$$

Let PL $= h_1$, MQ $= h_2$, LA $= x$, LM $= p$, then the equation becomes

$$t = \frac{(h_1^2 + x^2)^{\frac{1}{2}}}{V} + \frac{\{h_2^2 + (p - x)^2\}^{\frac{1}{2}}}{V}$$

If this time is a minimum, then $dt/dx = 0$, i.e.

$$\frac{x}{V(h_1^2 + x^2)^{\frac{1}{2}}} - \frac{(p - x)}{V'\{h_2^2 + (p - x)^2\}^{\frac{1}{2}}} = 0$$

or

$$\frac{\sin i}{V} - \frac{\sin i'}{V'} = 0$$

This gives

$$\frac{\sin i}{\sin i'} = \frac{V}{V'}$$

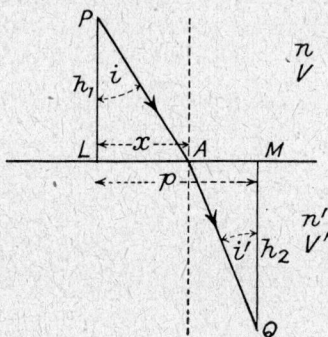

FIG. 39. FERMAT'S PRINCIPLE

Hence

$$\frac{\sin i}{\sin i'} = \frac{n'}{n} = \frac{V}{V'}, \text{ and } n'V' = nV . \qquad . \qquad . \quad (304)$$

Hence, Fermat's principle is in accordance with the law of refraction if the above equation is fulfilled; in spite of the somewhat irrelevant arguments on which it was first stated, this principle is one of the most fundamentally important ideas in optics, and will be discussed more fully later.

Although the minimum value of the optical path is seen to hold in some cases, it may be alternatively a maximum, or may have a stationary value. Thus it will be shown that various optical paths, through a lens, between an object and image point, may have a constant value, so that disturbances starting in the same phase and travelling by different paths may yet arrive in the same phase.

In 1676, Römer's observations on the eclipses of Jupiter's satellites showed that light had, in fact, a finite through very great velocity. His estimate was 192,000 miles per second. Modern researches have given a revised estimate of 299,860 km., or about 186,000 miles per second.

About the time when Newton's researches on "Dispersion" were in progress, a book by Grimaldi was published in 1665, two years after the death of its author. In it was described his work on *diffraction*. He had found that the boundaries of shadows were *not* exactly determined by the paths of possible rays between the source of light and the screen on which the shadows were observed;

light might appear within a region which (if the path of light in one medium were always precisely straight) should remain in darkness; conversely, certain dark shadows appeared larger than their strictly geometrical limits. These observations were taken up and further investigated by Newton, who also described the colours due to successive reflection of light at the surfaces of thin films, such colours as are seen in ring form at the point of contact between a convex lens and a glass plate when pressed together.*

Great as were Newton's services to experimental optics, his opposition to the wave-theory of light carried great weight against it after it had been propounded by Huygens in 1678. (Huygens' *Traité de la Lumière* was published later, in 1690.)

Huygens conceived that light is composed of pulses propagated with a definite velocity through a space-pervading medium which could be thought of as consisting ultimately of small elastic spheres in contact. Hence, any motion of one such sphere would tend to impart a motion to all those with which it was in contact. It would thus become the origin of a disturbance which would spread in all directions.

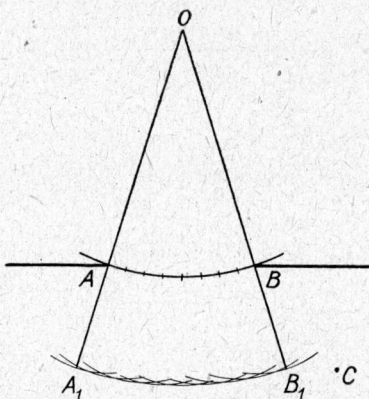

FIG. 40. HUYGENS' PRINCIPLE

His explanation of the rectilinear propagation of light will illustrate the theory. In Fig. 40, AB represents an opening in a screen. A pulse or "wave" of light, having spread with uniform velocity from O, is represented by the arc AB. Now each particle in the wave-front becomes a source of disturbance, and wavelets spread out from each such particle as centre. The envelope to such a series of wavelets will be an arc A_1B_1 with O as centre. In the immediate region of the arc A_1B_1 the density of the wavelets will be greatest, but at any point C outside the lines OA_1, OB_1, the wavelets will only arrive at different times, and their effects will be comparatively small. It is to be noted that the idea does not involve the propagation of a regular series of vibrations through the medium, as in the case of sound, but rather assumes the disturbance to consist of arbitrary pulses of no definite period. When the idea of periodicity is added, we can see that the secondary

* The theory is given in Chapter VI.

disturbances would arrive at points such as C in different phases, and would therefore cancel each other's effects. Thus "rectilinear propagation" becomes understandable.

The case of refraction at a plane surface was dealt with as follows: AB, Fig. 41, represents the trace of a plane "wave" incident on the surface AB' separating media of refractive indices n and n'. The normal to the wave lies in the plane of the diagram.

When the wave reaches the point A in the surface, this point becomes the centre of a secondary wavelet spreading out in the second medium. Suppose the velocity in the first medium is V, and in the second V', then, by the time that the part of the incident

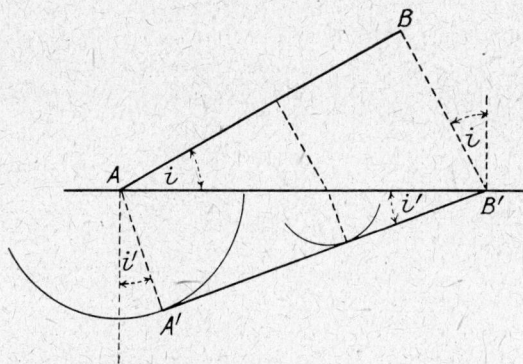

FIG. 41. HUYGENS' CONSTRUCTION FOR REFRACTION

wave at B has travelled to B', the radius of the wavelet will be BB' . V'/V. The envelope of all the secondary wavelets will be found by drawing a tangent from B' to the wavelet. Regarding the ray as the normal to the wave-surface, it is easy to see that BAB' is the angle of incidence and A'B'A the angle of refraction.

Then $\sin \widehat{BAB'}/\sin \widehat{A'B'A} = BB'/AA' = V/V' = n'/n$, as before.

Huygens also applied this type of "construction" to deal with the phenomenon of "double refraction" in substances such as Iceland spar or quartz; in this case the "wave" is assumed to spread out in two sheets or surfaces, one spherical, the other ellipsoidal. In this way he was able to explain the variation of direction between the "ordinary" and "extraordinary" rays, which generally result on refraction of a single ray by a doubly refracting body. (See Chapter VI.)

For the purposes of the present book, the development of the simple wave-theory of light into the electro-magnetic theory of the nature of the wave-displacements must be left without comment.

For the proper discussion of the theory of instruments it will, however, be necessary to follow some developments in the early growth
of the wave-theory.

Young's Experiment. It is not possible to follow the full history
of the investigations on the nature of light, but the corpuscular
theory was very generally accepted during the eighteenth century,
as, for example, by Robert Smith, whose *Compleat System of Opticks*
appeared in 1738. At the beginning of the nineteenth century,
Thomas Young, physician and physicist, took up the wave theory
and showed how it could be used to explain some of the phenomena
described by Grimaldi and Newton. He abandoned the idea of
single irregularly emitted pulses, and put forward the idea of continuous vibrations. Although Newton had not relinquished the

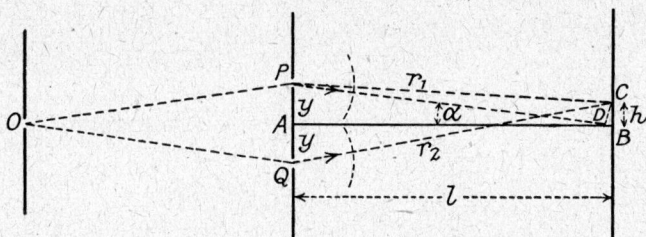

FIG. 42. TO ILLUSTRATE YOUNG'S EXPERIMENT

idea of the corpuscular theory of light, he had been driven to postulate a periodicity in light in order to explain the thin film phenomena.
Young ascribed colour variations to differences of frequency and
hence to differences of wave-length. The essential features of his
contribution to the theory of optics can best be explained in the
discussion of one of the experiments which he described.

Light from a very small origin O, Fig. 42, diverges to a screen A,
wherein are two small apertures P and Q; these apertures become
origins of light spreading to the region beyond A, and this is suggested by the dotted arcs, which are intended to suggest divergent
wave-fronts spreading from P and Q. Thus the illumination of the
further screen B is due to both sources.

The *principle of superposition* enunciated by Young states that
if the displacements at any instant at a point such as C in the plane
B, due to P and Q respectively, are s_1 and s_2, then the resultant
displacement D is

$$D = s_1 + s_2$$

In order that the algebraic addition may be valid, the direction of the displacements must be identical; in other words, they must be polarized in the same direction.

Similarly, if there were more than two sources, the displacement would be $s_1 + s_2 + s_3 +$ etc.

Let it be assumed that P and Q are single sources emitting simple harmonic waves of the same frequency and in the same phase, and let $PC = r_1$ and $QC = r_2$. Also assume that the displacements arriving at C can be added in accordance with the above principle, then if the amplitude at C due to P is a_1 and that due to Q is a_2, we may express the resultant displacement of the two simple harmonic wave-trains as

$$D = s_1 + s_2 = a_1 \sin 2\pi \left(\frac{t}{T} - \frac{r_1}{\lambda} \right) + a_2 \sin 2\pi \left(\frac{t}{T} - \frac{r_2}{\lambda} \right). \quad (305)$$

Putting $\delta_1 = \frac{2\pi r_1}{\lambda}$ and $\delta_2 = \frac{2\pi r_2}{\lambda}$ the expression becomes

$$D = a_1 \sin \left(\frac{2\pi t}{T} - \delta_1 \right) + a_2 \sin \left(\frac{2\pi t}{T} - \delta_2 \right)$$

Expanding the brackets and separating the terms, we obtain

$$D = \sin \frac{2\pi t}{T} (a_1 \cos \delta_1 + a_2 \cos \delta_2) - \cos \frac{2\pi t}{T} (a_1 \sin \delta_1 + a_2 \sin \delta_2)$$

If possible, let us find an angle $\triangle$ such that

$$A \cos \triangle = a_1 \cos \delta_1 + a_2 \cos \delta_2 . \qquad . \qquad . \qquad (a)$$

$$A \sin \triangle = a_1 \sin \delta_1 + a_2 \sin \delta_2 . \qquad . \qquad . \qquad (b)$$

Then $D = A \sin \dfrac{2\pi t}{T} \cos \triangle - A \cos \dfrac{2\pi t}{T} \sin \triangle = A \sin \left(\dfrac{2\pi t}{T} - \triangle \right)$

which would represent a simple harmonic vibration of the same frequency, but with a new phase term $\triangle$ and a new amplitude A. In order to find the significance of A and $\triangle$, square and add the equations (a) and (b) above.

Then $A^2 = a_1^2 + a_2^2 + 2a_1 a_2 (\cos \delta_2 \cos \delta_1 + \sin \delta_2 \sin \delta_1)$

or $\qquad A^2 = a_1^2 + a_2^2 + 2a_1 a_2 \cos (\delta_2 - \delta_1) \qquad . \qquad . \qquad (306)$

and, on dividing (b) by (a),

$$\tan \triangle = \frac{a_1 \sin \delta_1 + a_2 \sin \delta_2}{a_1 \cos \delta_1 + a_2 \cos \delta_2} . \qquad . \qquad (307)$$

If P and Q are acting as sources of the same intensity, and r_1 is only slightly different from r_2, equation (303) indicates that a_1 and a_2 will be very nearly equal. Supposing them equal, as they will be at certain points, within very small differences,

$$A^2 = 2a_1^2(1 + \cos \overline{\delta_2 - \delta_1}) = 2a_1^2\left\{1 + \cos \frac{2\pi}{\lambda}(r_2 - r_1)\right\}$$

Hence, when $r_2 = r_1$, $A^2 = (2a_1)^2$. When $(r_2 - r_1)$ is an odd number of half wave-lengths, the value of A^2 will be zero. In mechanical vibrations the energy of the wave-motion is proportional to the square of the amplitude. Therefore the intensity will evidently vary between zero and a value which is four times that contributed by either source acting separately.

To find the value of $(r_2 - r_1)$ in regard to the conditions of experiment, refer to Fig. 42 and join PB. (We imagine P and Q to be symmetrically disposed with regard to the common perpendicular to the parallel screens at A and B.) From C drop a perpendicular CD to the line PB. Then

$$\widehat{PBA} = \widehat{DCB} = \alpha \text{ (say)}$$

and if BC is very small, then PC = PD (within a small difference of the second order), and PB − PC = DB = $h \sin \alpha$, sufficiently nearly, where BC = h.

In a similar way, by joining QB it can be shown that

$$QC - QB = h \sin \alpha$$

Hence $\qquad\qquad QC - PC = 2h \sin \alpha$

If α is small, as it must be in Young's experiment, and AP = y and AB = l, then sufficiently nearly

$$QC - PC = r_2 - r_1 = \frac{2h \cdot y}{l} = \frac{hd}{l}, \text{ where } d = 2y$$

The distribution of intensity along the line BC, Fig. 42, can therefore be determined for the ideal conditions postulated above. At B, where $r_2 = r_1$ we should find the maximum intensity; when we have reached a point where

$$r_2 - r_1 = \frac{hd}{l} = \frac{\lambda}{2}, \text{ or } h = \frac{\lambda l}{2d}$$

there should be darkness, and so on for a succession of light and dark regions symmetrical on either side of the point B. The total width from one "light" region to another is $\lambda l/d$.

Of course, both a_1 and a_2 change in practice with r_1 and r_2, but the effect of this variation will be small.

While the above investigation relates only to the appearances on

the line BC, parallel to PQ, on the screen B, it is easy to deduce the
effects above and below this line. The intensity practically depends
on $r_2 - r_1$. Now Fig. 43 shows a point R on a hyperbola of which
P and Q are the foci. One of the properties of such a curve is that
PR − RQ is constant. We can draw any number of such curves for
any value of the difference up to a maximum PQ. If, then, we rotate
the diagram about the line PQ, we shall generate a set of surfaces
called hyperboloids of revolution; for any point on a particular
surface the distances to the foci will differ by a constant quantity.
Returning to Fig. 42 and imagining the surface B to be intersected
by such a set of hyperboloids,
we shall obtain the shapes of
the "fringes," each of which
marks the line of a constant
path difference. In the neighbourhood of the centre they
will evidently be practically
straight and perpendicular to
the line BC.

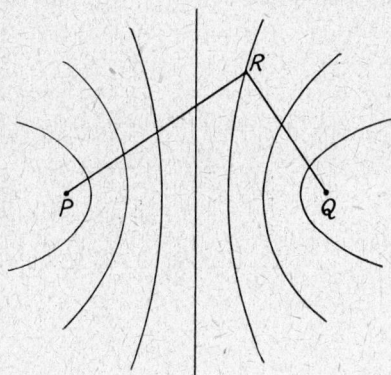

FIG. 43

We return to the actual
experiment, which should be
repeated by the student, on the
optical bench.

The origin of light O may be
represented by a ½ mm. hole
drilled and countersunk in a brass plate. It is illuminated by pro-
jecting on it the image of the carbon arc crater, pointolite lamp, or
high intensity mercury arc.

A is a screen of tin-foil in which two fine holes are pricked by a
needle point. They should not be more than about 0·2 mm. in
diameter and may be up to 1 mm. apart. OA may be about 50 cm.
and AB up to a metre in length. If it is desired, the fringes may
be registered by giving a sufficiently long exposure to a photographic
plate at B, precautions being taken to avoid stray light, but they
may be seen directly with the aid of an eyepiece or magnifier, which
can be used to examine the appearances in the region desired. The
eye looks in the direction BA, while the magnifier is focused in the
plane of B.

With such an arrangement, the fringes are not difficult to observe,
though the illumination is not very strong.

With apparatus of this kind (certain other methods of producing
interference fringes are described below) the following results can
be obtained.

1. In order to obtain visible interference, it is necessary that the interfering beams should be derived from the same source. (Vibrations derived from the same source are said to be "coherent.")

2. The width of the fringe varies with the colour of the light, the red regions of the spectrum giving the wider spacing. Fig. 44 shows approximately the relative spacing of red and violet fringes, of course highly magnified. The measurement of the width of a fringe in monochromatic light thus gives a means of determining the *wavelength* by using the formula given above. If white light is used to produce the interference, the fringes in the various spectrum colours are found to be apparently superposed; though the central fringe may appear white, those on each side will show coloured borders, and the difference of spacing is such that comparatively few fringes can be observed as compared with the number that can be seen when really monochromatic light is employed.

Red

Violet

FIG. 44. RELATIVE SPACING OF FRINGES

Before dealing with the other methods of exhibiting interference, however, it is necessary to inquire into the conditions obtaining in the actual experiment as compared with those assumed in the theoretical treatment given above.

First the origin of light O is of very finite size. The wave-length of light for the middle of the spectrum is about 0.5×10^{-3} mm., often written 0.5μ, and modern knowledge of the structure of matter has taught us to regard the origins of wave-trains of light as being comparable at most with the dimensions of an atom, which is very much smaller still, and is, in fact, of the order of 10^{-8} cm.

Hence, even if we put a flame very close to the opening O in order to make it practically self-luminous, we should still have a "source" which could be regarded as possibly consisting of millions of separate sources of light.

Again, the apertures at P and Q are of very finite dimensions, and similar considerations apply to them; how, then, can the observed interference phenomena be explained?

Before going more fully into the discussion of the actual experiment suggested by Young, we may describe an arrangement due to Fresnel. Referring to Fig. 45, OA and OB are the traces of two plane mirrors (imagined perpendicular to the diagram) inclined at a small angle, while *ab* is a small source of light, the images of which, a_1b_1 and a_2b_2, formed by reflection in the two mirrors, illuminate the screen *s*. It is evident that corresponding points in these images lie on a circle with O as centre, struck through the corresponding point of the object, and that the angle between the images subtended at the centre O is twice the angle between the mirrors. The two reflected beams overlap in the shaded portion of the diagram. In practice the source is a small pinhole brightly illuminated and placed close to the plane of the mirrors, which, when inclined at a very small angle, produce a pair of images which are very close together. The fringes are observed by an eyepiece. The mirrors must be optically polished; if they are of glass, the reflection from the back

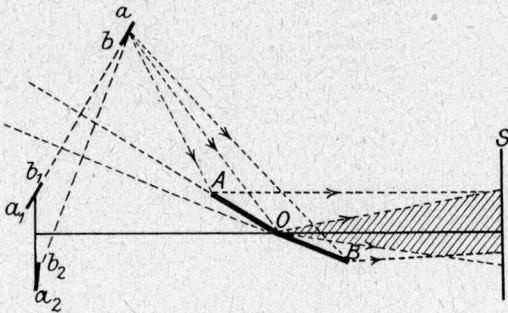

Fig. 45

surfaces must be prevented by blackening the latter or using dark "smoke" glass.

If we could regard the source of light as a point source, the two images must correspond to two equal sources emitting light in the same phase, and the theoretical treatment of page 78 would be applicable. But since they are actually of finite size, we can regard them as divided into a great number of corresponding elementary areas sufficiently small to be treated as origins of waves. Thus pairs of areas a_1 and a_2 would produce a set of fringes, and also b_1 and b_2, but the second set would overlap the first. In order to see how the overlapping occurs, it is evident that the central fringe for a_1a_2 lies on the line which bisects a_1a_2 at right angles and passes through O; similarly, the central fringe for b_1b_2 lies on the line bisecting b_1b_2 at right angles and passing through O. Hence, the amount of overlapping of the fringes depends on the angle subtended by the source at O.

The condition which must be fulfilled by the source, then, is that it shall subtend a very small angle at the mirrors; provided this condition is fulfilled, its actual size is of no importance. Thus Fresnel was able easily to observe the fringes when a star was used as the source.

A short illuminated *slit* parallel to the line of the two mirrors is often used in this experiment. We may still regard the "fringes" actually seen under experimental conditions as the resultant of many overlying systems, with maxima and minima of brightness more or less in the same regions; if the maxima become too widely spread, however, the fringes cease to be visible.

It was because of the somewhat complex considerations under-lying Young's experiment that Fresnel was led to devise his double mirror arrangement. In Young's experiment the interference takes place between diffracted beams, and it was thought that diffraction

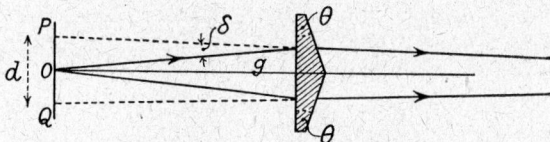

FIG. 46. THE BI-PRISM

might involve some change in the properties of light. There are a number of other methods of producing interference fringes. Fresnel's bi-prism is very useful. Its mode of action will be evident from Fig. 46. The deviation produced in a ray by transmission through a prism of small angle θ can be shown to be $\delta = (n - 1)\theta$. Hence d, the distance between the images, will be

$$d = 2g\delta = 2g(n - 1)\theta = g(n - 1)(\pi - A)$$

where A is the angular measure of the obtuse angle of the bi-prism. It is to be noted that the distance between the images is dependent on the refractive index. For the comparatively high refractive index characteristic of the shorter wave-lengths, the images will be further apart; hence the fringes will be more closely spaced on this account, as well as on account of the diminished wave-length. The distance from the central minimum to the first dark maximum for a given wave-length is naturally calculated by the formula derived in discussing Young's experiment, i.e. $h = \lambda l/2d$.

Billet has used the two halves of a converging lens, cut across a diameter and mounted so that the distance between them can be adjusted. Each half can thus be made to project the image of a small source of light, and the two images can be made to approach very closely.

Lloyd has produced interferences between light derived from a small source and from its image formed by reflection in a single mirror, Fig. 47, but the central band of zero path difference cannot be directly obtained.

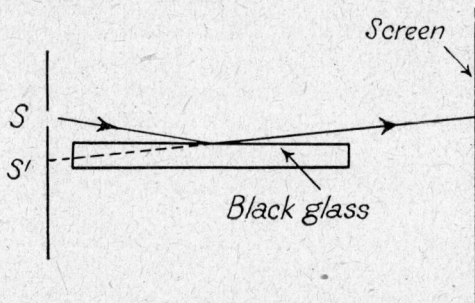

FIG. 47. LLOYD'S MIRROR ARRANGEMENT

Graphical Interpretation of the Superposition Formulae. Equations (306) and (307) can be illustrated graphically, as indicated in Fig. 48.

Let O be the origin of co-ordinates. Draw the line OA of length a_1, and making an angle δ_1 with the axis of x. From its extremity draw AB of length a_2 and making an angle δ_2 with the axis of x.

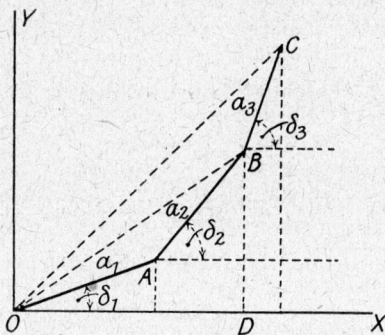

FIG. 48

The line OB then represents the amplitude of the sum of the vibrations by its length; the phase angle is represented by the angle it makes with the axis of x; for we see from the triangle OAB that

$$OB^2 = a_1{}^2 + a_2{}^2 + 2a_1 a_2 \cos (\delta_2 - \delta_1),$$

since $(\delta_2 - \delta_1)$ is the exterior angle between AB and OA produced,

and $\tan \widehat{BOX} = \dfrac{a_1 \sin \delta_1 + a_2 \sin \delta_2}{a_1 \cos \delta_1 + a_2 \cos \delta_2}$, which is easily seen by taking the projections of a_1 and a_2 on the axes of x and y.

If, now, a third component

$$s_3 = a_3 \sin\left(\frac{2\pi t}{T} - \delta_3\right)$$

is added to the sum, we shall easily see that it is done graphically by drawing BC of length a_3, and at an angle of δ_3 with the axis of x; as before, OC represents the length and phase angle of the resultant. We see that, generally, if there are several components, then A the amplitude of the resultant is such that

$$A^2 = (a_1 \cos \delta_1 + a_2 \cos \delta_2 + a_3 \cos \delta_3 + \text{etc.})^2$$
$$+ (a_1 \sin \delta_1 + a_2 \sin \delta_2 + a_3 \sin \delta_3 + \text{etc.})^2$$
$$= C^2 + S^2 \ . \quad . \quad . \quad . \quad . \quad . \quad . \quad (308)$$

where $\quad C = \Sigma a \cos \delta$, and $S = \Sigma a \sin \delta$,

and $\tan \triangle = \dfrac{S}{C}$ . . . . (309)

Mathematical Treatment of Superposition Formulae. A convenient and compact mathematical expression for use in the addition of simple harmonic vibrations is

$$A = a \exp i\delta \quad . \quad . \quad . \quad . \quad (310)$$

where a is the amplitude, i is the imaginary "square root of minus one," and δ is the characteristic phase angle. This is equivalent to

$$A = a(\cos \delta + i \sin \delta) \quad . \quad . \quad . \quad (311)$$

Hence, using the notation of the previous paragraphs, if the summation of a number of components of the same frequency is written conventionally

$$D = C + iS \quad . \quad . \quad . \quad . \quad (312)$$

the amplitude A is such that

$$A^2 = C^2 + S^2 \quad . \quad . \quad . \quad . \quad (313)$$

which is obtained by multiplying the displacement $C + iS$ by the "conjugate complex quantity" $C - iS$.

Diffraction. Fresnel extended the ideas of Huygens by considering that each point in a surface coincident with a wave-front can be treated as the origin of a *vibratory* disturbance (as distinct from mere arbitrary pulses) spreading out in all directions. Thus, if O, Fig. 49, represents a point source, the locus of points vibrating in the same phase (i.e. the wave-front) will be a circle such as AP struck with O as centre, and radius a.

Let the amplitude at unit radius from the centre be A_1, then the amplitude in the locus AP will be A_1/a, and the displacement will be

$$\frac{A_1}{a} \sin 2\pi \left(\frac{t}{T} - \frac{a}{\lambda}\right)$$

Take a point P on the locus, join PB, and call this length c. Then the amplitude ds_1 produced at B by the action of a very small area $d\sigma$ situated on the surface at P must be directly proportional to the area, and to the amplitude in the surface, and inversely proportional to the distance PB; i.e.

$$ds_1 = \frac{KA_1 d\sigma}{ac} \sin 2\pi \left(\frac{t}{T} - \frac{a+c}{\lambda} \right)$$

(where K is a factor to be discussed below), since the disturbance has to travel a total distance $(a+c)$ from O to B, via P.

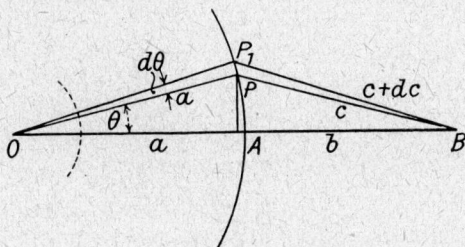

FIG. 49

In order to integrate for the effect of the whole wave, the surface may conveniently be divided into annular circular areas surrounding A as centre.

Let $\widehat{AOP} = \theta$; draw OP_1 so that $\widehat{AOP_1} = \theta + d\theta$. Join P_1B and call it $c + dc$. Imagine that $d\theta$ and dc are very small.
Now $c^2 = a^2 + (a+b)^2 - 2a(a+b) \cos \theta$.
Differentiating with regard to θ (remembering that a and b are constants),

$$2c\,dc = 2a(a+b) \sin \theta\, d\theta \quad . \quad . \quad . \quad . \quad (a)$$

Now, if we rotate the diagram about the axis OA, the arc PP_1 will strike out an annular area of amount $d\sigma$.

$$d\sigma = 2\pi a \sin \theta \,.\, a\,d\theta$$
$$= \frac{2\pi a c\, dc}{a+b}, \text{ from equation } (a) \text{ above.}$$

Hence, the expression for the effect at B of this elementary annular area becomes

$$ds_1 = \frac{KA_1}{ac} \left\{ \frac{2\pi a c\, dc}{(a+b)} \right\} \sin 2\pi \left(\frac{t}{T} - \frac{a+c}{\lambda} \right)$$
$$= \frac{2\pi KA_1 dc}{(a+b)} \sin 2\pi \left(\frac{t}{T} - \frac{a+c}{\lambda} \right)$$

We could now take a point P_2 such that $P_2B = P_1B + dc = PB + 2dc$; the effect of the annular strip P_1P_2 would then be

$$ds_2 = \frac{2\pi K A_1 dc}{a + b} \sin 2\pi \left(\frac{t}{T} - \frac{a + c + dc}{\lambda} \right)$$

If we take a number of rings with equal steps of "dc" we shall obtain zones which can contribute the same amplitude to the effect at B, provided K remains constant, but the phases of the contributions will vary *in equal steps*. The result will be of the type (n terms in each series)

$$A^2 = m^2 [\{\sin p + \sin (p + \delta) + \sin (p + 2\delta) + \dots$$
$$+ \sin (p + \overline{n - 1}\, \delta)\}^2$$
$$+ \{\cos p + \cos (p + \delta) + \cos (p + 2\delta) + \dots$$
$$+ \cos (p + \overline{n - 1}\, \delta)\}^2]$$

where m represents the contribution of an elementary ring.

The sums of these series are well known.* The expression becomes

$$A^2 = m^2 \left[\left(\frac{\sin \{p + \frac{1}{2}(n - 1)\delta\} \sin \frac{1}{2}n\delta}{\sin \frac{1}{2}\delta} \right)^2 \right.$$
$$\left. + \left(\frac{\cos \{p + \frac{1}{2}(n - 1)\delta\} \cdot \sin \frac{1}{2}n\delta}{\sin \frac{1}{2}\delta} \right)^2 \right]$$

$$= \frac{m^2 \sin^2 \dfrac{n\delta}{2}}{\sin^2 \dfrac{\delta}{2}}$$

or evidently
$$A = \frac{m \sin \dfrac{n\delta}{2}}{\sin \dfrac{\delta}{2}} \qquad \cdot \qquad \cdot \qquad \cdot \qquad \cdot \qquad (315)$$

If now n is very great but $n\delta$ is still finite and equal to P, say,

$$A = m \frac{\sin \dfrac{P}{2}}{\sin \dfrac{P}{2n}} = m \frac{\sin \dfrac{P}{2}}{\dfrac{P}{2n}}$$

$$= nm \frac{\sin \dfrac{P}{2}}{\dfrac{P}{2}} \qquad \cdot \qquad \cdot \qquad \cdot \qquad \cdot \qquad (316)$$

* See any book on higher trigonometry.

The coefficient nm is the total amplitude which would be contributed if the contributions of all the zones were in the same phase.

The required constancy of "K" is evidently a doubtful point. The contribution of a zone to the amplitude at B might be diminished as the angle made by PB with the normal to the surface increased. But evidently if we restrict the problem to finding the effect of a narrow area surrounding A, it will be justifiable to try the effect of regarding K as constant.

Suppose we first take a circular zone such that $PB = AB + \dfrac{\lambda}{2}$, and find the whole effect; then

$$nm = \frac{2\pi KA_1 n dc}{a+b} = \frac{2\pi KA_1 \left(\dfrac{\lambda}{2}\right)}{a+b}$$

The total phase difference P is $\dfrac{2\pi}{\lambda}\left(\dfrac{\lambda}{2}\right) = \pi$

Hence, a_1, the amplitude due to the whole zone as defined above, will be

$$a_1 = \frac{\pi\lambda KA_1}{(a+b)}\frac{\sin\dfrac{\pi}{2}}{\dfrac{\pi}{2}}$$

$$= \frac{2\lambda KA_1}{(a+b)} \qquad . \qquad . \qquad . \qquad (317)$$

To find the phase of the resultant, we may evaluate

$$\tan \triangle = \frac{\sin p + \sin \overline{p+\delta} + \ldots + \sin (p + \overline{n-1}\delta)}{\cos p + \cos \overline{p+\delta} + \ldots + \cos (p + \overline{n-1}\delta)}$$

and from the sums of the series appearing in the expression above, we find

$$\tan \triangle = \tan \left\{ p + \frac{n-1}{2}\delta \right\}$$

and thus evidently $\qquad \triangle = p + \dfrac{n-1}{2}\delta$

This equation shows that the phase of the resultant in such a case is the mean of the phases of the first and last "contributions"; this is otherwise obvious from considerations of symmetry. Hence, the phase of the resultant of the whole zone considered above, where

$PB = AB + \dfrac{\lambda}{2}$, would be $\dfrac{\pi}{2}$ behind that of the disturbance arriving from the centre, if we consider the secondary waves from points such as P to start out with the same phase as the vibrations in the wave-surface. The expression for the displacement is therefore

$$ s = \frac{2\lambda KA_1}{(a+b)} \cos 2\pi \left(\frac{t}{T} - \frac{a+b}{\lambda} \right) \qquad . \qquad (318) $$

the cosine appearing instead of the sine.

If, now we take a wider zone given by making $PB = AB + \dfrac{\lambda}{2}$ and $AB + \lambda$ for the limits, the amplitude a_2 produced at B may be slightly smaller numerically than that from the first zone; on the same suppositions the phase would be $3\dfrac{\pi}{2}$ behind that of the disturbance from A, and therefore the amplitude contributions, being in exactly opposite phases, can be subtracted to find the resultant of both.

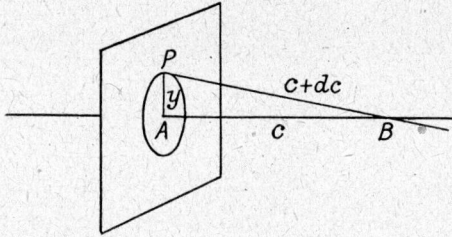

Fig. 50

Amplitude from first two zones $= a_1 - a_2$ (and similarly the resultant amplitude for any number of zones will be $a_1 - a_2 + a_3 - a_4 +$ etc. . . .).

With respect to $(a_1 - a_2)$, this will be very small in comparison with either a_1 or a_2, and it thus appears that if we screen off the outer parts of the surface so as to allow only the first two zones to send light to B, the illumination should be much smaller than when only the first zone is allowed to act. If the aperture is opened so as to admit the third zone, there will again be a maximum illumination. Such "zones" were used for the discussion of diffraction problems by Fresnel, and are often termed Fresnel zones.

For finding the general effects of the first few zones, it is quite legitimate to use formula (316).

Suppose it is desired to find the effect, at a point on the axis of symmetry, of the diffraction of a plane wave-train at a circular aperture, assuming that the incident wave-fronts are parallel to the plane of the aperture.

In Fig. 50, the aperture has centre A and radius $AP = y$. B is a point on the axis, so that $AB = c$ and $PB = c + dc$.

Then $y^2 + c^2 = (c + dc)^2 = c^2 + 2cdc$, if dc is small of the first order, so that $(dc)^2$ can be neglected.

Then $y^2 = 2cdc$ and $dc = \dfrac{y^2}{2c}$.

The difference of phase between disturbances arriving at B from A and P is therefore

$$\frac{2\pi}{\lambda} \left(\frac{y^2}{2c} \right) = \frac{\pi y^2}{\lambda c}$$

In formula (316), nm appears as the total amplitude which would result if all the elementary zones gave their contributions at B in

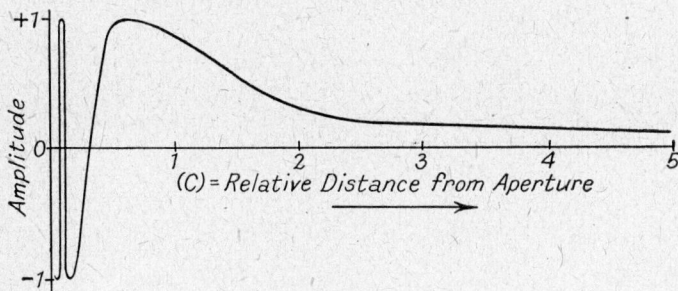

$$(C) = Relative\ Distance\ from\ Aperture$$

FIG. 51

the same phase. It is evidently proportional to the area of the aperture, and inversely proportional to the distance of B from the point A. Hence (316) becomes in this case, writing k as a constant of proportionality,

$$A = k\frac{\pi y^2}{c} \frac{\sin\left(\dfrac{\pi y^2}{2\lambda c}\right)}{\left(\dfrac{\pi y^2}{2\lambda c}\right)} = 2k\lambda \sin\left(\frac{\pi y^2}{2\lambda c}\right) = K_1 \sin\left(\frac{K_2}{c}\right)$$

where K_1 and K_2 are constants for a given aperture and wavelength. The values of A are plotted against c in Fig. 51.* As we approach the point A from a distance which is very great in comparison with the radius, the amplitude on the axis slowly increases to a maximum; it then falls through zero and becomes negative, going thus through a series of maxima of alternate signs, the more rapidly as the distance from the aperture decreases. The *intensity*, which is proportional to the square of the amplitude, can naturally show no changes of sign, but varies between zero and a more or less uniform maximum value. The accuracy of the expression diminishes as the distance c becomes shorter.

* K_1 and K_2 are taken as unity, to exhibit the form of the curve.

The discussion just given is only applicable to points on the axis, but we may gain some idea of the distribution of intensity away from the axis by the following argument. Let us consider the plane of B, Fig. 50, where, as we approach A, the first maximum on the axis is found. From the expression above, we shall then have

$$\frac{\pi y^2}{2\lambda c} = \frac{\pi}{2}, \text{ or } y^2 = \lambda c,$$

the sine term then becoming unity. The aperture then includes the first of the Fresnel zones mentioned above, and $PB - AB = \lambda/2$.

The area of the zone is

$$\pi y^2 = \pi c\lambda \quad . \quad (319)$$

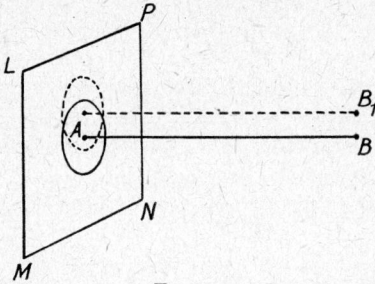

Fig. 52

Imagine that LMNP, Fig. 52, is a portion of the plane wavefront *unobstructed by a screen*, and let B_1 be a point in the plane of observation so that B_1B is perpendicular to AB, and is equal, say, to $y/2$.

If we draw the first Fresnel zone for the point B_1 we shall obtain a circular area suggested by the dotted line. Now imagine the screen replaced in the original position with respect to B. As far as B_1 is concerned, the aperture obviously includes a part only of the first Fresnel zone, and also a portion of the second. The radii of successive zones, enclosing rings of equal area, are 1, $\sqrt{2}$, $\sqrt{3}$, etc., so that a small portion of the third begins to appear. Clearly the illumination is very much lower than at the axial point, and we may therefore infer a concentration of light at B of which the dimensions are comparable with the aperture itself. Exact calculation shows that the effective concentration is even smaller than the aperture; a "focus" can be found where the bright *axial spot* has only one-third of the diameter of the aperture.

The Pinhole Camera. Calculation will show that the ratio y/c must be very small if the first Fresnel zone only is to be included. If c is 50 cm. and we assume $\lambda = 0.5 + 10^{-3}$ mm., the radius of the zone is 0.5 mm.

Fig. 53 shows a set of photographs of the diffraction effects at a circular aperture. The enlargement is so great as to show the grainy structure of the photographic image. As the aperture is approached, the concentration of light becomes more definite and a dark ring begins to appear surrounding it. The illumination at the centre falls, and a dark spot appears (the first two Fresnel zones are now included); further inwards still, a dark ring appears to grow out of the centre, while a bright spot increases to a maximum on the axis.

It is owing to the comparatively great concentration of light, which appears when the first Fresnel zone is included by the aperture, that the pinhole camera can be used to produce quite well-defined photographs. Further diminution of the size of the pin-hole causes the image patch to become more and more diffuse.

A serious disadvantage of the photographs is that when wide-angle views are taken, the effec-tive area of the aperture varies with the obliquity; this factor adversely affects both the illum-ination and definition towards the margin.

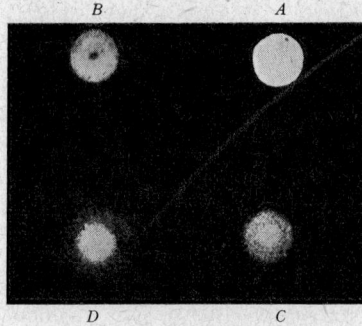

FIG. 53

A. Circular aperture. *B.* Diffraction pattern when the aperture includes two Fresnel zones. *C.* Pattern when the aperture includes the first Fresnel zone. *D.* Pattern at a still greater distance.

Results of Advanced Theoretical Studies of Diffraction. The effect at the point B, Fig. 49, of the disturbances due to the whole wave-front is

$$a_1 - a_2 + a_3 - a_4 + \text{etc.}$$

If the successive terms are of slowly diminishing magnitude, the higher ones being comparatively small, it is easy to show that the sum of the series must be very nearly $\left(\dfrac{a_1}{2}\right)$*.

* The sum
$$S = a_1 - a_2 + a_3 - a_4 + \ldots \ldots + a_{n-1} + a_n$$
can be written
$$S = \frac{a_1}{2} + \left(\frac{a_1}{2} - a_2 + \frac{a_3}{2}\right) + \left(\frac{a_3}{2} - a_4 + \frac{a_5}{2}\right) + \text{etc. to} \ldots$$
$$+ \left(\frac{a_{n-2}}{2} - a_{n-1} + \frac{a_n}{2}\right) + \frac{a_n}{2}$$
$$= a_1 - \frac{a_2}{2} - \left(\frac{a_2}{2} - a_3 + \frac{a_4}{2}\right) - \left(\frac{a_4}{2} - a_5 + \frac{a_6}{2}\right) - \text{etc. to} \ldots$$
$$- \left(\frac{a_{n-3}}{2} - a_{n-2} + \frac{a_{n-1}}{2}\right) - \frac{a_{n-1}}{2} + a_n$$

If the terms a_1, a_2, a_3 only decrease in magnitude very slowly, we may conclude that the terms in the brackets would probably all be positive or all negative. The sum is seen to lie between
$$\frac{a_1}{2} + \frac{a_n}{2} \quad \text{and} \quad \left\{\left(a_1 - \frac{a_2}{2}\right) - \left(\frac{a_{n-1}}{2} - a_n\right)\right\}$$
and therefore cannot differ greatly from $\dfrac{a_1}{2} + \dfrac{a_n}{2}$, or from $\dfrac{a_1}{2}$ if $\dfrac{a_n}{2}$ can be neglected.

Now $$\frac{a_1}{2} = \frac{\lambda K A_1}{(a + b)} \qquad . \qquad . \qquad \text{from (317)}$$

On the other hand, the displacement at B can be calculated directly; it is

$$\frac{A_1}{(a + b)} \sin 2\pi \left(\frac{t}{T} - \frac{a + b}{\lambda} \right)$$

Hence, if we put $K = \dfrac{1}{\lambda}$ in our equation (318) for the use of Huygens' principle, the correct value of the amplitude will be obtained.

There is a difficulty regarding the phase, however, for if it be assumed that the effect at B is simply half that of the first Fresnel zone, the phase of the resultant would (as shown above) be $\pi/2$ behind that of the disturbance from the centre; but it is, of course, the central disturbance which is being investigated. Therefore, in order to find the correct phase by the application of Huygens' principle, we must assume that the secondary disturbances start with a phase $\dfrac{\pi}{2}$ in advance of the vibrations in the wave-front, or that the length of the optical path is diminished by a quarter of a wave-length. This procedure must be regarded primarily as a practical basis of calculation, the Huygenian account of wave propagation being merely pragmatically useful. Naturally, the exact absolute phases of disturbances are seldom of significance, provided the *relative* phases are correctly assigned.

However, if real oscillating systems take part in wave propagation, the phase retardation of the secondary waves is taken into account in the theory of dispersion. (See p. 230.)

Suppose we have a source of light O emitting radiation, and a point B at which the total effect is to be found, a permissible modification of Huygens' principle is to imagine a surface surrounding B which, while the waves are passing, will clearly be a seat of disturbances of various amplitudes and phases. With certain restrictions we may find the effect at B by adding up the contributions derived from all points of this surface which are capable of sending them, taking account of their amplitudes and relative phases on arrival. A little consideration will, however, make it appear that the disturbances arriving at B in any instant must be regarded as having been possibly derived from *all points in the space surrounding B* and arriving with the phases which were characteristic of these points at a time r/V before arrival (where r is the distance of a point from B and V is the velocity). This latter method is clearly the most general, and it is possible to obtain a mathematical solution of the problem as to the conditions under which the effect of the *surface* can be regarded as equivalent to the effect of the *space*. The results confirm those which have already been obtained tentatively above, and show that we must not regard the modified Huygens' principle as a physical description of the mechanism of these diffraction phenomena, but rather as a helpful "short cut" to be applied with due reservations in order to escape considerations of a much more complex character.

Diffraction Phenomena with Convergent Light. *Effects on the Axis.* Let a convergent wave-train with spherical wave-fronts be limited by a circular diaphragm symmetrically placed with respect to the axis. The centre of the spherical loci is, of course, equidistant from all points on a wave-front, but at any other point on the axis the distances to the marginal and axial zones will be unequal. Let p_m be the difference of the marginal and axial distances, then, if this magnitude is calculated, the wave-surface can be divided up into Fresnel zones. A trigonometrical investigation will

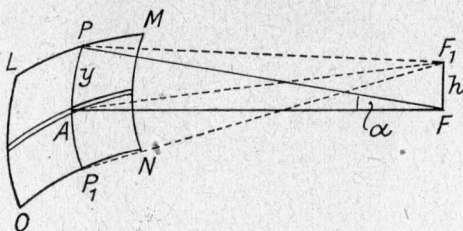

FIG. 54

be given in Chapter IV; in the meantime, we note that when $p_m = \pm \lambda$ the surface includes two Fresnel zones, and the intensity on the axis will be zero. From the investigation on p. 86, which is valid for the present case, it appears that the zones will be equal in area, and for any elementary ring in the first zone there will be another of equal area in the second zone which gives an amplitude contribution equal in magnitude but opposite in sign. Hence, there will be a series of maxima and minima, practically symmetrically spaced along the axis on each side of the focus.

Effects in the Focal Plane. It is worth while to examine the effects in the plane of the focus at right angles to the axis, but an easy discussion is only possible when the aperture is rectangular. This case is represented in Fig. 54, where F is the centre of curvature of the wave-front, LMNO is a portion of the wave-front supposed to be transmitted by a rectangular aperture symmetrically placed, and A is the central point. Take $FF_1 = h$, parallel to one side of the aperture and perpendicular to AF. The line P_1AP is a mid-line of the rectangle. Let $P_1A = AP = y$.

The conditions are such that we might imagine FF_1 a portion of the axis of a globe on which LM, ON were parallels of latitude.

The point F_1 is equidistant from all points on such lines, and consequently the phase contribution from a whole strip parallel to LM will be the phase of the contribution from its mid-point.

From the similar case encountered in discussing Young's experiment, we find where y is relatively small

$$P_1F_1 - PF_1 = 2h \sin \alpha, \text{ or } AF_1 - PF_1 = h \sin \alpha.$$

Evidently when $AF_1 = PF_1 + \lambda/2$, we shall always be able to find a pair of horizontal strips in the sections above and below A which give their contributions in opposite phases, so that the results

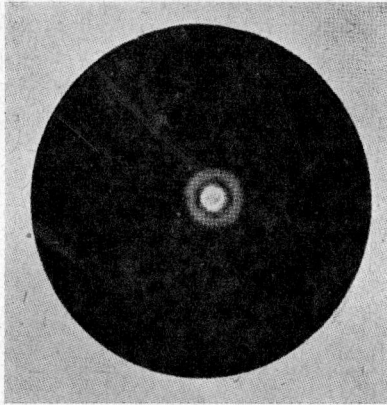

FIG. 55. PHOTOGRAPH OF THE AIRY DISC

neutralize. It may be inferred that there will then be a minimum illumination at F_1, when

$$hy/f = \lambda/2$$

or

$$h = f\lambda/2y$$

(taking $\sin \alpha = y/f$ approximately), and there will be additional minima when $h = 3f\lambda/2y$, $5f\lambda/2y$, etc.

The conditions when the aperture is circular are not so easily dealt with, but it can be shown that the first minimum will be found when

$$h = 0 \cdot 61\lambda/\sin \alpha \qquad . \qquad . \qquad . \qquad (320)$$

or by an allowable approximation

$$h = 0 \cdot 61\lambda_o f/n'y \qquad . \qquad . \qquad . \qquad (321)$$

λ_o/n' being now written for λ, the actual wave-length of the light; λ_o is the wave-length in air and n' the refractive index.

In this case there will be central symmetry, the minima are

represented by dark rings, and the general appearance of the concentration in the focal plane is shown by Fig. 55. The central condensation of light is called the "Airy disc," since the distribution of light in the image was first worked out by Sir George Airy in 1834.

Intensity near the Focus. General Method for Circular Aperture.*
Let F in Fig. 56 represent a point on the axis of a circular aperture limiting a symmetrical, spherical, convergent wave-train. FF_1 is a line of small height h perpendicular to the axis OF. Imagine a spherical reference surface (with centre F) limited by the aperture; then the circular ring ACBD, having a radius y, with *its centre* O in the axis, is drawn in the surface. The diameter CD is parallel to, and the diameter AB perpendicular to, FF_1. The surface is the seat of disturbances in various phases.

Take the point P in the ring so

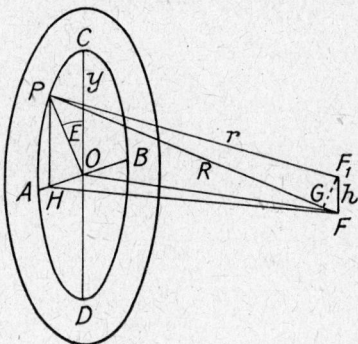

FIG. 56

that $\widehat{COP} = E$. Join PF_1, PF, and HF, having drawn PH perpendicular to AO and F_1G perpendicular to PF as shown.

If h is a small quantity of the first order, $PG = PF_1$ within a small error of the second order. Hence, if $PF_1 = r$, and $PF = R$

$$r = R - h \sin \widehat{GF_1F}$$

It will appear from the diagram that the points P, H, F_1, F, and G are all in one vertical plane, and that $\widehat{GF_1F} = \widehat{PFH}$. Hence,

$$r = R - h \sin \widehat{PFH} = R - h\,\frac{PH}{R} = R - \frac{hy \cos E}{R}$$

The area of an element of surface at P is $ydEdy$. Hence, by Huygens' principle the displacement at F_1 produced by this element can be written

$$ds = \frac{A}{\lambda r}\,(ydEdy)\,\sin\left\{2\pi\left(\frac{t}{T} - \frac{r}{\lambda}\right) + \delta\right\}$$

where δ represents a term to express the phase of the disturbance

* Those who are not acquainted with Bessel Functions should note that the integrals can be evaluated by "mechanical integration." (See Conrady, *R.A.S.*, "Monthly Notices," 79 (1919), 575.)

in the element *plus* the phase correction term of $\pi/2$ and A is the amplitude in the surface.

The total displacement is therefore

$$s = \frac{A}{\lambda R} \int \int \sin \left[2\pi \left\{ \frac{t}{T} - \frac{R - hy\,(\cos E)/R}{\lambda} \right\} + \delta \right] ydEdy$$

in which the approximation of writing R for r in the denominator of the co-efficient outside the integral has been introduced; the integration is to be performed over the whole surface. The expression may be simplified by writing it

$$s = \frac{A}{\lambda R} \int \int \sin \left\{ x + \frac{2\pi hy \cos E}{\lambda R} \right\} ydEdy$$

$$= \frac{A}{\lambda R} \int \int \sin (x + W \cos E)\, ydEdy$$

where $\qquad W = \dfrac{2\pi hy}{\lambda R}$ $\qquad . \qquad . \qquad . \qquad . \qquad . \qquad . \qquad$ (322)

Writing in the limits,

$$s = \frac{A}{\lambda R} \int_{E\,=\,o}^{E\,=\,2\pi} \int_{y\,=\,o}^{y\,=\,y_1} (\sin x \cos \overline{W \cos E} + \cos x \sin \overline{W \cos E})\, ydEdy$$

In integrating with respect to E, the elements of the integral involving $\sin (W \cos E)$ will cancel each other in pairs if δ (which is contained in the term x) is independent of E, since for every one value of E there will be another for which the cosine is numerically equal and opposite in sign.

The integral therefore reduces to

$$s = \frac{A}{\lambda R} \int_o^{2\pi} \int_o^{y_1} \sin x \cos \overline{W \cos E}\; ydEdy$$

$$= \frac{A}{\lambda R} \int_o^{y_1} \sin x \left\{ 2\pi \, J_o \left(\frac{2\pi hy}{\lambda R} \right) \right\} ydy$$

where J_o is the Bessel function of the zero order.* If now x is independent of y, which will be the case of a spherical wave-front with centre in F, the expression is integrable, and becomes

$$s = \frac{Ay_1}{h} J_1 \left(\frac{2\pi hy_1}{\lambda R} \right) \sin x$$

* Tables of these "Bessel functions" are available, and thus it is convenient to express results in terms involving them.

The sin x is the periodic term; the other part represents the amplitude. Hence the intensity is given by

$$I = \text{constant} \left\{ \frac{Ay_1}{h} J_1 \left(\frac{2\pi h y_1}{\lambda R} \right) \right\}^2 \qquad . \qquad . \quad (323)$$

This subject will be continued in Chapter IV (see p. 121). The
form of the above expression, when plotted, is shown in Figs. 59
and 70. The general form of the curve corresponds to

$$\text{Intensity} = \text{constant} \left\{ \frac{J_1(h)}{h} \right\}^2$$

THE OPTICAL IMAGE AND ITS DEFECTS

THE distribution of light near the focus of a convergent spherical wave-train has been shown to depend upon the ratio of the aperture to the focusing distance. Hence the study of the limitations of the image-forming pencils of light is a matter of the greatest importance.

Fig. 57 represents in a conventional way the optical system of centered lenses which is forming the image B′ of an axial object B. All the lenses are mounted in circular mounts which limit their

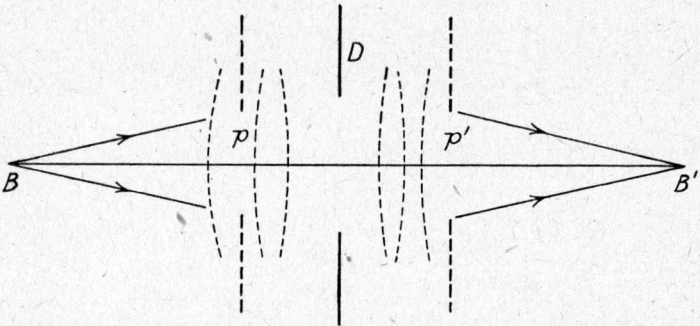

FIG. 57

diameters and, in addition, the system may comprise circular diaphragms, such as D, introduced at various points to limit the beams. An eye placed at B and looking into the system might observe (under proper illumination) the images of a number of the lens boundaries and diaphragms; thus the mount limiting the nearest lens of the system would be "seen" directly; others *might* appear under a smaller angle, and spaced at various distances. The limitation of the rays which pass quite through the system is evidently performed by that diaphragm, the *image* of which subtends the smallest angle at B. This image is the *entrance pupil*. If the rim of the first lens or a diaphragm in front of the system subtends the smallest angle, it will itself constitute the entrance pupil.

Thus, to find the entrance pupil, theoretically it would be necessary to construct for each lens mount or diaphragm in turn, the image of it formed by that part of the lens system lying to the left of it, imagining for this purpose light to be travelling from right to left. That diaphragm image which subtends the smallest angle at the object point will be the entrance pupil. The image of the *same diaphragm*, formed by the part of the system lying to the right, is called the *exit pupil*. These pupils are evidently in conjugate planes with respect to the lens system; their radii will be denoted by p and p'.

It is not the case that the exit and entrance pupils are necessarily constant for all positions of the object; this will be understood from Fig. 58, in which 1, 2, 3 represent diaphragm images formed as set forth above. An axial object point B will have (1) as its effective entrance pupil; the point B_1 will have (3).

The limitations of the pencils from extra-axial object points at finite distances from the axis may be of a complex character, as

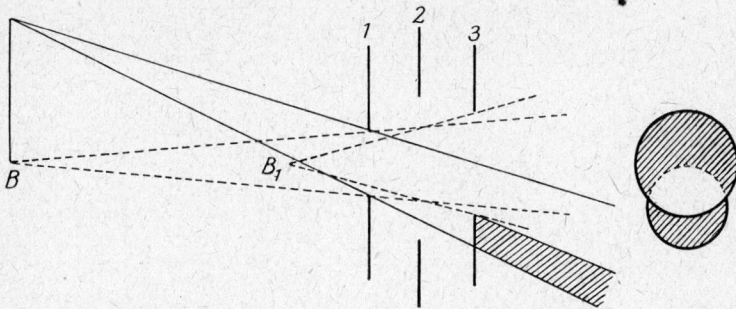

FIG. 58

indicated in the diagram; the approximately conical pencil transmitted by (1) will be partly cut off by (3). Hence it is to be remembered in discussing extra-axial images that the effects characteristic of a circular aperture cannot always be assumed to be present.

Resolving Power. As already mentioned, the distribution of light in the focal plane of a "spherical" wave-train was calculated by Airy with results of the type shown by the full line in Fig. 59. In order to compute the ability of the system to form distinct images of close point sources, we assume that each of the sources has an image giving the characteristic distribution of light. Since the light from the two object points will be mutually incoherent, there will be no visible interference effects between their images. Hence the intensity along the line through the image centres will be represented by the sum of the ordinates of the intensity curve for each. There will be a decided dip when the maximum of one falls on the first minimum of the next, but when the images are a trifle closer this dip will vanish, and it is approximately in this condition that it would begin to be

difficult to detect the double nature of the image, when it is registered by a photographic plate or other means.

Although it is not a conception which is necessarily optically
exact, the limit of resolution is conveniently accepted as that
when the centre of one Airy disc falls upon the first dark minimum
of the other. The separation h' of the centres of the two images is
thus given by equation (320),

$$h' = 0.61\lambda'/\sin \alpha'$$

where α' is the angular semi-aperture of the convergent cone from

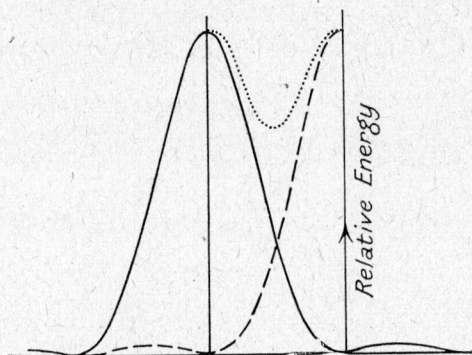

FIG. 59

Full line:　　Airy disc distribution.
Broken line: Second image with maximum coincident with first dark minimum of Airy disc.
Dotted line: Sum of ordinates.

the boundary of the circular diaphragm to the centre of each image
point, and λ' is the wave-length of light in the image space.

In actual practice there may be possibilities of resolution beyond
the above limit, as will be seen below.

Fermat's Theorem. We have already discussed the conception
of the optical image as the meeting point of congruent rays originating from the object point; our discussion of the diffraction effects
of a convergent wave by a circular aperture has prepared us for the
concept of the image as being the point where vibratory disturbances from the object point meet in the same phase. If the wave
surface is spherical and converging to its central point, we can
visualize the "rays" as being the normals to the wave-surface.

Following Huygens' principle, it is seen generally that a wave-
surface must spread along lines normal to its own direction, i.e.
along the rays, and this leads to a very general theorem regarding
the path of a ray, which has already been justified for the particular
cases of reflection and refraction.

*The path of a "ray" of light from one point to another is such that
the time taken in the journey by a disturbance has no more than an
infinitesimal* difference from the time which would be occupied in
travelling along other very close adjacent paths between the same points.*
(The adjacent path must lie everywhere close to the ray path
within a distance which is small of the first order, and must similarly
make only very small angles with the ray path.)

Thus the time may be either a minimum or maximum, or genuinely
stationary; the minimum property was shown to hold for reflection
and refraction at plane surfaces. The more formal proof of the
general theorem will be found in textbooks of theoretical optics.

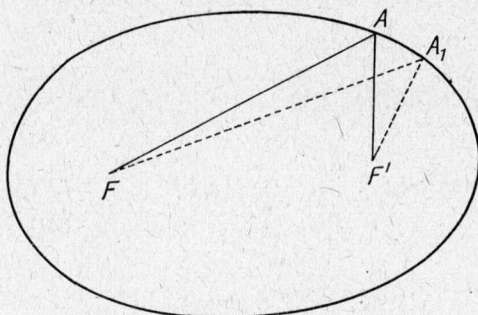

FIG. 60. SECTION OF ELLIPSOIDAL SURFACE
Foci *F* and *F'*.

An optical example of a stationary optical path is found in the
case of Fig. 60, in which F and F' are the two foci of an ellipsoid of
revolution having a smooth inner reflecting surface. By a well-
known property of the ellipse FA + AF' = FA$_1$ + A$_1$F', where A
and A$_1$ are any two points on the surfaces. It will also be remembered
that FA and AF' make equal angles with the normal to the surface
at A; hence we have a case in which the total path of a reflected
beam between two points is really stationary. Reflection at a plane
surface tangential at A would have given a minimum path. A more
highly curved surface than that of the ellipsoid, tangential to the
latter at A, would have provided an example in which FA + AF'
represented a maximum path.

Analytical Statement of Fermat's Theorem. Let the length of
path of light in a medium "*a*" be dl_a and let the refractive index
be n_a. Let the velocity in the medium be V_a and the velocity in
vacuo be V_o. Then

$$V_o = n_a V_a$$

The time occupied $= dl_a/V_a = dl_a n_a/V_o.$

* i.e. as compared with the total time of the journey.

Hence, the total time occupied in traversing the media a, b, c, etc., through which the ray passes will be

$$t = (n_a dl_a + n_b dl_b + n_c dl_c + \text{etc.})/V_o$$

Hence, if the time is to have a stationary value, then Σndl must also have a stationary value for the same conditions, i.e. under the very small variations of path between two points as contemplated in Fermat's theorem. This is expressed analytically

$$\delta(\Sigma ndl) = 0$$

The use of this theorem enables us to answer the following question: Supposing that B and B' are conjugate points of an optical system, the optical path between them being stationary for all variations

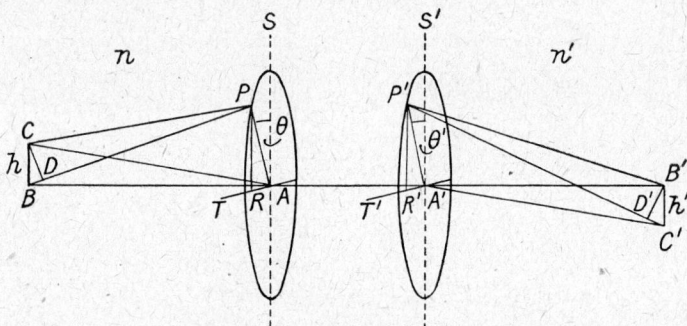

FIG. 61

of the route, consider a *very short* line BC perpendicular to the axis. Where will the image C' of the point C be found?

The Optical Sine Relation. In Fig. 61, BC and B'C' are two very short lines perpendicular to the axis BAA'B' of a centred optical system. They lie in the same axial plane.

Imagine a circle drawn on a plane touching the first refracting surface of the system, so that its centre is on the axis, and P to be a point through which we can track a ray BP to its final destination, which we will assume to be the image point B'. It will pass through the point P', which we can imagine to lie on a similar circle on a plane touching the last surface.

The general condition that B' may be the image of B is that (Σndl for the actual path BP . . . P'B') = (Σndl for BA . . . A'B'). Consider now the image of a point above the axis. Let us investigate the condition that C' may be the image of C; if this is the case, we shall be able to track the rays CP and CA through the system to their final destination, which will be C', but the points of intersection of the last surface may *not* exactly coincide with P' and A'; Fermat's theorem allows us, however, to calculate the optical lengths of these paths as

$$(\Sigma ndl \text{ for CP } \ldots \text{ P'C'}) \text{ and } (\Sigma ndl \text{ for CA } \ldots \text{ A'C'})$$

where the paths (P to P') and (A to A') *are taken as the same as those for the disturbances from* B. This is because these "paths" are adjacent paths to the actual ones, lying everywhere very close to them and making only small angles with them at any point.

Let the refractive indices of the object and image spaces be n and n' respectively, then if disturbances are to meet in the same phase at C' as well as at B',

$$n . \text{CP} + (\text{P to P'}) + n' . \text{P'C'} = n . \text{CA} + (\text{A to A'}) + n' . \text{A'C'},$$

and $n . \text{BP} + (\text{P to P'}) + n' . \text{P'B'} = n . \text{BA} + (\text{A to A'}) + n' . \text{A'B'}.$

Subtracting, we find

$$n(\text{BP} - \text{CP}) + n' (\text{P'B'} - \text{P'C'}) = n(\text{BA} - \text{CA}) + n'(\text{A'B'} - \text{A'C'}).$$

If h and h' are assumed to be small of the first order, then

$$\text{CA} = \text{BA, and A'B'} = \text{A'C', sufficiently nearly.*}$$

This will make the right-hand side of the above equation vanish, and we then have

$$n(\text{BP} - \text{CP}) = n'(\text{P'C'} - \text{P'B'}) . \qquad . \qquad . \qquad (a)$$

We may draw AS and A'S' in the reference planes parallel to BC and B'C'. Let the angle $\widehat{\text{PAS}} = \widehat{\text{P'A'S'}} = \theta$. (Note that P and P' must lie in the same axial plane if the system is centered.) Draw also AT, A'T', at right angles to AS and A'S' respectively in the reference planes, and drop perpendiculars PR, P'R' to AT, A'T'. Also draw CD perpendicular to BP and B'D' perpendicular to P'C'.

The points C, B, D, P, R are evidently in one vertical plane. Imagining the line BR to be drawn, we see

$$\widehat{\text{BCD}} = \widehat{\text{RBP}}$$

Now, if h is small of the first order CP = DP within a small quantity of the second order; hence

$$\text{BP} - \text{CP} = \text{BD} = h \sin \widehat{\text{BCD}} = h \sin \widehat{\text{RBP}} = h . \frac{\text{PR}}{\text{BP}}$$

$$= h \left(\frac{\text{AP}}{\text{BP}}\right) \cos \theta$$

* Note that $\text{CA}^2 = h^2 + \text{BA}^2$, whence

$$\text{CA} = \text{BA} \left(1 + \frac{h^2}{\text{BA}^2}\right)^{\frac{1}{2}} = \text{BA} \left\{1 + \frac{1}{2} \left(\frac{h}{\text{BA}}\right)^2 - \frac{1}{8} \left(\frac{h}{\text{BA}}\right)^4 + \text{etc.}\right\}$$

If h is taken sufficiently small in comparison with BA, it will be seen that the terms beyond the first in the expansion can be neglected, since $h^2/2\text{BA}^2$ will be extremely small even in comparison with h.

Let the angle $\widehat{ABP}$ be α, as usual, then

$$BP - CP = h \sin \alpha \cos \theta$$

Note that $\sin \alpha$ and $\cos \theta$ are not very small quantities. Hence, the difference between BP and CP is not negligible in comparison with h, as was the difference between CA and BA.

Similarly, it may be shown that

$$P'C' - P'B' = h' \sin \alpha' \cos \theta$$

whence $nh \sin \alpha \cos \theta = n'h' \sin \alpha' \cos \theta$, from equation ($a$) above, or

$$nh \sin \alpha = n'h' \sin \alpha' \quad . \qquad . \qquad . \qquad . \qquad (401)$$

This is the "optical sine relation," evidently an extended form of the Lagrange relation (see equation (109)). The above proof is due to Conrady.

The so-called "sine condition," is derived from it. Provided that the system is free from spherical aberration (see below), so that the disturbances from all zones of the system meet in the same phase in the axial image point, the "sine condition" is the law which the rays through the optical system should fulfil if the disturbances from all zones are similarly to meet in the same phase in image points away from the axis. Thus, if the ratio of h' to h is to be the same for all zones, *then the ratio* $\sin \alpha/\sin \alpha'$ *must be constant for all zones also.* This will free the system from the defect known as coma, i.e. inequality of magnification for the different zones; see p. 131.

A case in which it is encountered is in the "aplanatic" refraction at a spherical surface. (See Vol. II.) The term "aplanatic" signifies freedom both from spherical aberration and coma.

Resolving Power in the Object Space. The separation h' of the centres of two images placed at the least distance for conventional resolution is

$$h' = \frac{0 \cdot 61 \, \lambda_o}{n' \sin \alpha'}$$

whence
$$0 \cdot 61 \lambda_o = n'h' \sin \alpha'$$
$$= nh \sin \alpha$$

by the optical sine relation, where h is the corresponding separation of the object points in the object space. This gives

$$h = \frac{0 \cdot 61 \, \lambda_o}{n \sin \alpha} \qquad . \qquad . \qquad . \qquad . \qquad (402)$$

This is a very general equation and one of great importance in connection with the theory of the microscope. The minimum separation of two object points for possible resolution is thus directly proportional to the wave-length, and inversely proportional to the refractive index of the object space and to the sine of the semi-apical angle of the cone of rays entering the optical system from the object.

Diffraction Phenomena with Convergent Light. Path Differences on the Axis. Let disturbances from a spherical wave front AP arrive in the same phase at the centre point B. This point will be the position of maximum vibration. In order to calculate the relative amplitude at other points we must consider the optical path differences. Take, for example in Fig. 62, the axial point B_1 at a distance δl from B. Let s be written for PB_1. The refractive index of the space is n.

Produce PB; with

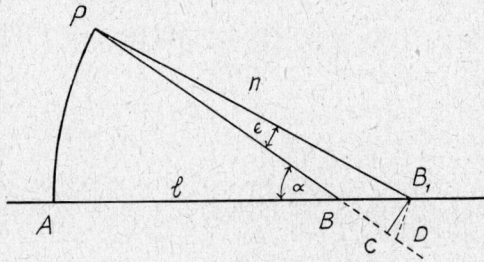

FIG. 62

P as centre and PB_1 as radius, strike the arc B_1D cutting PB (produced) in D. Drop the perpendicular B_1C from B_1 to BD.

On Huygens' principle, the disturbances reach B_1 from all parts of the wave-front AP. Since $PD = PB_1$, the extra path for the marginal disturbance from P, as compared with the path to B, is BD. The extra path for the axial disturbance from A is BB_1. Hence we write the relative retardation p_m at B_1 of the marginal disturbance as the difference of optical paths, i.e.

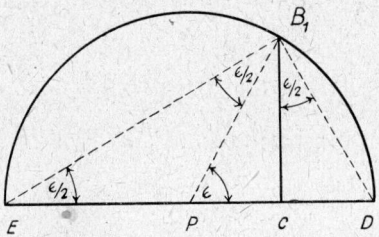

FIG. 63

$$p_m = n(BD - BB_1),$$
$$= n(BC + CD - BB_1),$$
$$= n\{BB_1(\cos \alpha - 1) + CD\}$$

Now, when BB_1 is very small, the angle BPB_1, written as ε, will be very small also. But with the aid of the auxiliary diagram, Fig. 63, we can write down an expression for the intercept CD between the arc and perpendicular. The whole semicircle is shown, and since the angle $\widehat{EB_1D}$ is a right angle, the triangles EB_1D and B_1CD are similar, and $\widehat{CB_1D} = \varepsilon/2$. Hence

$$CD = B_1D \sin (\varepsilon/2) \qquad . \qquad . \qquad . \qquad . \qquad . \qquad (403)$$

but $\qquad B_1D = ED \sin (\varepsilon/2) = 2PB_1 \sin (\varepsilon/2) \qquad . \qquad . \qquad (404)$

Hence $\qquad CD = 2s \sin^2(\varepsilon/2) \qquad . \qquad . \qquad . \qquad . \qquad (405)$

In many cases of interest, CD will be small in comparison with the other part of the retardation expression, which thus becomes, on writing,

$$\cos \alpha = 1 - \frac{\alpha^2}{2!} + \frac{\alpha^4}{4!} - \text{etc.} \quad . \qquad . \qquad . \qquad . \quad (406)$$

and again taking the case where α is so small that α^4 is negligible,

$$p_m = - \tfrac{1}{2}n \, BB_1\alpha^2,$$
$$= - \tfrac{1}{2}n \, \delta l(y/l)^2, \text{approximately} \quad . \qquad . \quad (407)$$

where y is the height of P above AB, and AB is written as l.

If the restrictions under which the above formula was obtained are not valid, we must go back to the original equation for retardation, writing it

$$p_m = n \, \{\delta l(\cos \alpha - 1) + 2s \sin^2 (\varepsilon/2)\}.$$

If ε is small, though not so small that its square is negligible, a legitimate approximation will usually be that

$$\sin^2 (\varepsilon/2) \simeq \tfrac{1}{4} \sin^2 \varepsilon \, ;$$

Also
$$\sin \varepsilon = \frac{BB_1 \sin \alpha}{PB_1} = \frac{\delta l \sin \alpha}{s}$$

so that
$$CD = 2s \sin^2 (\varepsilon/2) \simeq 2\frac{(\delta l)^2}{s} \sin^2 (\alpha/2) \cos^2 (\alpha/2).$$

Since also
$$\cos \alpha = 1 - 2 \sin^2 (\alpha/2),$$

we obtain, on using these results in the retardation expression,

$$p_m = 2n \left\{ - \delta l \sin^2 (\alpha/2) + \frac{(\delta l)^2}{s} \sin^2 (\alpha/2) \cos^2 (\alpha/2) \right\},$$

$$= - 2n\delta l \sin^2 (\alpha/2) \left\{ 1 - \frac{\delta l}{s} \cos^2 (\alpha/2) \right\} \quad . \qquad . \qquad . \qquad . \quad (408)$$

Hence in cases where $(\delta l)^2$ is negligible, though α may be large, a convenient formula for calculation is—

$$\text{Marginal retardation} = p_m = - 2n\delta l \sin^2 (\alpha/2) \quad . \qquad . \qquad . \quad (409)$$

A numerical example is to calculate the axial displacement from the focus which will produce a marginal retardation of one wave-length i.e. $p_m = 0\cdot5 \times 10^{-3}$ mm., supposing that $\alpha = 30°$, and $n = 1$. On inserting these quantities δl is found to be $- 0\cdot0037$ mm., i.e. a displacement towards the wave front from the focus.

The degree of approximation involved in the approximate formula above where the cosine is taken as $1 - \alpha^2/2$, neglecting $\alpha^4/4!$ etc., can be appreciated by a numerical case. If $\alpha = \tfrac{1}{8}$ radian, the aperture would be fairly large for an optical system, yet the term $\alpha^4/4!$ is only $1/768$ of the term $\alpha^2/2$. For such reasons it is possible to use the simplified formula (407) in the majority of cases as representing the relative effect, on the optical path differences, of axial shifts of the reference point. A similar trial will show the close numerical equality of (407) and (409) in most cases of practical interest.

Refraction at a Spherical Surface Discussed on the Wave Theory.

Referring to Fig. 64, let it be supposed that disturbances travelling along the directions LP and MA would meet in the same phase at the point B, provided they are unhindered. Introduce now a spherical refracting surface so situated that its centre falls on the line MAB. We may consider that the disturbances meet the surface in the points P and A, and that these points become the origins of disturbances which will meet in various phases at different points;

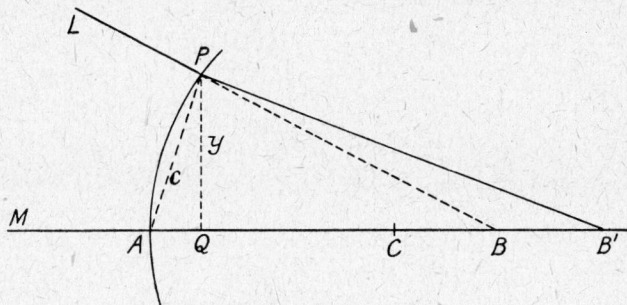

FIG. 64

let us investigate the optical path difference with which the disturbances will meet at a new axial point B'. The refractive indices of object and image spaces are n and n', as usual.

The increase in path for the marginal disturbance

$$= n' \cdot \mathrm{PB}' - n \cdot \mathrm{PB}$$

while the increase in path for the axial disturbance

$$= n' \cdot \mathrm{AB}' - n \cdot \mathrm{AB}$$

Hence, the net increase (marginal *minus* axial) will be

$$p = (n' \cdot \mathrm{PB}' - n \cdot \mathrm{PB}) - (n' \cdot \mathrm{AB}' - n \cdot \mathrm{AB})$$
$$= n'(\mathrm{PB}' - \mathrm{AB}') - n(\mathrm{PB} - \mathrm{AB})$$

We can next calculate a simple expression for $(\mathrm{PB}' - \mathrm{AB}')$, and a similar one for $(\mathrm{PB} - \mathrm{AB})$.

From P drop PQ perpendicular to AB, and let the length be y. Let AB, AB' be l, l' respectively, and let r be the radius of the spherical surface.

If we imagine Fig. 64 completed by drawing the semicircle, above the axis, with centre C, and remember that the angle in a semicircle is a right angle, it is easily seen that

$$\mathrm{AP} = 2r \cos \widehat{\mathrm{CAP}}.$$

Since $\qquad$ $AQ = AP \cos \widehat{CAP}$ then $AQ = AP^2/2r$.

Now $\qquad$ $PB^2 = AP^2 + AB^2 - 2\,AP.AB \cos \widehat{CAP}$

$$= AP^2 + AB^2 - 2\,AQ.AB$$

$$= AB^2 + AP^2\left(1 - \frac{AB}{r}\right)$$

Writing $AB = l$, we obtain the formula (still free from approximation for our case)

$$PB = l\left\{1 + \frac{AP^2}{l}\left(\frac{1}{l} - \frac{1}{r}\right)\right\}^{\frac{1}{2}}$$

Writing c for the chord AP,

$$PB = l\left\{1 + \frac{c^2}{l}\left(\frac{1}{l} - \frac{1}{r}\right)\right\}^{\frac{1}{2}}$$

$$= l\left\{1 + \frac{c^2}{2l}\left(\frac{1}{l} - \frac{1}{r}\right) - \frac{c^4}{8l^2}\left(\frac{1}{l} - \frac{1}{r}\right)^2 + \frac{c^6}{16l^3}\left(\frac{1}{l} - \frac{1}{r}\right)^3 - \text{etc.}\right\}$$

if we ensure that the rays considered make only small angles with the axis, so that c is small in comparison with l, then the fourth term in the expansion, containing the factor c^6 will tend to be small in comparison with the third; we will only discuss the cases in which it may be neglected. If the direction PB is more steeply inclined, then the higher order terms become of increasing importance.

In a similar manner we thus obtain (neglecting the terms in c^6 and c^8, etc.)

$$PB' = l'\left\{1 + \frac{c^2}{2l'}\left(\frac{1}{l'} - \frac{1}{r}\right) - \frac{c^4}{8l'^2}\left(\frac{1}{l'} - \frac{1}{r}\right)^2\right\}$$

then, since $AB = l$, and $AB' = l'$, the previously obtained equation for the optical path difference—

$p = n'(PB' - AB') - n(PB - AB)$ becomes

$$p = \left\{\frac{n'c^2}{2}\left(\frac{1}{l'} - \frac{1}{r}\right) - \frac{n'c^4}{8l'}\left(\frac{1}{l'} - \frac{1}{r}\right)^2\right\} - \left\{\frac{nc^2}{2}\left(\frac{1}{l} - \frac{1}{r}\right) - \frac{nc^4}{8l}\left(\frac{1}{l} - \frac{1}{r}\right)^2\right\}$$

$$= \frac{c^2}{2}\left\{n'\left(\frac{1}{l'} - \frac{1}{r}\right) - n\left(\frac{1}{l} - \frac{1}{r}\right)\right\} + \frac{c^4}{8}\left\{\frac{n}{l}\left(\frac{1}{l} - \frac{1}{r}\right)^2 - \frac{n'}{l'}\left(\frac{1}{l'} - \frac{1}{r}\right)^2\right\} \qquad (410)$$

This equation shows that if c is so small that the second term above can be neglected, the optical path differences become zero at the values of l and l' given by

$$n\left(\frac{1}{l} - \frac{1}{r}\right) = n'\left(\frac{1}{l'} - \frac{1}{r}\right)$$

which is identical with equation (107).

This shows that if we restrict the region considered to the paraxial region, imagined as a very narrow thread-like space surrounding the axis, then if the disturbances start out from an axial object point at a distance l from the surface, they will arrive in the same phase at the corresponding paraxial focus point. On the other hand, when the aperture is finite, and we may picture the image forming rays as inclined at a few degrees to the axis, then the disturbances arriving at the paraxial focus (where the "c^2" term is zero) from various zones of the refracting surface will have optical path differences (zonal path *minus* axial path) approximately proportional to the fourth power of the radius of the zone. This is the simplest case of *spherical aberration* and is called "Primary."

When the rays have larger inclinations to the axis, the above expression for PB does not become accurate until more terms in the expansion are included. By taking in the c^6 term we obtain the expression for the "secondary" spherical aberration. Even terms in c^8 (and higher) may be needed to express the law of optical path differences accurately under some conditions.

The aberration equations can be expressed in terms of y, the height of incidence, since

$$y^2 = c^2 - \mathrm{AQ}^2 = c^2 - \frac{c^4}{4r^2},$$

whence

$$c^4 - 4r^2c^2 + 4r^2y^2 = 0.$$

Solving for c^2 we obtain

$$c^2 = 2r^2 \left\{ 1 \pm \left(1 - \frac{y^2}{r^2} \right)^{\frac{1}{2}} \right\},$$

and on expanding we find for the relevant case

$$c^2 = y^2 + \frac{1}{4}\frac{y^4}{r^2} + \frac{1}{8}\frac{y^6}{r^4} + \text{etc.}$$

$$c^4 = y^4 + \frac{1}{2}\frac{y^6}{r^2} + \text{etc.,}$$

$$c^6 = y^6 + \text{etc.}$$

Substituting for the terms in c, we obtain the full expression for the retardation

$$p = \frac{y^2}{2}\left\{ n'\left(\frac{1}{l'} - \frac{1}{r}\right) - n\left(\frac{1}{l} - \frac{1}{r}\right) \right\}$$

$$+ y^4\left[\frac{1}{8r^2}\left\{ n'\left(\frac{1}{l'} - \frac{1}{r}\right) - n\left(\frac{1}{l} - \frac{1}{r}\right) \right\} - \frac{1}{8}\left\{ \frac{n'}{l'}\left(\frac{1}{l'} - \frac{1}{r}\right)^2 - \frac{n}{l}\left(\frac{1}{l} - \frac{1}{r}\right)^2 \right\} \right]$$

$$+ y^6\left[\frac{1}{16r^4}\left\{ n'\left(\frac{1}{l'} - \frac{1}{r}\right) - n\left(\frac{1}{l} - \frac{1}{r}\right) \right\} - \frac{1}{16r^2}\left\{ \frac{n'}{l'}\left(\frac{1}{l'} - \frac{1}{r}\right)^2 \right.\right.$$

$$\left.\left. - \frac{n}{l}\left(\frac{1}{l} - \frac{1}{r}\right)^2 \right\} + \frac{1}{16}\left\{ \frac{n'}{l'^2}\left(\frac{1}{l'} - \frac{1}{r}\right)^3 - \frac{n}{l^2}\left(\frac{1}{l} - \frac{1}{r}\right)^3 \right\} \right]$$

$$+ \text{etc.} \quad\quad\quad\quad\quad\quad\quad\quad\quad\quad\quad (411)$$

Alternatively, the above may be written

$$p = y^2\frac{A}{2} + y^4\left(\frac{A}{8r^2} - \frac{B}{8}\right) + y^6\left(\frac{A}{16r^4} - \frac{B}{16r^2} + \frac{C}{16}\right) + \text{etc.} \quad . \quad (411\text{A})$$

where
$$A = n'\left(\frac{1}{l'} - \frac{1}{r}\right) - n\left(\frac{1}{l} - \frac{1}{r}\right)$$

$$B = \frac{n'}{l'}\left(\frac{1}{l'} - \frac{1}{r}\right)^2 - \frac{n}{l}\left(\frac{1}{l} - \frac{1}{r}\right)^2$$

$$C = \frac{n'}{l'^2}\left(\frac{1}{l'} - \frac{1}{r}\right)^3 - \frac{n}{l^2}\left(\frac{1}{l} - \frac{1}{r}\right)^3$$

A type of series which often arises in optical calculations is one such as

$$p = \frac{C_1 y^2}{l'^2} + \frac{C_2 y^4}{l'^4} + \frac{C_3 y^6}{l'^6} + \text{etc.}$$

where C_1, C_2, C_3, etc., may have various *finite* numerical values and y is small compared with l'. Suppose $y/l' = 1/8$ at the maximum. By taking smaller and smaller values of y, the third term can always be made very small in comparison with the second, no matter what the (finite) values of the coefficients, and the second very small in comparison with the first. The student should take trial numerical values and verify this statement. Such trials will help to explain the reason why the primary aberrations term is often a sufficient approximation to the aberration, and conversely, why the higher aberration terms may often reach relatively large values when y/l' increases.

Primary Spherical Aberration of a Thin Lens. The optical path difference (marginal path *minus* axial path) arising at the *paraxial focus* after a single refraction is (retaining the primary term only),

$$p = \frac{y^4}{8}\left\{\frac{n}{l}\left(\frac{1}{l} - \frac{1}{r}\right)^2 - \frac{n'}{l'}\left(\frac{1}{l'} - \frac{1}{r}\right)^2\right\} = -\tfrac{1}{8}By^4$$

Since $n\left(\frac{1}{l} - \frac{1}{r}\right) = n'\left(\frac{1}{l'} - \frac{1}{r}\right)$ at the paraxial focus,

$$p = \frac{y^4}{8}\left[\frac{n}{l}\left(\frac{1}{l} - \frac{1}{r}\right)^2 - \frac{1}{n'l'}\left\{n'\left(\frac{1}{l'} - \frac{1}{r}\right)\right\}^2\right]$$

$$= \frac{y^4}{8}\left\{n^2\left(\frac{1}{l} - \frac{1}{r}\right)^2\left(\frac{1}{ln} - \frac{1}{l'n'}\right)\right\} = \frac{y^4}{8}\left\{n'^2\left(\frac{1}{l'} - \frac{1}{r}\right)^2\left(\frac{1}{ln} - \frac{1}{l'n'}\right)\right\}$$

In the case of a thin lens with surfaces 1 and 2, we shall put $n_1 = n_2'$ $= 1$ and $n_1' = n_2 = N$, and the sum of the path differences arising at the two surfaces (the same value for y is valid at each, since the lens is assumed "thin") is therefore

$$\frac{y^4}{8}\left\{\left(\frac{1}{l_1} - \frac{1}{r_1}\right)^2\left(\frac{1}{l} - \frac{1}{Nl_1'}\right) + \left(\frac{1}{l_2'} - \frac{1}{r_2}\right)^2\left(\frac{1}{l_2N} - \frac{1}{l_2'}\right)\right\} = A_1 y^4, \text{ (say)}.$$

The value of the new coefficient A_1 can be expressed as a function of

the power of the lens F, the vergence of the rays from the object
$L_1 = \dfrac{1}{l_1}$ and the curvature $R_1 = \dfrac{1}{r_1}$ of the first surface.

Since we have

$$L_1' = \frac{L_1 + (N - 1)\, R_1}{N} = L_2$$

$$L_2' = F + L_1$$

$$R_2 = R_1 - \frac{F}{N - 1}$$

$$A_1 = \tfrac{1}{8}\left[(L_1 - R_1)^2 \left\{ L_1 - \frac{L_1 + (N - 1)R_1}{N^2} \right\} + \left\{ F + L_1 - R_1 \right. \right.$$
$$\left. \left. + \frac{F}{N - 1} \right)^2 \left\{ \frac{L_1 + (N - 1)\, R_1}{N^2} - F - L_1 \right\} \right]$$

After somewhat lengthy algebraical reductions, the value of the coefficient proves to be (writing n for the refractive index of the lens in place of N)

$$A_1 = -\tfrac{1}{8}\left\{ F^3 \left(\frac{n}{n - 1} \right)^2 + F^2 L_1 \left(\frac{3n + 1}{n - 1} \right) - F^2 R_1 \left(\frac{2n + 1}{n - 1} \right) \right.$$
$$\left. + FL_1^2 \left(\frac{3n + 2}{n} \right) - FR_1 L_1 \left(\frac{4n + 4}{n} \right) + FR_1^2 \left(\frac{n + 2}{n} \right) \right\} . \quad (412)$$

The most instructive manner to deal with this equation is to assume a set of values for n, F, and L, then to plot graphically the aberration coefficient as a function of the curvature R_1 of the first surface for different cases. This will be done in connection with the discussion of telescope object glasses in Part II of this book.

The equation can be applied without serious difficulty to the second lens of a "thin" telescope object glass, and the spherical aberration of the combination can then be found. Graphical methods permit of finding the "bendings"* of two lenses which will remove the spherical aberration when used together.

It is not, however, within the scope of the present book to discuss the subject of the correction of aberrations at length. Reference should be made to Conrady's *Applied Optics and Optical Design*.[1] The above equation is also discussed in *The Formation of Images in Optical Instruments*[2] (Von Rohr).

It leads to the conclusion that no bending of an ordinary glass

* The term "bending" as applied to a lens denotes the process (carried out on paper) of altering the shape without altering the power. Thus, one might add a power of $+ 4D$ to the first surface, and a power of $- 4D$ to the second.

lens will entirely remove the spherical aberration or change its sign when used with incident parallel light, but where a meniscus converging lens is placed in convergent light it may be freed from aberration, and the sign of the aberration may even be reversed.

The minimum spherical aberration form for a double convex converging lens in parallel light is the "crossed lens." Assuming a refractive index of about 1·51, the curvature of the front surface is about 6·4 times the curvature of the second.

Relations between Geometrical and Physical Expressions of Aberration.

Referring to Fig. 65, AQT represents a portion of a spherical surface with centre at B. If this represents the locus of a

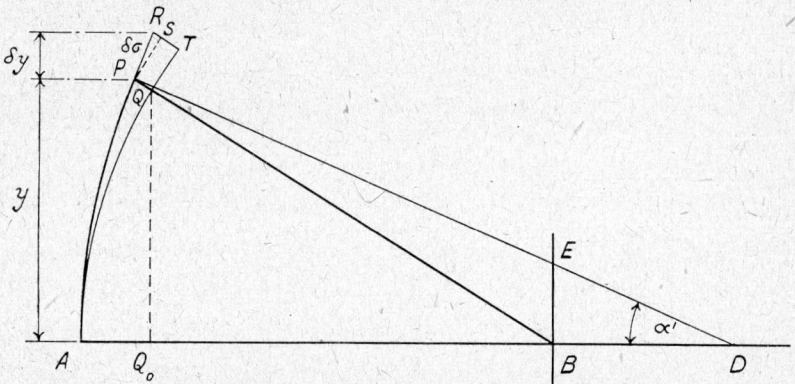

Fig. 65

wave-front, all disturbances will arrive at B in the same phase; but if, however, there are phase differences depending on the zonal radius, the wave-front subject to spherical aberration will have a trace represented by some other curve APR. If it be supposed that B is the paraxial focus, then the actual wave-front has the same curvature as the spherical surface at the centre, but it diverges towards the margin. The actual cases considered will be those in which the divergence is not large, amounting perhaps to a few wave-lengths of light.

Whatever be the shape of the wave surface, consider a zone of height y, marked by the point P. Take another point R on the same trace very close to P and drop perpendiculars PQ, RT to the spherical surface, also produce PQ to B; the difference between RT and PQ represents the extra path which a disturbance from R will have to travel on its way to the centre B, as compared with the disturbance from P. The optical path difference discussed above is seen in the distortion of the wave surface. The focus for a very narrow zone, at P, of the actual wave-front, is found by drawing PD perpendicular to the wave-front and cutting the axis in D; this represents a "*ray*," and if the point B is the paraxial focus, then the intercept BD is a measure of the "longitudinal spherical aberration,"[*] in the geometrical sense, of the chosen zone.

The ray intercepts a plane through B, perpendicular to the axis, in the point E; then BE is a measure of the "*lateral* aberration."

If we draw PS parallel to the short intercept QT of the spherical surface (the intercepts are considered so short as to be practically straight) and call PR $= \delta\sigma$ (a short segment of the wave-surface), RS $= \delta p/n'$ (δp representing an element of *optical* path difference so that the linear path difference is obtained by dividing by n'), then

$$\sin \widehat{\text{RPS}} = \frac{1}{n'} \frac{\delta p}{\delta \sigma}$$

but since PD and QB are perpendicular to PR, PS respectively, we see that $\widehat{\text{RPS}} = \widehat{\text{BPD}}$ (a measure of the "angular aberration"). Hence, if the angles are small and $\widehat{\text{PDB}} = \alpha'$, while $\widehat{\text{BPD}} = \beta$,

$$\sin \beta = \frac{1}{n'} \frac{\delta p}{\delta \sigma} = \frac{\text{BE} \cos \alpha'}{\text{PB}}$$

But $\delta\sigma = \delta y \sec \alpha'$; thus writing PB $= l_m'$, the equation involving the lateral intercept BE of the ray, which may be written T', becomes

$$\frac{dp}{dy} = \frac{n'\text{T}'}{l_m'} \qquad . \qquad . \qquad . \qquad . \qquad (413)$$

In cases of practical interest, the intercept PQ will be often only a few wave-lengths, and thus (in general) negligibly small with respect to the geometrical aberrations BE or BD, and still more with respect to the intersection distances. Thus if l_m' differs inappreciably from l', the paraxial intersection distance, we shall have

$$\text{T}' = \frac{l'}{n'} \frac{dp}{dy} \qquad . \qquad . \qquad . \qquad . \qquad (414)$$

We may calculate the transverse aberration if the law connecting p

[*] The early discussions of "Aberration" were all given in terms of the intercepts between the crossing points of such rays from chosen zones of the wave-front.

with y is known. In the case of a *single refracting surface*, we refer to equation (411) and obtain the expression

$$(l'/n')\left\{-\frac{B}{2}y^3 + \frac{3}{8}\left(C - \frac{B}{r^2}\right)y^5 + \text{etc.}\right\}$$

for the transverse aberration at the paraxial focus, which is thus seen to be represented by a series in odd powers of y. This will be true in other cases also; the angular aberration β will also be represented by a series in odd powers of y, starting with y^3.

Conversely, if the transverse aberration has been determined experimentally or by ray-tracing, we can find p by integration, since

$$p = \frac{n'}{l'}\int_0^Y T'dy \ . \quad (415)$$

the integration to be performed over the whole radius Y, say. If p is positive, the marginal path will be greater than the axial. Note that p is the "marginal" path *minus* axial path calculated for a zone of radius Y, which may be the marginal or any intermediate zone.

If by any means, then, we can measure or calculate the lateral intercepts of the rays from different zones, these can be plotted as abscissae against y as ordinates, as in Fig. 66. The area between the curve and the lines $x = o$ and $y = Y$ is proportional to the optical path differences between disturbances arriving at the focus from zones $y = o$ and $y = Y$.

For another focus at a distance m from B, the transverse or lateral intercept becomes T_m', where

$$T_m' = T' - \frac{my}{l'}$$

Some degree of approximation is involved, which will be examined below. But we can see at once that if m is of the same order of smallness as $(y/l')^2$, then my/l' is of the same order of smallness as the primary component of T', which depends on y^3. Hence the equation is accurate enough to deal with cases in which y^4 terms are negligible.

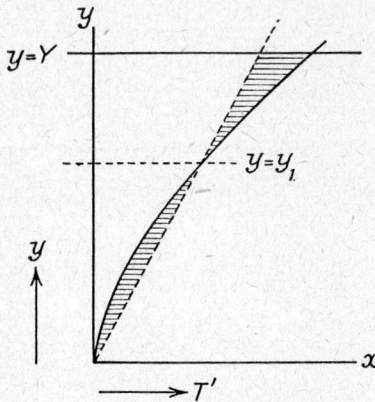

FIG. 66

Within the limits to which the equation applies, the path differences at the new focus are

$$p_m = \frac{n'}{l'} \int_o^Y \left(T' - \frac{my}{l'} \right) dy$$

$$= \frac{n'}{l'} \left\{ -\frac{mY^2}{2l'} + \int_o^Y T' dy \right\} \quad . \quad . \quad . \quad (416)$$

The term $\dfrac{mY^2}{2l'}$ represents the triangular area included between the same two lines mentioned above and the line

$$x = my/l'$$

Therefore, in a case of a lens system which gives large path differences for one focus, the condition of affairs might evidently be greatly improved by choosing another focus which would make the above areas for curve and triangle equal; this would make the optical path difference between central and marginal disturbances disappear, and the residual path differences for other paths would be much smaller.

Note that the approximate path difference between a marginal and axial disturbance, arising through a change of focus, is given by the first term in equation (416). Compare with (407). Since (407) gives a close numerical approximation in the majority of cases of practical interest, the above graphical construction is usually allowable even in cases where secondary aberration is present.

Relation Between the Transverse and Axial Aberration. Consider the relation between the transverse aberration BE (Fig. 65) and the axial or "longitudinal" aberration BD (supposing B to be the paraxial focus). If α' is small, then (approximately),

$$\tan \alpha' \approx \frac{y}{l'}$$

and
$$BD = \frac{T'}{\tan \alpha'} \approx \frac{l'^2}{n'y} \frac{dp}{dy} \quad . \quad . \quad . \quad (417)$$

In this case, since we have seen that the path difference p at the paraxial focus will be represented by a series in even powers of y starting with the fourth power (and this will be true for a system of any complexity, as will be shown below), we infer that the longitudinal aberration (LA') will be represented by a series starting with y^2. Suppose it is

$$LA' = by^2 + \text{terms in } y^4, \text{ etc.}$$

Owing to the axial symmetry, rays from a zone of height $-y$ will have the same value of LA' as those from $+ y$. Hence, *even* powers only are involved.

We must, however, make a closer estimate of $\tan \alpha'$. Noting that QQ_o is the perpendicular from Q to the axis, we write

$$\tan \alpha' = \frac{QQ_o}{Q_oD}$$

Now QQ_o differs from y by the vertical projection of PQ, i.e. $PQ \sin \alpha'$. But we know that PQ will be represented by a series in powers of y commencing with y^4. Suppose it is

$$PQ \text{ (numerical value)} = b_1 y^4 + \text{etc.,}$$

then

$$PQ \sin \alpha' \approx b_1 y^4 \left(\frac{y}{l'} \right)$$

so that

$$QQ_o = y \left(1 - \frac{b_1}{l'} y^4 \right) \text{ very nearly.}$$

Note that there should be terms with higher powers of y in the bracket in this last equation, but none smaller than the fourth power. Again,

$$Q_oD = l' - AQ_o + BD.$$

We can introduce approximate expressions for AQ_o and BD which will exhibit their dependence on y. By the accurate "spherometer formula,"

$$AQ_o = \frac{QQ_o^2}{2l'} + \frac{QQ_o^4}{8l'^3} + \text{etc.}$$

$$= \frac{y^2}{2l'} \left(1 - \frac{b_1}{l'} y^4 + \text{etc.} \right)^2 + \frac{y^4}{8l'^3} \left(1 - \frac{b_1}{l'} y^4 + \text{etc.} \right)^4 + \text{etc.}$$

Further, if $BD = by^2 + \text{etc.}$, where b is the coefficient of primary LA',

$$Q_oD = l' + gy^2 + \text{etc.,}$$

where

$$g = b - \frac{1}{2l'}$$

Consequently

$$\tan \alpha' = \frac{y \left(1 - \frac{b_1}{l'} y^4 + \text{etc.} \right)}{l' \left(1 + g \frac{y^2}{l'} + \text{etc.} \right)}$$

$$= \frac{y}{l'} \left(1 - g \frac{y^2}{l'} + \text{terms in } y^4 + \text{etc.,} \right) \qquad . \qquad . \qquad . \quad (418)$$

It will be seen that the calculation of the exact expressions in the series would be complicated, but the most important correction to our approximate expression for $\tan \alpha'$ is the factor containing y^2. Hence, more accurately,

$$LA' = \frac{T' . l'}{y} \left(1 + g \frac{y^2}{l'} + \text{etc.} \right) = \frac{l'^2}{n'y} \frac{dp}{dy} \left(1 + g \frac{y^2}{l'} + \text{etc.} \right) . \quad (419)$$

It may be pointed out that it is not the absolute value of y which is so significant as its ratio to the conjugate distances and to the radius.

In the optical path aberration for the single surface the aberration coefficient is seen to have the dimensions L^{-3}, and it depends upon the reciprocals of l, l', and r. In a large telescope objective (say $12''$ diameter) y may reach several inches, while the aberration is still largely primary, and the secondary is still inappreciable; in a microscope objective, the higher aberrations may be appreciable for zones at a few millimetres from the axis. The matter is best considered in relation to the *angles of incidence and refraction* at the surfaces; when these amount to more than a few degrees, the growth of aberration can be expected. Expressions can be derived in which these angles appear in the formulae, and this influence on the aberrations can then be seen more directly, but such equations are less convenient for our present purposes.

Calculation of Optical Path Difference for a Series of Surfaces. A typical aim in the discussion of aberrations is to obtain a method of calculating the aberration for a ray at a small finite aperture, having given the results of a paraxial ray trace.

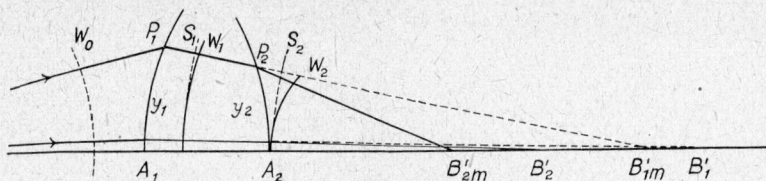

FIG. 67

The expression for the optical path difference in the case of a single surface (obtained above) assumed no special values for l and l', but supposes that the object point is the same both for paraxial and marginal disturbances, so that the wave is spherical before refraction. Such a condition is suggested in Fig. 67, where W_0 is the incident spherical wave. After refraction at the first surface, however, the paraxial focus is B_1' and the marginal B_{1m}'. The retardation of the marginal ray is shown as negative, and thus the wave front W_1 is in advance of the spherical surface S_1, the gap between the two being, say, proportional to Y^4. After refraction by a second surface the paraxial focus is B_2' and the marginal focus B_{2m}'; the gap between W_2 and S_2 is now increased (in the sense of optical path difference) by the contribution of surface 2; each surface adds to or subtracts from the retardation of the marginal ray relative to the paraxial, and it is evident that the contributions are additive. The exact form of the final wave-surface can be found by tracing a set of rays diverging from the object point and passing through the system; then marking on each emergent ray those points which have the same optical path length from the object point. Then, according to the modern form of Huygens' principle we can treat the final wave surfaces as the origin of secondary disturbances of which the total effect can be calculated on the principle of superposition; this is known to give a valid result for points near the general centre of curvature of such a wave. If we take any such point and draw a spherical surface, with the point as centre, touching or intersecting the wave surface, the relative radial distances of surface and sphere will determine the relative phases at which disturbances will meet in such a point.

This is not to be taken as a complete or accurate account of what actually occurs in the physical sense; but it has the merit that the results of such a calculation agree with observation. We note that Fermat's principle is involved; it would be unwise to think that the actual elements of the energy travel as it were along the tramlines of ray tracks until they reach a certain wave surface and then spread out in diffraction.

The procedure suggested in the analytical sense is somewhat different; in this case a paraxial ray is traced through the system, and the relative heights of intersection of the successive surfaces found from

$$y_1 = l_1 u_1, \; y_2 = l_2 u_2, \text{ etc.} \qquad \qquad \qquad (420)$$

We now conceive a *fictitious ray track* intersecting the successive surfaces in heights

$$\dot{Y}_1 = m y_1, \; Y_2 = m y_2, \; \ldots, \; Y_l = m y_k$$

where m is some constant factor, and apply an analytical formula (such as 411A) to find the sum of the successive optical path differences or

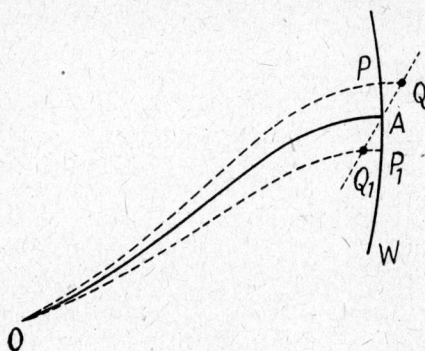

FIG. 68

retardations, each reckoned from one paraxial focus to the next. The relative optical path length along this fictitious track is thus obtained, and since the analytical form of the contributions from each surface is known we finally calculate an expression for the manner in which the retardation varies with the height of the fictitious track in some final reference surface. The validity of this procedure must now be examined.

Fermat's theorem may be invoked again. We note that the fictitious path lies everywhere close to the actual ray-path, and makes only small angles with it. The angular separation between these tracks will vary, as we have seen, by angles depending on the cube and higher powers of the intersection height, and if the angular separation after the first surface is (say) $\sigma Y_1^3 + \tau Y_1^5 +$ etc., where σ and τ are appropriate aberration coefficients, and d_1 is the distance (along the path) between the first and second surfaces, then the lateral separation of the two tracks near the second surface will be approximately $d_1 (\sigma Y_1^3 + \tau Y_1^5 +$ etc.). Similarly, the separation of the paths near the third surface will *further* contain the product of d_2 with the cube and higher powers of Y_2. It may therefore be asked: Is it legitimate to calculate the position of the wave surface by calculation of optical paths along the fictitious ray track? Fermat's theorem points to the answer.

In Fig. 68, O is the origin of some ray path OA in a medium not necessarily homogeneous, and WP_1AP is an associated wave surface. OP is a close continuous neighbouring path such that the separation AP between the two paths is *everywhere* very small (1st order), and the angle between the two paths in adjacent elements is correspondingly small. Then Fermat's theorem states that the difference between the optical paths reckoned along the paths OA and OP will be very much smaller (2nd order), and it will depend on powers of AP not smaller than the second; for if it should depend on the first power, the sign of the path difference would differ for points P, P_1 on the wave surface on either side of A; then if truly equal optical paths (OQ, OQ_1, say) were marked off along the tracks OP, OP_1, the locus QAQ_1 of equal paths would intersect the wave front; but the latter *is* by definition the locus of equal optical paths. Therefore the magnitude of the optical path difference must depend on at least the square of AP.

In our case then, if the (1st order) separation of the real and fictitious paths depends on the cubes of the heights, the position of the wave surface can be reckoned correctly along the fictitious path within quantities depending on the square of the separation; this will begin with the squares of the cubes of the heights, i.e. on terms in "Y^6." If, therefore, we are content only to allow values of Y so small that, while the fourth power is appreciable, the sixth power is negligible, the calculation along the fictitious track is valid for calculating the *primary* but not the higher aberrations.

Finally, then, we can calculate and add the successive contributions to find the primary value of p, i.e. (referring to 411)

$$p = - \tfrac{1}{8}\{B_1Y_1^4 + B_2Y_2^4 + \ldots + B_kY_k^4\} . \qquad . \quad (421)$$

If it be desired to write down the coefficient of the total aberration in terms of Y_k the intersection height in the final surface, we may write for any surface j

$$Y_j = Y_k \frac{l_j{'}\alpha'_j}{l_k{'}\alpha'_k} \qquad . \qquad . \qquad . \qquad . \qquad . \qquad (422)$$

then

$$p = - \frac{Y_k^4}{8} \Sigma^k{}_1 \left[B_j \left(\frac{l_j{'}x'_j}{l_k{'}\alpha_{k'}} \right)^4 \right] . \qquad . \quad . \quad (423)$$

the quantities in the last bracket will be found by means of a par-axial trace, which will also give the necessary quantities for the calculation of B. The term Σ denotes the sum of all such terms from 1 to k.

Phase Relation at Points Near the Focus of a Wavefront. Axial symmetry being assumed, the expression for marginal path *minus* axial path at the paraxial focus of a wave-front showing spherical aberration will be of the type

$$p = C_2 y^4 + C_3 y^6 + \text{etc.}$$

If the path differences are required at another axial point close to the first at a distance dl, equation (407) shows that we should add an amount proportional to y^2, and it was also indicated that this would usually be adequate in the quantitative sense, other additional terms being relatively small in most cases of interest. If primary aberration only is present, the path equation valid for axial points near the focus is thus of the type

$$p = C_1 y^2 + C_2 y^4 \qquad . \qquad . \qquad (424)$$

The rays are represented diagrammatically in Fig. 69. B_p is the paraxial focus and B_m the marginal focus. The rays from a zone $Y/2$ come to a focus at the point C where the distance $B_p C = B_p B_m/4$. The rays coming to a focus at the mid-point between B_p and B_m come from the zone $Y/\sqrt{2} = 0.707Y$.

It can easily be shown (see Vol. II) that the location of the focus, where the circle containing all the rays from the whole wave surface

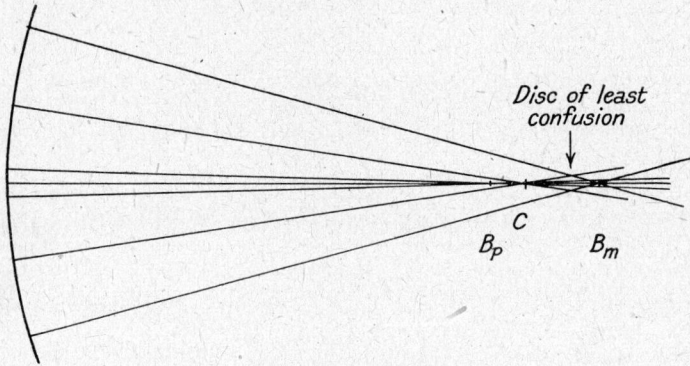

Disc of least confusion

C

B_p B_m

FIG. 69

has a minimum diameter, is in this case three-quarters of the distance from the paraxial focus to the marginal focus.

Focus with Minimum Residuals of Path Differences. Using the notation of equations (416) and (424), and referring to Fig. 66, let us represent the variation of m by differing slopes of the dotted line passing through the origin. The area between the curve and between the lines $x = 0$ and $y = y_1$ (say), *less* the corresponding triangular area, represents the optical path difference between disturbances arriving at the focus m from the zone given by $y = y_1$ and from the centre. It is easily seen that the area of "curve *minus* triangle" (in our figure) reaches a maximum negative value at about $Y/2$, while at Y the whole difference is very small. On the other hand, the path differences between disturbances from $y = Y/2$ and $y = Y$ will have reached a positive amount of about the same numerical value as the negative maximum. The maximum residuals are clearly least when the two shaded areas are equal, and this means that the total areas for curve and triangle are equal, the path difference for the margin then being zero—

$$p_Y = C_1 Y^2 + C_2 Y^4 = 0.$$

If we assume that $Y = 1$, then $C_2 = -C_1$, and the general equation will become: $p = -C_2y^2 + C_2y^4$, a form which holds only for the special focus which makes $p = o$ for $y = 1$.

The radius for the maximum optical path difference at this special focus is found by differentiating the expression for p and equating the result to zero, giving

$$\frac{dp}{dy} = -2C_2y + 4C_2y^3 = o$$

whence $y = 1/\sqrt{2}$. As we have seen, the rays from this zone intercept the axis half-way between the paraxial and marginal foci. The value of p for this focus ($y = 1/\sqrt{2}$) proves to be $-C_2/4$.

The maximum path differences at the paraxial focus are found between disturbances from the centre and from the extreme margin. At the paraxial focus,

$$p = C_2y^4$$

and the maximum path difference is therefore C_2.

Remembering that a ray is the normal to the wave surface, the criterion for the marginal focus is that

$$\frac{\delta p}{\delta y} = o \text{ for } y = 1,$$

i.e.
$$2C_1y + 4C_2y^3 = o$$

when $y = 1$, so that $C_1 = -2C_2$. The maximum path difference is now $-C_2$. Hence at the mid-focus we find a point where the residual path differences are numerically only one-quarter of those existing at either the marginal or paraxial foci.

Numerical Calculations for the Distribution of Light in the Neighbourhood of an Image. In Chapter III the method of calculation of the distribution of light was worked out for points in the focal plane. To obtain numerical results in the general case it is convenient to divide up the spherical reference surface, which may be assumed to be of unit radius, into a series of annular zones of equal areas. Thus the bounding radii may be $(1/n)^{\frac{1}{2}}$, $(2/n)^{\frac{1}{2}}$, etc. Each narrow ring will thus produce a numerically equal effect of amplitude at the centre, but at a point such as F_1 (Fig. 56) the contribution of one ring will be proportional to

$$\int_o^{2\pi} \overline{\cos W \sin E} \, dE$$

where W has the significance of the previous investigation, i.e. it is the difference of phase at F_1 with which a disturbance from C, Fig. 56, meets one derived from A or B; it is half the maximum difference of phase between disturbances arriving from the zone considered, the extreme difference being for C and D. In presenting the results it is convenient to specify the distance FF_1 by that maximum value of W which relates to the outermost ring in the surface. Thus the W value for intermediate zones will be

$$W_{max}(1/n)^{\frac{1}{2}}, W_{max}(2/n)^{\frac{1}{2}}, \text{ etc.}$$

and the contributions of the various zones can easily be computed by evaluating the integral. If the contributions of amplitude are all in the same phase they can be added directly; this was the case for points in the focal plane, for the phase of the resultant at F_1 for any one ring must be the phase of the elements derived from A or B, and this will be identical for all zones when we deal with a spherical wave-surface.

It is otherwise if the various rings of the reference surface give contributions which arrive at the focus with differences of phase. The relative phases of the resultants arriving at F_1 may be considered to be essentially the same as at F. Let the phase for one ring be "δ" and the amplitude contribution be "a," then the final intensity will be found by evaluating, as shown in Chapter III, the equivalent of

$$\{\Sigma(a \sin \delta)\}^2 + \{\Sigma(a \cos \delta)\}^2$$

The integration can be carried out by mechanical quadratures. Full details of the method will be found in Conrady's original paper.[3] See also a paper[4] by the present writer.

A more formal study of the problem was carried out by Lommel[5] in 1884, and a comprehensive review has been given in an article by Jentsch.[6] The methods of integration are still attracting attention; see, a paper by Hopkins.[7] Maréchal[7a] has built a mechanical integrator.

For points away from the paraxial focal plane the phase differences for various rings will be expressed sufficiently nearly in the absence of aberration by equation (407). Moreover, in the presence of primary spherical aberration we have seen that the general expression for the optical path differences for disturbances was

$$p = C_1 y^2 + C_2 y^4$$

Hence, $$\delta = \frac{2\pi p}{\lambda} = \mathbf{C_1} y^2 + \mathbf{C_2} y^4,$$

the use of thicker type indicating the application of the factor $2\pi/\lambda$, gives the requisite phase angles. The results of numerical computation are shown in Figs. 70 and 71. The vertical scale for intensity is given for the lowest curve. The radius of the marginal zone is taken as unity.

In Fig. 70 (no aberration) $\mathbf{C_1}$ is given the values $0°, 45°, 90° \ldots 540°$, the light intensities being calculated for $W = 0°, 40°, 80°, \ldots 600°$ in all the corresponding planes. There will be symmetry of the results on each side of the focus (the symmetry is not *absolute* with real systems).

The case of primary spherical aberration is shown in Fig. 71. The maximum radius is again assumed to be unity, and $\mathbf{C_2}$ is given the value $360°$, while $\mathbf{C_1}$ varies in steps of $90°$ from $-1080°$ to $0°$. From foregoing results we have—

$\mathbf{C_1} = 0$: paraxial focus
$\mathbf{C_1} = -720°$: marginal focus
$\mathbf{C_1} = -360°$: focus with least residuals of phase.

At $\mathbf{C_1} = -360°$ the outstanding phase residuals are $\dfrac{\mathbf{C_2}}{4} = 90°$.

The positions of the limiting rays are shown in the diagrams. Let k be the distance, measured perpendicular to the axis, between a point on the limiting ray (from the zone of radius y) and the axis at an axial distance δl from the axial crossing point of the ray. Then from equation 407, if $n = 1$,

$$k = \delta l . y/l = -2p_m l/y$$

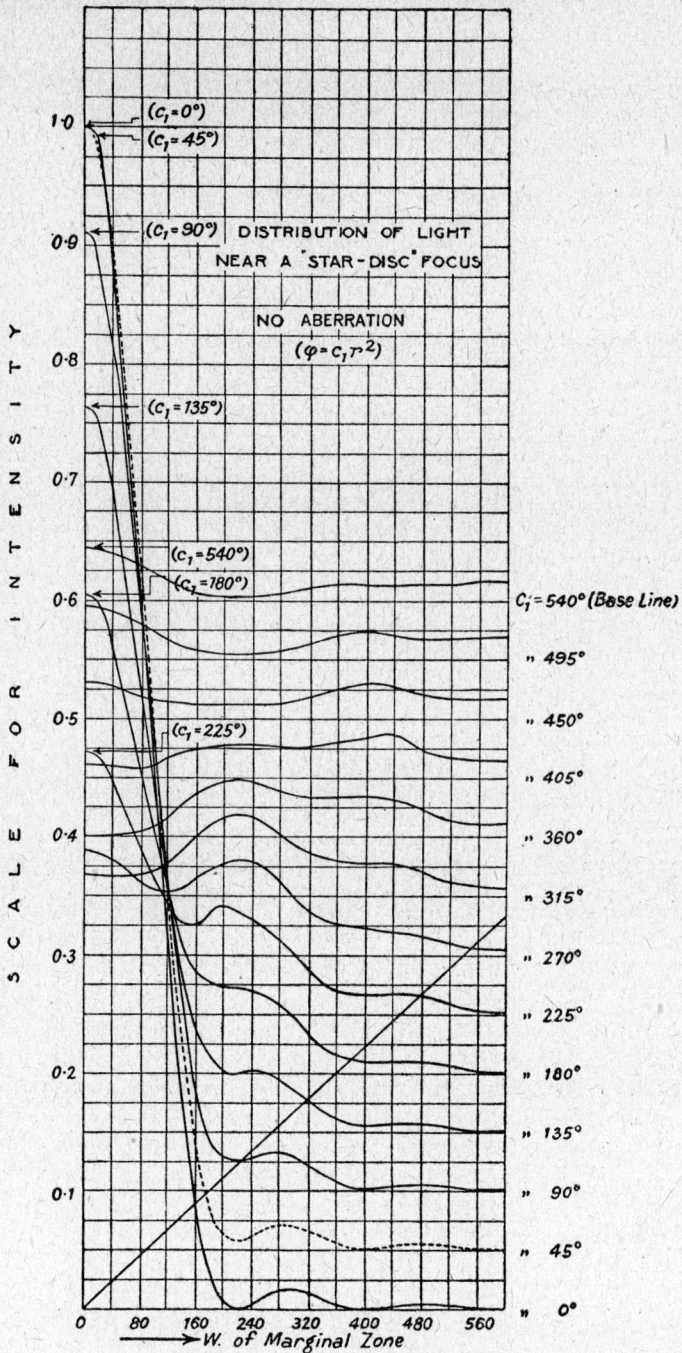

FIG. 70

Hence, W_k, the value of W* for a displacement k at the point fixed by δl is given by

$$W_k = \frac{360°}{\lambda} \cdot \frac{ky}{l} = -\frac{360°}{\lambda} 2p_m = -2d\omega$$

from which it is seen that W is numerically equal to twice the phase difference $d\omega$ (for marginal path *minus* axial) calculated for the zone of radius y, arising from a shift of the axial focussing point through a distance δl.

In the case of primary spherical aberration the geometrical "circle of least confusion" through which all rays pass, lies at three-quarters of the distance from the paraxial to the marginal focus, and is bounded by the intersection of the ray from the opposite mid-zone of half radius and the marginal ray (see Heath's *Geometrical Optics*, p. 113). One extreme marginal ray is easily drawn through the marginal focus, by means of the above relation $W_k = -2d\omega$,† while the other mid-zone ray is drawn through its axial intersection point (one-quarter of the distance from the paraxial to the marginal focus) at an angle the tangent of which is numerically one-half that of the marginal ray. The radius of the "circle of least confusion" is thus found, the corresponding W value being 360°.

In the case of no aberration, the maximum central intensity is unity, but when $C_1 = 90°$ (corresponding to a path difference of a quarter of a wavelength) the actual intensity is still 0·8102, but as the first dark ring of the Airy disc is almost filled with light, the loss of definition in a complex image would probably just be noticeable. Hence, a total "permissible depth of focus" corresponding to a path difference of not more than $\pm \lambda/4$ may be inferred. The corresponding focal depth in the object space of a lens system could be calculated. The symmetry of the diffraction effects on each side of the focus has already been noted.

In the case of primary spherical aberration the diffraction patterns are found to be markedly dissimilar on the two sides of the focus. On the one side is a very pronounced set of ring systems, but on the other side a gradually weakening patch of light appears. The intensity at the focus giving least residuals of phase (90° in this case) is still 0·8 of the greatest intensity possible when no aberration is present, but the first dark ring here is not completely devoid of light, and the first bright ring has double the intensity of that surrounding the ideal Airy disc. The *radius* of the first dark ring (W = 220°) at this point is practically identical with that of the aberration-free image. It is thus much smaller than the geometrical "disc of least confusion," and does not lie in the same plane as the latter.

Higher Aberration. In actual practice, spherical aberration of more complex character is often encountered, in which the effects must be represented by such an expression as

$$p = C_1y^2 + C_2y^4 + C_3y^6 + C_4y^8$$

* The optical phase difference $360° \dfrac{(AF_1 - CF_1)}{\lambda}$ (Fig. 56).

† In Fig. 71, the marginal focus is found at $C_1 = -720°$ (see scale on right-hand of figure). On going to $C_1 = -540°$, the change of phase $d\omega$ between axial and marginal disturbances is 180°. The W value is therefore 360°. We thus obtain two points on the ray from the extreme margin.

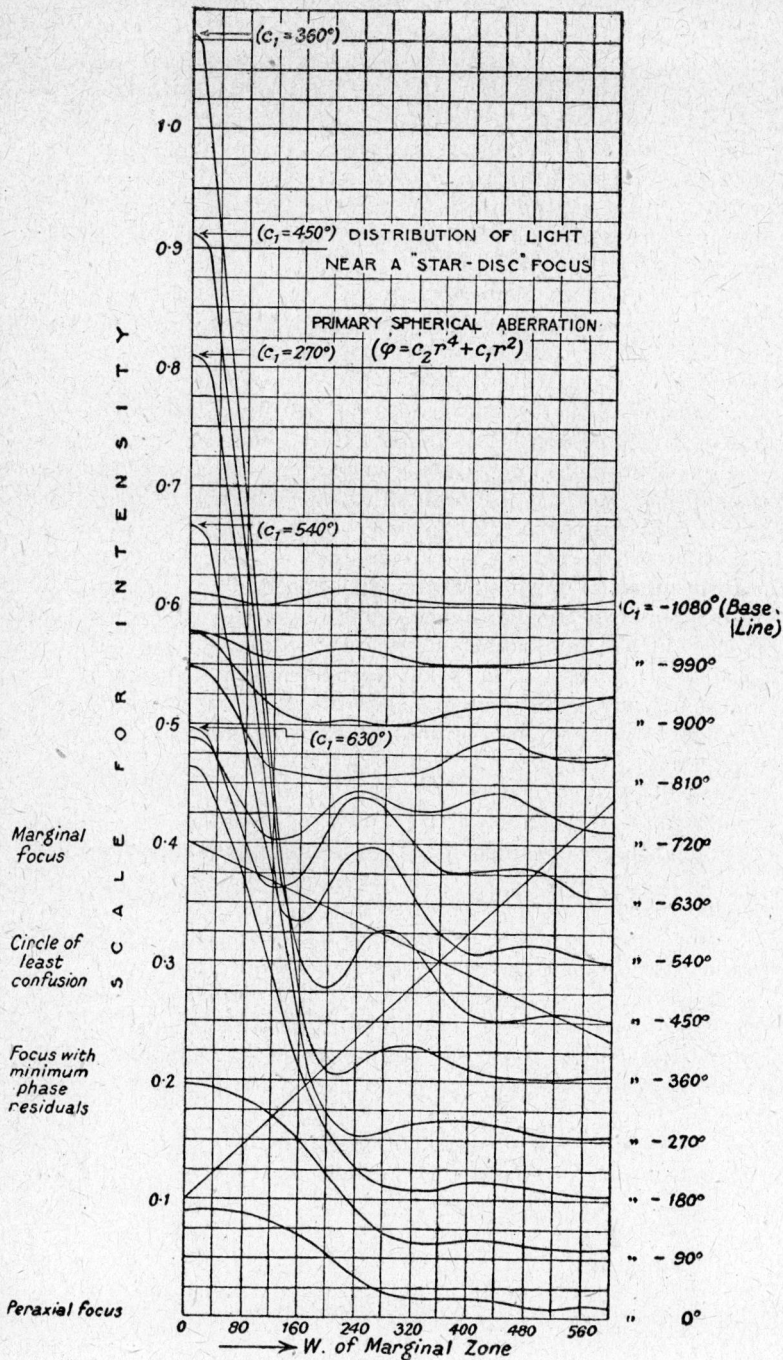

FIG. 71

the contribution of the terms in y^6, y^8, and so on, being known as the higher aberrations. For further details, see papers by Prof. Conrady[3] and the author[4]. It frequently occurs that one or more of the constants in the equation above have different signs, and cases are thus represented in which the wave surface has a double bend, so that there is a zone of maximum or minimum focussing distance (Zonal Spherical Aberration).

There is a remarkable persistence, at some focus, of a concentration closely resembling the Airy disc, even in the presence of considerable spherical aberration. It may be surrounded by more or less "haze" when the aberration is large, but its size, as given by the diameter of the first dark ring, can usually be calculated very closely from equation (321), Chapter III, although it may even be smaller, if anything, under some conditions. *It is seen that mere resolution or sharpness of detail in an image is no criterion of the optical perfection of the system, unless the good definition is accompanied by the maximum possible contrast.*

Distribution of Light in Extra-axial Images. The foregoing investigations have related to the simpler case when the convergent wave-front has an axial symmetry, as is secured when we have an axial object point and an axially symmetrical optical system.

It is now necessary to inquire as to the variations of optical path which arise when the object and image are no longer on the axis of symmetry.

We will consider first of all a single spherical refracting surface with a stop, as shown in Fig. 72; then the results so obtained can be extended without difficulty to a system containing a number of coaxial spherical surfaces.

The circular stop at E is located in the diaphragm S, while B_1 is the object point situated at a distance h from the axis of symmetry passing through the centre C of the refracting surface.

The *principal ray* is the one which passes through the centre of the stop; it intersects the refracting surface in the point P, and the outer limiting rays intersect the surface in an approximately circular figure shown in end-view in Fig. 73. Note that E' is the image of E, and the distance AE' is designated l_{pr}'.

The restrictions applied to the present discussion are that h is a small quantity of the first order, and also that the radius of the stop is small. Hence, if we draw the line B_1C through the centre of curvature (cutting the surface in A_1), the perpendicular distance of any point on the circle of intersection just mentioned from the line B_1C will be assumed to be small. The inclination of any ray to the axis is also assumed to be small.

If we drop a perpendicular from P to B_1C, the portions of the perpendicular lying above and below the axis AC will be seen to be both proportional (within allowable approximation) to h'. This perpendicular distance can be represented with sufficient accuracy under the limitations of the inquiry by the length of the line PA_1, Fig. 72. The parts are very nearly equal to the elements A_1A and AP of the arc. When h' is very small, we may write within the

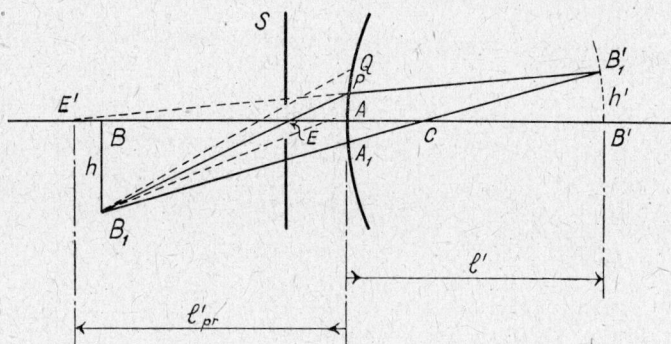

FIG. 72

necessary limits of accuracy (remember that l_{pr}' in Fig. 72 is numerically negative),

$$AP = h'\left(\frac{-l_{pr}'}{-l_{pr}' + l'}\right) = h'\left(\frac{l_{pr}'}{l_{pr}' - l'}\right)$$

and

$$A_1A = h'\left(\frac{r}{l' - r}\right)$$

and thus,

$$A_1P = Mh',$$

where

$$M = \left\{\frac{l_{pr}'}{l_{pr}' - l'} + \frac{r}{l' - r}\right\}$$

If Q be any point on the circle of intersection, QA_1 will be, in a similar way, a sufficiently accurate measure of the perpendicular distance of Q from the line B_1A_1C.

Produce the line B_1C to B_1', the "paraxial focus"* which would be realized in the absence of the stop; then the optical path difference with which the disturbance from the point P would meet the "paraxial" disturbance at B_1' would be given by

$$p_P = C_2(A_1P)^4$$

* Regarding, for the moment, the line $B_1A_1CB_1'$ as the axis.

since the above restrictions make it possible to assume the presence of primary aberration only.

Similarly, the optical path difference with which the disturbance from Q would arrive at the "paraxial" focus B_1' would be

$$p_Q = C_2(A_1Q)^4$$

It is convenient to represent the co-ordinates of Q, Fig. 73, in the circle by y and z, as shown. Hence, we find

$$(A_1Q)^2 = (A_1P + y)^2 + z^2,$$

so that $\quad A_1Q^4 = \{(Mh' + y)^2 + z^2\}^2$

The net optical path difference between disturbances arriving at the "paraxial" focus discussed above from Q and P will therefore be

$$p = C_2[\{(Mh' + y)^2 + z^2\}^2 - (Mh')^4]$$

On expansion this expression reduces to

$$p = C_2[(y^2 + z^2)^2 + 4My(y^2 + z^2)h' + 2M^2(3y^2 + z^2)h'^2 + 4M^3yh'^3]$$

If there are a number of such surfaces, each one will produce an optical path difference of this type with its own values of C_2 and M. The value of h' at the various surfaces will vary according to the original position of the object point and to the magnification of the intermediate image, which is presented as the object to any surface; but for any one surface it may be written as $\phi_r h$, say, for the rth surface, where h represents the value in some definite stage, possibly for the object or the final image.

Similarly, the y and z co-ordinates of a ray vary as the pencil passes through successive refracting surfaces, but for any one ray path they will bear a sufficiently constant ratio to each other in the various surfaces; denoting their values in the exit-pupil by y and z, their values in the rth surface will be given sufficiently accurately by

$$y_r = \theta_r y, \ z_r = \theta_r z$$

Substituting these values for h', y, and z, and adding up all the optical path differences arising at successive surfaces, the total optical path difference for a disturbance passing along the principal ray, and one which passes through the edge of the "stop" to the final image, will be given by an expression of the form

$$p = a_1(y^2 + z^2)^2 + a_2y(y^2 + z^2)h + a_3(3y^2 + z^2)h^2 + a_5yh^3 \quad . \quad (425)$$

This expression of the optical path is a particular form of the

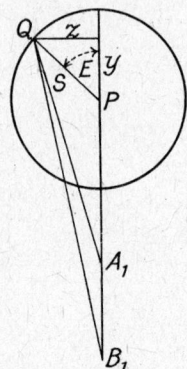

Enlarged View of End Projection

FIG. 73

Characteristic Function, the theory of which was originated by Sir William Rowan Hamilton (whose collected works should be consulted), and has been developed by many later writers; especially by T. Smith (see Ref. 8, and many articles in the *Transactions of the Optical Society*).

The terms of the above equation represent four kinds of aberration which may arise in an optical system, and their characteristics will be discussed below. They correspond to four of the five "aberrations" deduced by von Seidel[9] in 1856, and often called after his name. They are, in succession, characteristic of

Seidel's $\begin{cases} \text{1. Spherical aberration.} \\ \text{2. Coma.} \\ \text{3. Astigmatism.} \\ \text{4. Distortion.} \end{cases}$

No. 4 of Seidel's aberrations is the "Curvature of Field" of the surface containing the sharp image found when the first three aberrations are absent. Referring again to Fig. 72, we see that in the case of a single refracting surface, a spherical object surface concentric with C would have a corresponding image surface also concentric with C. If the object surface has a different curvature it is possible (see below) to calculate the curvature of the image surface for one surface, imagining image formation to be effected by narrow pencils passing through the centre of curvature; this is done one by one for all the surfaces of the system, and the curvature of a final "image" surface can thus be found. A little consideration will show that the foregoing investigation must relate to the optical path differences arising in this particular surface.

The matter was first investigated by Coddington and later, independently, by Petzval. The above surface is usually known as the "Petzval surface," but it may not contain the best physical image.

It is natural to find that the above equation contains no reference to the curvature of field, in view of the particular assumptions on which it was derived. A discussion of the magnitude of the curvature of the field, and its dependence on the optical properties of the system, will be found below.

Discussion of the Aberrations in Terms of Ray Intercepts. The optical designer tests his designs by the method of tracing "rays" through the system, using the method described briefly in Chapter I. It used to be thought that the distribution of light in the image plane could be predicted fairly accurately from the relative concentration of ray intersections, but exact inquiry has now shown this to be erroneous. A case of the discrepancy between the magnitude of the calculated "least disc of confusion" and the actual "Airy disc" patch in the presence of spherical aberration, has been already met with. In one case[4] of "zonal spherical aberration" the size of the ray diffusion patch was eight times that of the actual concentration of light in the Airy disc, even though the residual differences of phase between disturbances arriving in the image from all zones amounted to no more than 90°.

The designer should understand these facts, and to be able to interpret the ray intercepts, which are obtained as the direct results of ray tracing, in terms of optical path differences.

It can be shown that equation similar to (414) hold for both the y and z displacements; note the *partial* differential coefficients. Thus,

$$T_z' = \frac{l'}{n'}\left(\frac{\partial p}{\partial z}\right)$$

where T_z' is the lateral aberration in the focal plane, measured in the z direction, while the corresponding equation,

$$T_y' = \frac{l'}{n'}\left(\frac{\partial p}{\partial y}\right)$$

gives the lateral intercept in the y direction in the focal plane. Thus the point of intersection of the ray in the focal plane (or rather, the part of the focal surface near the axis) can be calculated.

Differentiating equation (425) with regard to y and z, we find

$$y \text{ displacement} = T_y' = \frac{l'}{n'}\left[4a_1 y(y^2 + z^2) + a_2 h\,(3y^2 + z^2) \right.$$
$$\left. + 6a_3 h^2 y + a_5 h^3\right]$$

$$z \text{ displacement} = T_z' = \frac{l'}{n'}\left[4a_1 z\,(y^2 + z^2) + 2a_2 hyz + 2a_3 h^2 z\right]$$

The easiest way of discussing the equations is to use polar coordinates. Put

$$y = S \cos E, \; z = S \sin E, \; y^2 + z^2 = S^2$$

taking E as the angle made with the y axis by the radius vector PQ, which is of length S. Whence

$$\left. \begin{aligned} T_y' &= \frac{l'}{n'}\left[4a_1 S^3 \cos E + a_2 hS^2\,(2 + \cos 2E) \right. \\ &\qquad\qquad \left. + 6a_3 h^2 S \cos E + a_3 h^3\right] \\ T_z' &= \frac{l'}{n'}\left[4a_1 S^3 \sin E + a_2 hS^2 \sin 2E + 2a_3 h^2 S \sin E\right] \end{aligned} \right\} . \quad (426)$$

The terms involving the various coefficients $a_1 \ldots a_5$ may now be discussed. Take h to be the radial distance of intersection, in the focal surface, of the ray from the centre of the exit pupil. Equation (425), when expressed in polar co-ordinates, becomes

$$p = a_1 S^4 + a_2 S^3 h \cos E + a_3 S^2 h^2 (2 + \cos 2E)$$
$$+ a_5 S h^3 \cos E \qquad . \qquad . \qquad . \qquad (427)$$

Spherical Aberration. The terms in a_1 indicate an optical path difference proportional to the fourth power of the distance from the central axis at which the ray leaves the exit pupil, or a lateral aberration proportional to S^3. This is characteristic of primary spherical

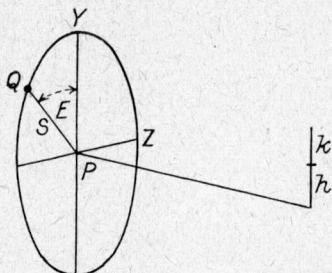

FIG. 74

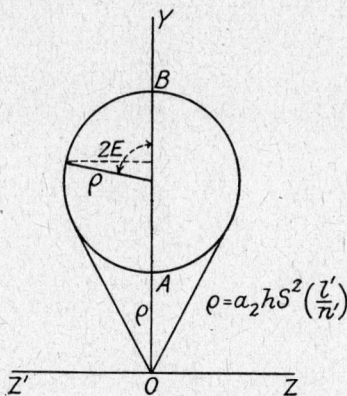

$$\rho = a_2 h S^2 \left(\frac{l'}{n'}\right)$$

FIG. 75

aberration, and this type of aberration, therefore, if present on the axis, will exist also in the other parts of the field in the same magnitude.

Coma. The terms in a_2 give the components of the displacement for the ray intersection as

$$\left.\begin{aligned} T_y' &= \frac{l'}{n'} (2a_2 h S^2 + a_2 h S^2 \cos 2E) \\ T_z' &= \frac{l'}{n'} (a_2 h S^2 \sin 2E) \end{aligned}\right\} \qquad . \qquad . \qquad (428)$$

and they are shown as a circle for a given value of S in Fig. 75. For smaller values of S, the figure will be similar and the circle will still lie within the same tangential lines. The point A of the circle nearest the origin lies at a distance $(a_2 h S^2) (l'/n')$ from it.

Now a displacement of amount $(+k)$ (see Fig. 74) parallel to the y direction produces an optical path difference between the central disturbance from P and the marginal disturbance from the point Q given by

$$p_1 = \frac{n'k\mathrm{S}\cos \mathrm{E}}{l'} = \begin{array}{l}\text{(increase of axial path } less \text{ increase of} \\ \text{marginal path)}\end{array}$$

(compare the expression derived on p. 103). When

$$k = (a_2 h\mathrm{S}^2)\left(\frac{l'}{n'}\right)$$

$$p_1 = a_2 h\mathrm{S}^3 \cos \mathrm{E}$$

but this is the optical path difference due to coma, which is shown by the second term in equation (427). When $\frac{\partial p}{\partial y}$ and $\frac{\partial p}{\partial z}$ are reckoned positive, it signifies a greater marginal than axial path. Hence, the disturbances from the entire ring of the exit pupil of radius S meet

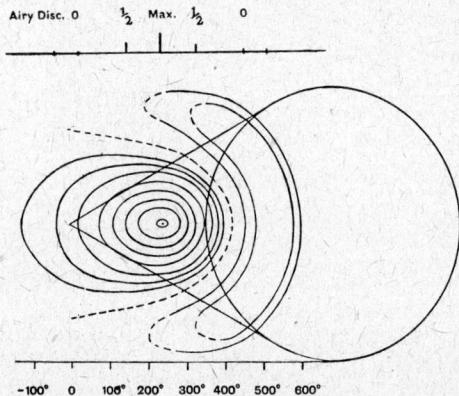

FIG. 76. CONTOURS OF LIGHT INTENSITY IN THE PRESENCE OF COMA COMPARED WITH THE OUTLINE OF THE GEOMETRICAL COMA FIGURE

in the same phase at the point A of the coma figure (Fig. 75). The point A can thus be looked upon as the physical focus of the corresponding ring of the wave surface, and the foci for intermediate rings are distributed between O and A at distances proportional to S^2. After what has been said above, it will be appreciated that, while the ray intersections with the focal surface may be distributed round the complete circle AB, the physical focus for the ring of the wave surface may be at the one point A.

When the focusing points for all zones of the surface are identical, the magnification is the same for all zones; thus the sine condition is fulfilled and "coma" disappears. Provided that spherical aberration is absent, the "offence against the sine condition" is thus a measure of the coma present.

When the optical path differences are not large, the great proportion of the energy is concentrated into the region of these physical focal points. Fig. 76 shows the results of some calculations of the energy distribution in comparison with the figure showing the boundaries of the patch into which the rays are distributed. The great discrepancies between the distribution of energy calculated from physical theory and that which might be inferred from a corpuscular theory are obvious. In the case shown, the optical path

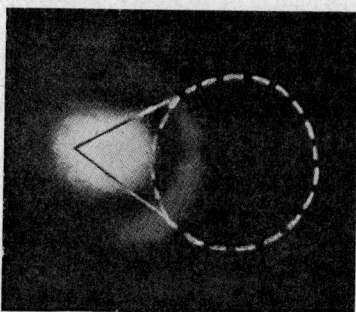

FIG. 77. PHOTOGRAPH OF STAR IMAGE EXHIBITING SLIGHT COMA
The corresponding geometrical figure is drawn in outline.

differences for the extreme marginal zone amounted to $\pm$ one wavelength. It is not until the aberration amounts to several wavelengths that more resemblance to the geometrical "coma patch" figure begins to be found in the image.

Astigmatism. The terms in a_3 in the displacement equations

$$\left. \begin{aligned} T'_y &= (6a_3h^2S \cos E)\,\frac{l'}{n'} \\ T'_z &= (2a_3h^2S \sin E)\,\frac{l'}{n'} \end{aligned} \right\} \qquad \cdot \qquad \cdot \qquad \cdot \quad (429)$$

show that the figure representing the ray intersections in the Petzval surface from a zone of radius S, is an ellipse with a y axis having three times the length of the z axis (Fig. 78 shows a case in which the lateral intercepts are negative). The rays from the extremity of the Y diameter (the direction of the image point from the centre of the field represents the Y direction) therefore intersect at a distance from the Petzval surface three times the distance of those from the extremity of the Z diameter. The former focus is the focus of the "tangential" pencil, the latter is that of the "sagittal" pencil; both these foci lie on the same side of the Petzval surface. We thus have the tangential and sagittal focal

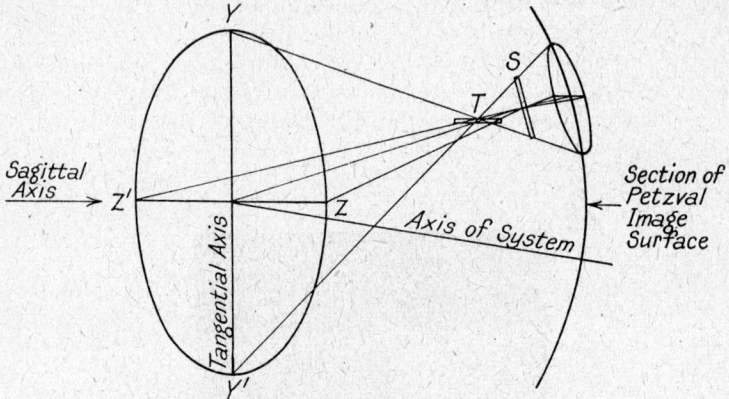

FIG. 78. TANGENTIAL AND SAGITTAL FOCAL LINES

surfaces, as suggested in Fig. 79.* The contours for light distribution in the presence of astigmatism have also been worked out in one or two cases. Typical results are shown in Fig. 80, in which the results of calculation have been supplemented by observation. The

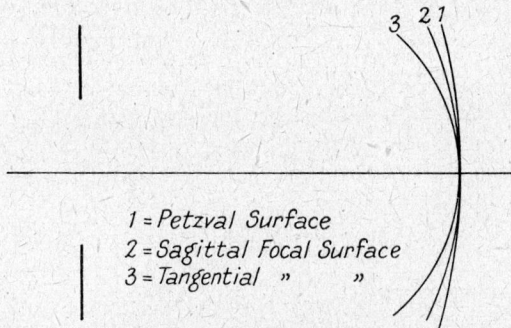

1 = Petzval Surface
2 = Sagittal Focal Surface
3 = Tangential   "   "

FIG. 79

Note that the distance of the tangential focal surface from the Petzval
is three times that of the sagittal surface.

geometrical theory leads to the conclusion that all the rays from a given zone pass through two mutually perpendicular focal *lines*. These are suggested in Fig. 78. The line at the "tangential" focus

* The power of a thin lens in an oblique direction is worked out on pages 37 *et seq.*

is perpendicular to the radial direction of the image point in the field; the sagittal line is parallel to this radius.

Actually, in cases where the astigmatism may be present in combination with other aberrations, the sagittal line for any zone will not in general lie perpendicular to the principal ray from the centre of the aperture, but will lie in the plane containing the principal ray and the axis of the system, at an angle with the principal ray, depending on the values of the astigmatism and coma.

It will be understood that if the lens system suffering from the astigmatism of oblique pencils is being employed to form an image

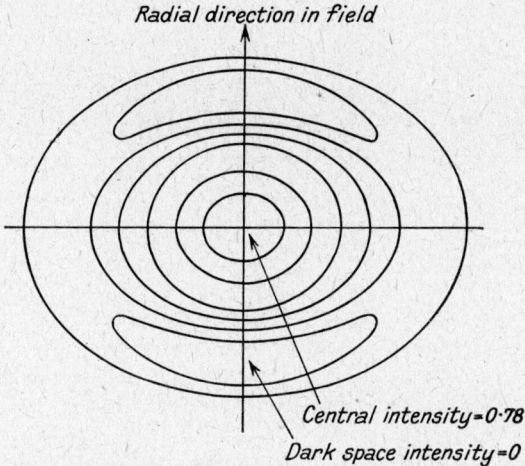

FIG. 80. LIGHT DISTRIBUTION CONTOURS IN THE ELEMENTARY IMAGE NEAR THE TANGENTIAL IMAGE SURFACE
The amount of aberration corresponds to the Rayleigh limit.

of any object, any one point of the object away from the axis will be imaged as a short line, tangential in the tangential surface, radial in the sagittal. Thus a diagram consisting of circles concentric with the axis would be imaged as reasonably sharp circles in the tangential focal surface, while radial lines would be imaged as apparently sharp radial lines in the sagittal focal surface, even though the image of an object *point* would appear as a line in either case.

Curvature of Field. Imagine a lens, and a plane object perpendicular to the axis. The image formed by refraction at the first surface of the lens will have a definite curvature. Hence, in order to calculate the final curvature of the image field formed by the whole lens, we must be able to deal with the general case of a curved "object field" such as is presented to the second surface of the lens.

Having given the radius of curvature R_i of the object field (which is assumed to be centred on the axis of the lens system), one has to find the corresponding radius R_i' of the image field. A single refracting surface is first considered, and the image formation is assumed to be effected by pencils passing through the centre of curvature.

In Fig. 81, the dotted arcs BE and B'G with centres at C represent surfaces which are conjugate with respect to each other, B and B' being conjugate points on the axis ACB'B (see Chapter I, p. 26, for a similar case). The actual object field passes through B, but

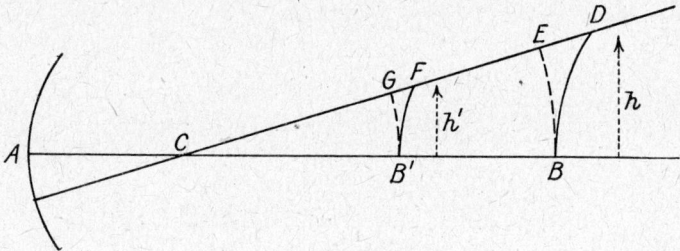

FIG. 81

it has a radius of curvature R_i; it is indicated by the trace BD; similarly, the trace of the image field is shown by B'F. The points C, G, F, E, and D lie on a straight line passing through the centre of curvature C. Hence the intercept GF is the "image" of the intercept ED.

Let h and h' be the object and image heights, then by dropping perpendiculars from E and D to the axis and applying the "spherometer formula" to find the intercepts between the foot of each perpendicular and the point B, we shall find—

Distance between feet of perpendiculars = ED very nearly when h' and h are very small; then in such a case

$$\text{ED} = \frac{h^2}{2(l - r)} + \frac{h^2}{2R_i}$$

where $l = $ AB and $r = $ AC, the radius of curvature of the refracting surface. Similarly,

$$\text{GF} = \frac{h'^2}{2(l' - r)} + \frac{h'^2}{2R_i'}$$

But the formula (206) for axial magnification gives

$$\frac{dx'}{dx} = \left(\frac{h'}{h}\right)^2 \frac{n'}{n}, \text{ hence } \frac{\text{GF}}{\text{ED}} = \left(\frac{h'}{h}\right)^2 \frac{n'}{n}$$

Hence $\dfrac{h'^2}{2}\left(\dfrac{1}{l'-r}+\dfrac{1}{R_i'}\right)=\left(\dfrac{h'}{h}\right)^2\dfrac{n'}{n}\times\left(\dfrac{h^2}{2}\right)\left(\dfrac{1}{l-r}+\dfrac{1}{R_i}\right)$

Whence $\dfrac{1}{n'R_i'}-\dfrac{1}{nR_i}=\dfrac{1}{n(l-r)}-\dfrac{1}{n'(l'-r)}$ . . (430)

In order to simplify the right-hand side of the expression, we make use of equation (106),

$$\frac{(l-r)l'}{(l'-r)l}=\frac{n'}{n}$$

and obtain $\dfrac{1}{n'R_i'}-\dfrac{1}{nR_i}=\dfrac{1}{n(l-r)}-\dfrac{1}{n(l-r)\left(\dfrac{l'}{l}\right)}$

$$=\frac{1}{n(l-r)}\left\{1-\frac{l}{l'}\right\}\qquad . \quad . \quad (431)$$

Equation (107), $\dfrac{n'}{l'}-\dfrac{n}{l}=\dfrac{n'-n}{r}$, gives

$$\frac{l}{l'}=\frac{nr+(n'-n)l}{n'r}$$

Substituting,

$$\frac{1}{n'R_i'}-\frac{1}{nR_i}=\frac{1}{n(l-r)}\left\{1-\frac{nr+(n'-n)l}{n'r}\right\}$$

$$=-\left(\frac{n'-n}{nn'r}\right)\qquad . \quad . \quad . \quad (432)$$

The equation may be applied successively to any number of refracting surfaces; if n^* and R_i^* are the final values of refractive index and curvature of field, we have

$$\frac{1}{n^*R_i^*}-\frac{1}{nR_i}=\Sigma\left(\frac{n-n'}{nn'}\cdot\frac{1}{r}\right)\qquad . \quad . \quad (433)$$

The formula is not completely adequate. For example, the simple treatment on p. 23 of this book showed that when the object field for a single refracting surface contains the centre of curvature, the image field has then the same curvature as the object field. In order to obtain a more general result, the variation formula (204) should be applied in the investigation in place of the differential formula (206). This has been done by F. Gilbert Brown,[10] who obtains the expression,

$$\frac{X'}{n'Y'^2}-\frac{X}{nY^2}=-\frac{1}{2}\frac{n'-n}{nn'r}\left\{1+\tan^2\tfrac{1}{2}\theta-2\frac{n'}{n}m_o\left(\frac{X}{Y}+\tan\tfrac{1}{2}\theta\right)^2\right\}$$

$$. \quad . \quad . \quad (434)$$

where X, Y; X', Y' represent the co-ordinates of the extra-axial object and image points (e.g. D and F, Fig. 81) with respect to the axial points B and B' as origins. Also θ is the angle of the field, e.g. $\widehat{FCB'}$, and m_o is the lateral magnification associated with the conjugates B and B'. Suppose, then, that a plane object is situated at the centre of curvature; clearly X = o and tan $\frac{1}{2}\theta = 1$; the curly bracket on the right vanishes; hence X' must vanish, i.e. the image is also plane. The simple Petzval equations, however, give adequate accuracy except where the object or image is fairly close to a centre of curvature.

Applying the equation (433) to the two surfaces of a thin lens in air, and writing n for the refractive index of the lens, we obtain, assuming R_i infinite (plane object)

$$\frac{1}{R_i{}^*} = -\frac{1}{nf'} \qquad \qquad (435)$$

This equation was first given by Coddington. For a number of coaxial thin lenses,

$$\frac{1}{R_i{}^*} = \Sigma\left(-\frac{1}{nf'}\right) \qquad \qquad (436)$$

It should be noted that the curvature of the field of a lens system is independent of the relative aperture and also of the object distance.

This discussion, then, enables us to find the curvature of the surface referred to above as the "Petzval surface."

Distortion. The term in a_5 shows a displacement of the image point along the radius of that point drawn from the centre of the field. It is independent of S, and therefore occurs, however small the stop may be which limits the optical system. It is proportional to the cube of the radius of the image point.

It is to be noted, however, that the distortion usually of interest in practice is that which is found in a plane image surface, not generally the curved Petzval surface.

The general result is that the scale of the image presentation is not constant over the field, and, usually, the displacement is exaggerated the greater the distance from the centre. In the case where the distortion is inwards, the scale of representation for the peripheral object is too small, this giving barrel-type distortion; in the other case, the peripheral scale is too great, giving pincushion distortion. These effects are shown in Fig. 82, which is self-explanatory.

The subject of distortion will be discussed in greater detail in the chapter on Photographic Lenses, Vol. II.

General Remarks on the Aberrations. The Seidel aberrations arise with monochromatic light and are quite independent of the chromatic aberrations arising through variations of refractive index with wave-length, except in the sense that chromatic variations of the Seidel aberrations are usually experienced to some extent.

It should be noticed that the aberrations of *spherical aberration*, *coma*, and *astigmatism* affect the *definition* of the image point ; those of *curvature of field* and *distortion* affect its position.

The laws of the aberrations discussed above are a useful guide in many cases, though no relation has been worked out here between

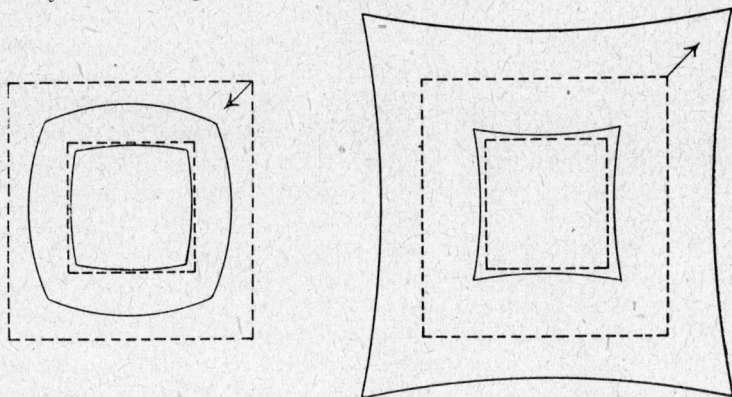

(a) Barrel Type   *(b) Pincushion Type*

FIG. 82. TYPES OF DISTORTION

the amounts of these aberrations and the construction of the systems; this is a subject belonging to the province of optical designing and computing.

With large apertures, we saw (p. 108) how the spherical aberration becomes more complex; there is a corresponding complexity in the extra-axial aberrations affecting the outer parts of the field, but although it is possible to discuss the higher order aberrations on the lines adopted above, the investigation will not be attempted here. The theory already developed will suffice for a general understanding in many cases, and will be referred to in the discussion of various instruments. A short discussion of the higher oblique aberrations will be found in Vol. II.

Tolerances for Aberration. The somewhat inviting method of ray-tracing by the law of refraction, and the application of the results to estimate the distribution of light in the image, has been shown to be by no means always reliable. The ideal type of image characteristic of spherical convergent waves has been examined, and also the variation from this type consequent on the presence of aberration. The late Lord Rayleigh was the first to show in particular cases that when the disturbances met in the image with optical path differences exceeding one-quarter of a wave-length, the deterioration of the image would begin to be noticeable. This has led to an extremely useful general guide for designers of optical systems by which to test the merits of their designs; a rule which, however, has to be applied with discretion. In cases where the highest definition is required, as in the images formed by the objective of a telescope or microscope, the optical path differences in the image should not be allowed to exceed this "Rayleigh limit" of one-quarter of a wave-length. In other cases, such as photographic lenses, much larger aberrations must be tolerated in order to obtain other ends, such as the covering of a large field with reasonably good definition.

Depth of Focus in the Image. From a study of the results of integration of the effects of light from all parts of a finite lens aperture, it appears that it is possible to travel in the axial direction from the centre of a spherical wave till the optical path difference (extreme marginal path *minus* axial path) of the disturbances reaches $\pm \lambda/4$, before a serious deterioration in the concentration of light begins. This is in agreement with the "Rayleigh limit," and is a very useful approximation.

The optical path difference p_m between marginal and axial disturbances produced by a shift δl along the axis is given by equation (409). If p_m may reach a value of $\pm \lambda/4$, the value of δl may be such that

$$\delta l = \pm \frac{\lambda}{8n \sin^2 (\alpha/2)} . \qquad . \qquad . \qquad (437)$$

If α is so small that the angular measure of $\alpha/2$ may be substituted for the sine, then, using the symbol of equation 407,

$$\delta l \simeq \pm \lambda/2n\alpha^2 \simeq \pm \lambda l^2/2ny^2 \qquad . \qquad . \qquad (438)$$

The total focal depth is therefore approximately $\lambda l^2/ny^2$ (supposing y very small in comparison with l).

These equations are only valid where the focal depth so calculated is small in comparison with the value of f. A fuller discussion of focal depth will be given in connection with photographic lenses. In practice, it is found, for example, that an eyepiece of a telescope or microscope may be pushed in or withdrawn through a definite interval corresponding to this depth of focus without the manifestation of any serious deterioration of the image. There is, however, no *very* sharply-marked limit.

Chromatic Defects of the Image. The fuller discussion of chromatic aberration and its correction in "achromatic" systems must be postponed till the properties of optical glass are discussed. Considering two wave-lengths "D" and "F," the simple formula for a thin lens gives—

$$\frac{1}{f_D{}'} = (n_D - 1) \, \mathbf{R}$$

$$\frac{1}{f_F{}'} = (n_F - 1) \, \mathbf{R}$$

Whence
$$\frac{f_F{}' - f_D{}'}{f_F{}' f_D{}'} = (n_D - n_F) \, \mathbf{R}$$

By dividing the last equation by the first—

$$\frac{(f_D{}' - f_F{}')}{f_F{}'} = \frac{\delta f}{f_F{}'} = \frac{-\delta n}{(n_D - 1)} \qquad . \qquad . \quad (439)$$

Hence, for a given change of wave-length, the fractional change of focal length is given by the expression on the right of the equation, and is thus proportional to the change of refractive index. In a simple lens, therefore, which is forming an image of an axial point source, the foci for the different wave-lengths are drawn out along the axis.

Chromatic Variation of the Focal Point. The chromatic variation of the focal point in the above sense causes coloured haloes around the focus. It is easy to arrange a spectacle lens to form the image of a distant but bright source of light, and to examine this image by a suitable eyepiece, mounted coaxial with the lens. As the star focus of such a simple lens is approached, the red focus is first found, which is surrounded by a halo of green and an outer one of violet. Further inwards, the central spot appears whitish from the superposition of radiations, but it is surrounded by a reddish-violet halo which becomes more strongly red as the point of observation shifts inwards to the violet focus, where surrounding rings of green and red are seen.

Chromatic Difference of Magnification. In addition to this axial shift of the focal point with wave-length, there are frequently found chromatic differences of magnification which may arise through variation of the "focal length" with wave-length. In such a case the star image in the outer parts of the field formed by the optical system is drawn out into a short spectrum lying in a direction radial from the centre of the field. These two are the most important types of chromatic aberration, but, in addition, there is usually a certain degree of chromatic variation in the other aberrations of a complex system. Thus, spherical aberration, even when corrected for one wave-length, may be found in another, and so on.

Tolerance for Chromatic Axial Shift of the Focal Point. As seen above, the "focus" of any homogeneous component of the radiation may be regarded as a concentration of energy in a finite region of space. The depth of focus in the image up to the optical path difference of $\pm \lambda/4$ is (in air) by (438), $\pm \lambda l^2/2y^2$. Hence, if the full and dotted lines in Fig. 83 respectively indicate the foci of two homogeneous radiations (each having a definite wave-length), their

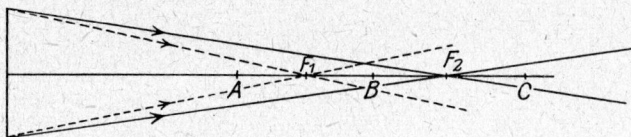

FIG. 83

depth of focus may be shown by AB and BC. At the point B there will just be a reasonable concentration of each of them, and a better concentration for all intermediate wave-lengths.

Suppose for a moment that these wave-lengths were those of the orange and blue radiations of the visible spectrum, then the point B would have a reasonable concentration of all wave-lengths of good luminosity. Thus, the distance F_1F_2 = the sum of half the total focal depths for each wave-length, and for a thin lens of focal length f'

$$\delta f' = F_1F_2 = \tfrac{1}{2}(\lambda_1 + \lambda_2)\,(f'/y)^2$$

Combining this with equation (439) in the form

$$\delta f = -f'\,\frac{\delta n}{n-1}$$

we obtain

$$\frac{f'}{y} = 2\,\frac{y\,\delta n}{(n-1)\,(\lambda_1 + \lambda_2)}$$

(numerically, disregarding the sign).

In practice, with ordinary crown glass, $\delta n/(n-1)$ might amount to something like $\tfrac{1}{80}$. Take $y = 4$ cm., say, and $\lambda_1 + \lambda_2 = \cdot000048 + \cdot00006$ cm. $= \cdot0001$ cm. sufficiently nearly, then

$$\frac{f'}{y} = \frac{2 \times 4}{80 \times \cdot0001} = \frac{8}{\cdot008} = 1000$$

Hence, f' required for a colour-free image $= 4,000$ cm. From this investigation, the reason for the extraordinarily long astronomical telescopes employed before the invention of the achromatic lens can be understood. The small aperture and long focal length were essential to obtain reasonably colour-free images.

Achromatic Lens. In the case of an ordinary doublet achromatic lens, the axial spreading of the colours is greatly reduced. Applegreen ($\lambda = \cdot000055$ cm.) is found nearest the lens, while red and blue are superimposed at a distance of about $\frac{1}{2000}$ of the focal length beyond. Since the extreme ends of the spectrum are relatively faint, it may be assumed that none of the components should arrive with path differences greater than $\lambda/2$, a doubled tolerance. This is expressed by

$$\delta f_1 + \delta f_2 = \frac{f}{2000} = (\lambda_1 + \lambda_2)\left(\frac{f}{y}\right)^2$$

Assuming $\lambda_1 = \cdot000055$, and $\lambda_2 = \cdot000048$ cm., this gives very nearly: $f = 5y^2$, where f and y are to be given in centimetres. Conrady, who first drew attention to the importance of this limit of tolerance, uses a similar expression to show that the majority of big telescopes have focal lengths which are too short in relation to their diameters to satisfy the above requirement, and their images probably suffer in consequence.

REFERENCES

1. Conrady: *Optical Designing and Computing* (Oxford University Press, 1929).
2. von Rohr: *The Formation of Images in Optical Instruments* (H.M. Stationery Office, 1920).
3. Conrady: *Monthly Notices, R.A.S.*, 79, 575 (1919).
4. Martin: *Trans. Opt. Soc.*, XXVII, 249 (1925–26).
5. Lommel: *Abhand. bayer Akad. d. Wiss.* II Kl. Bd. 15, pp. 233–328, (1884).
6. Jentsch: *Handbuch d. Physik.* XXI, pp. 885–955.
7. Hopkins: Thesis for Ph.D., London (1945).
7 (a). Maréchal: *Communications des Laboratoires de l'Institut d'Optique*, III, 68 (1944).
8. T. Smith: *Dictionary of Applied Physics*, IV, 309 (1923).
9. v. Seidel: *Ast. Nach.*, 43, 289–332 (1856).
10. Brown: Proc. Phys. Soc., 57, 403 (1945).

THE EYE AND PHYSIOLOGICAL OPTICS

THE majority of optical instruments function as direct aids to vision, hence it is most important for the optician to understand the action of the human eye, its capabilities, its limitations, and the conditions which govern its efficiency. Its mode of action was unknown to the ancients, and it was left for *Kepler* to show that the refracting parts of the eye produce a clear image upon the retina. Descartes describes, in Chapter V of the *Dioptrice*, an experiment in which a freshly-excised eye is placed in a hole cut in a window shutter. The opaque membranes at the back of the eye being removed, a sharp image of external objects is found on a piece of paper held against the retina.

Although we shall not deal with binocular vision in this chapter, it must be remembered throughout that two eyes are concerned in ordinary "seeing." Some special considerations regarding binocular instruments and vision will be dealt with in Vol. II of this book.

Anatomy of the Eye. The eyeball is an approximately spherical body about 1 in. in diameter; the front, however, exhibits the protrusion of the *cornea*, a spherical segment of smaller radius, while the posterior is somewhat flattened. The *cornea* in front and the *sclerotic* behind are the coats which enclose the media of the eye; the general shape is preserved by the internal pressure in the eyeball, which is equivalent to 20–30 mm. of mercury.

The eyeball is situated within the *orbit*, the funnel-shaped bony cavity which is usually called the socket; it is held in position at the rear by the lymph-filled elastic sheath known as the capsule of Tenon, and is protected at the front by the inner surfaces of the lids, i.e. a part of the *conjunctiva*; its movements are controlled by the group of muscles comprising the four *recti* and two *obliques*.

The eyeball is rotated round a vertical axis by the action of the two horizontal recti; the vertical recti rotate it about the transverse axis, which lies in a horizontal plane and intersects the vertical axis in the centre of rotation. The transverse axis is inclined at about 70° to the optic axis.

The *oblique* muscles rotate the eye about the oblique axis, which also lies in a horizontal plane; it makes an angle of about 35° with the optic axis. The oblique axis also passes through the centre of rotation. This centre of rotation is a point of great importance, and is situated about 15·5 mm. behind the cornea and 9 mm. in front of the retina; it is about 1·5 mm. to the nasal side of the visual axis for horizontal rotations.

Fig. 84 shows a section of the eyeball; passing from front to rear the *cornea* is first encountered, a transparent, horny layer, of thickness about 0·5 mm.,* which is kept moist and transparent by a surface-tension film of lachrymal fluid constantly distributed by the involuntary action of the lids in winking. The diameter of the cornea is about 12 mm. horizontally and 11 mm. vertically, the

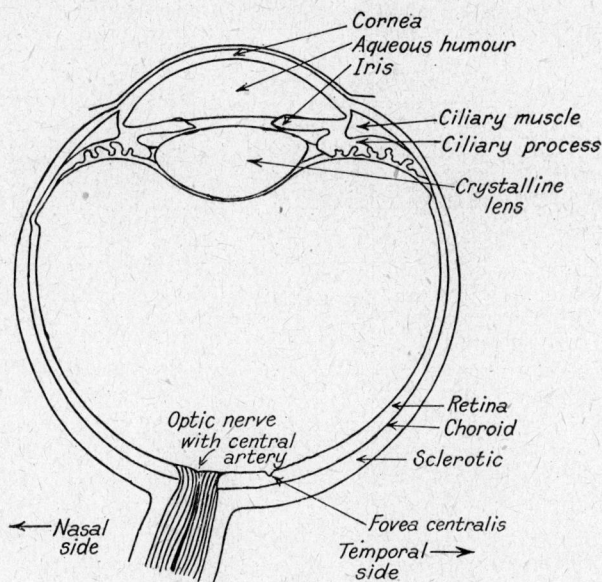

FIG. 84. HORIZONTAL SECTION OF RIGHT EYE

remainder of the eye being covered by the opaque *sclerotic*. Several layers of the cornea can be distinguished, but for these and other details, works on physiology must be consulted.

Behind the cornea is found the *anterior chamber*, which is filled with a watery, slightly saline fluid of refractive index 1·336, the *aqueous humour*. The axial thickness of the anterior chamber is about 1·3 mm.

At the back of the anterior chamber is the *crystalline lens* on the anterior surface of which the *iris* rests. The central opening of the iris is known as the *pupil*. The heavy pigmentation of the iris renders it practically opaque. The diameter of the pupil, which is immediately controlled by the action of radial and circular muscular

* The thickness at the pole is somewhat less than at the sides.

fibres in the iris, depends (through reflex action) both on the accommodation and on the amount of stimulation of the retinae of the
two eyes; it determines the effective aperture of the optical system
of the eye. In ordinary light the diameter may be 3 to 4 mm.; in
excessive light it may shrink to 2 mm., but after some time in darkness it may rise to 8 mm. It will contract in three or four seconds on
re-exposure to light. Blanchard[1] and Reeves have published results,
shown in Fig. 85, in which the diameters of the pupil in millimetres
are plotted as ordinates against the logarithms of the corresponding

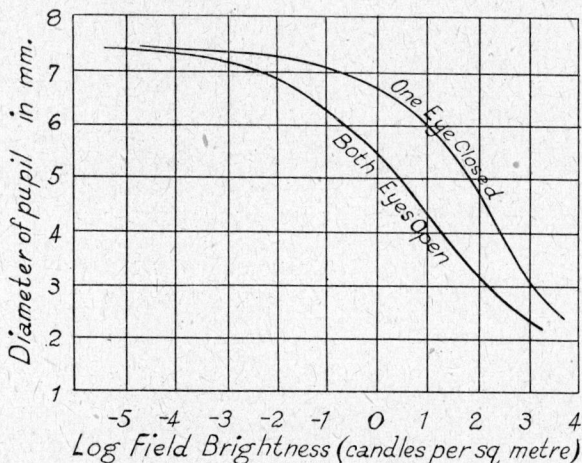

FIG. 85. VARIATION OF THE DIAMETER OF THE PUPIL

field brightnesses as abscissae. It must always be remembered that
the pupil shrinks when the eye is accommodated for near objects.
The *crystalline lens* is bi-convex in form, the normal radii of front and
back surfaces being about 10 mm. and 6 mm. respectively, and the
thickness about 3·6 mm. It is built up of successive fibrous layers,
and the refractive index of the material rises from the outer parts,
where it is about 1·38, to the inner nuclear portions where it is
about 1·41. The anterior covering, or capsule, of the lens has a
maximum thickness about 3 mm. from the pole; the thin posterior
capsule is thickest at the periphery. The lens is held in position by
the *suspensory* ligament, which is attached to the *ciliary body* (see
below).

At the back of the lens is found the *vitreous humour*, transparent,
and of jelly-like consistency (refractive index 1·336), which occupies
the main volume of the eyeball between the lens and the *retina*.

The retina is a coat of several layers which constitutes the receiving screen of the eye; it will be more fully described below. Immediately behind the retina is situated the *choroid*, a "vascular" layer of tissue richly supplied with dark brown pigment cells and blood vessels; together with the retina it extends over all the inner surface as far as the ciliary body, and it is concerned with the nourishment of the retina. Finally, the tough outer coating of the eyeball (the sclerotic) is encountered; it is about 1 mm. thick, opaque, and usually white in colour; it merges into the transparent cornea in the region of the ciliary body.

Accommodation. The *ciliary body* lining the inner surface of the sclerotic near its junction with the cornea contains both circular and radial muscle fibres; the *suspensory ligament* attaches it to the capsule or outer sheath of the crystalline lens.

It is well established that the lens itself is in youth highly elastic and deformable, and it is also well known from optical observations of reflected images that accommodation, or change in power of the optical system of the eye, is accompanied by variation of the curvature of the anterior surface of the lens, and not by any variations in the curvature of the cornea or in the optical length of the eye. The precise mechanism is, however, still the subject of discussion. According to Helmholtz's theory, the effect of accommodation is obtained by an action of the muscles which relieves the normal outward radial tension exerted by the suspensory ligament; the lens therefore takes up its natural more highly-curved figure, the anterior apex of the crystalline moving slightly outwards. On the other hand, Tscherning correctly observed that the act of accommodation is accompanied by a relative increase of curvature of the polar part of the anterior surface and a flattening of the peripheral part; the changes in the posterior surface (which is not displaced at the pole during accommodation) are slighter. In order to account for the lenticonus of the anterior surface, Tscherning at one time maintained that an outward radial pull of the ciliary muscle in accommodation made manifest the bulging of the denser central nucleus. Later he supposed that the action of the ciliary muscle is to press the vitreous forward upon the posterior parts of the lens while the outward tension of the suspensory ligament is maintained; this was expected to produce a depression in the periphery of the posterior surface and a bulging of the pole.

Observations by Hess, Graves, and others have, however, established that the radial tension of the suspensory ligament is relaxed during accommodation, thus confirming the theory of Helmholtz. The phenomenon of non-sphericity of the surfaces is, according to Fincham,[2] explainable by the variable thickness of the anterior capsule, which has its greatest thickness in a mid-zone of the surface, and is thus capable of relieving the relative tension of the membrane at the pole and allowing a bulging effect in that region.

The crystalline lens loses its elasticity with advancing years, and accommodation usually vanishes entirely by the age of 75, see p. 287.

The Retina. The optic nerve enters the eye at the rear, its centre being up to 3·5 mm. from the posterior pole of the axis of symmetry. The sclerotic is continuous with the lining of the nerve channel. Debouching from the entrance of the channel, the nerve fibres run

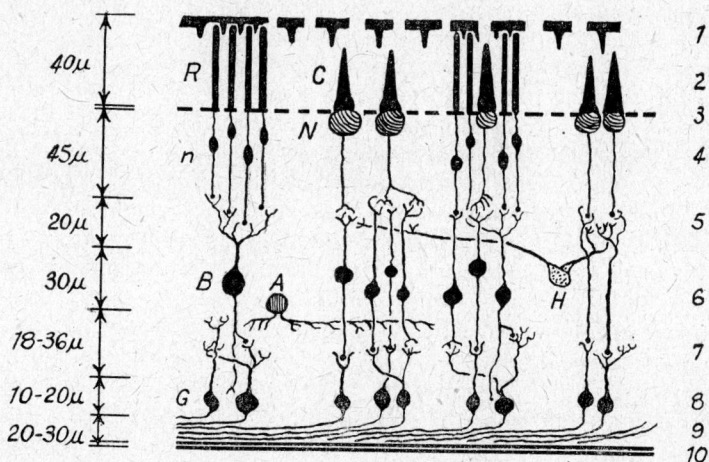

FIG. 86. STRUCTURE OF THE RETINA
Diagrammatic.

in all directions over the inner surface of the retina. Since all the various structures of the retina have practically the same refractive indices, such fibres remain transparent; they are not themselves sensitive to light, but they convey the impulses derived from the special sensitive elements of the retina. The structure of the retina has been the subject of much microscopical study; differentiation of the various parts is effected by the use of selective staining by appropriate dyes, etc., which have been found to colour some parts of the structure more strongly than other parts.

The retina varies in thickness from about 0·56 mm. near the optic disc to less than 0·1 mm. at the scalloped termination (the ora serrata) nearest the lens. The retinal membrane is continuous, however, with the ciliary epithelium or covering membrane. Fig. 86 suggests the relative thickness of the various layers in an intermediate part. The light would traverse the structures upward in the diagram. Some ten layers of the retina are distinguished, and the following numbering is conventional—

1. Pigment epithelium.
2. Bacillary layer (rods and cones, R and C, Fig. 86).
3. Outer limiting membrane.
4. Outer nuclear layer (n and N).
5. Outer plexiform or synapse layer.
6. Inner nuclear layer (Horizontal, Bipolar, and Amacrine Cells, H, B, A).
7. Inner plexiform or synapse layer.
8. Ganglion cell layer (G).
9. Nerve fibre layer.
10. Inner limiting membrane.

The pigment epithelium absorbs much of the light which passes through the retina and thus prevents degradation of the contrast of the retinal image. The rods and cones are the sensitive elements in which the nerve impulses (probably electrical in character) originate. They pass on through the nuclei of the fourth layer to the synaptic layer (5). A "synapse" is the junction or structure at the junction of two nerves or "neurons"; it may have the function of a valve, permitting currents or impulses to pass in one direction only. In many cases there is opposing arborization or twig-like formation at the synapse, and thus a single neuron may collect pulses from a number of photo-receptors, or a pulse may be presented with a variety of pathways, so that pulses from one element might be distributed into several channels. The inner nuclear layer shows three main types of cells. The horizontal cells are supposed by Polyak to receive pulses from the cones and transfer them to other cones or rods; the bi-polar cells pass on the pulse along a single channel; the function of the "Amacrine" cells is speculative, although the derivation of the word (presumably from the Greek αμα (together) and κρα'τοσ (strength) indicates that they have been considered to act in some way in integrating the action of the photo-receptors.

The region where the optic nerve enters the eye is from 2·0 to 2·5 mm. in diameter, and is seen as the "optic disc" when the retina is examined with the ophthalmoscope. Radiation falling on this area gives rise to no sensation of light. (Draw two small crosses 3 in. apart on a sheet of paper. Observing the left-hand one with the right eye only when both are on a level with the eye, bring the paper gradually closer to the face. The right-hand cross will vanish in a certain range of positions in which its image falls on the blind spot.) The "blind spot" subtends 5° horizontally and 7° vertically at the posterior nodal point.

On the temporal side of the pole is found the *macula lutea*, a round or slightly elliptical area, about 2·0 to 3·0 mm. in diameter, in which the retina is covered by a yellow pigment; some degree of pigmentation exists up to a zone perhaps 5·0 mm. in diameter, but the greatest amount is found in the margin of the fovea (see below). There is evidence that individual eyes differ considerably in pigmentation.

In the centre of this pigmented area there is a region (the *fovea*) where the thinning-out of the inner layers (5–8 inclusive) of the retina forms a depression, about 0·37 mm. deep, having a diameter about 1·5 mm. The retinal structures here consist mainly of cones, cone nuclei, and nerve fibres. The pigmentation largely disappears with the layers now absent.

The central region of the depression (about 0·35 mm. in diameter) is called the *foveola*. A region of about 0·5 mm. in diameter containing the foveola has no rods at all; it would subtend 50′ on each side of the point of fixation. The fovea, as a whole, subtends 2·5°, and the pigmented area about 5°, on each side of the fixation point.

The cones are elongated to a length of 70μ in the foveal region; the diameter of the outer segments, where contact is closest, is variously estimated; the figure most frequently given is 2μ–3μ; recent work by Polyak resulted in a result of $1\cdot2\mu$–$1\cdot8\mu$. The main difficulty is associated with the shrinkage and deformation of the sections made for microscopic examination. We shall adopt 2μ as a not unlikely value for discussion. The cones in the outer retinal regions are shorter and thicker, i.e. 2μ to perhaps 5μ in diameter. The diameters of the rods near the fovea approximate to 1μ.

The foveal cones are closely packed, the "dead" separating interval being only about $0\cdot3\mu$. The packing shows a tendency to hexagonal sections (honeycomb pattern) in the cones; but though photomicrographs often show "rows" of elements, they run in various directions, and there are not any three main row directions for the whole area such as would be characteristic of a uniform hexagonal structure. The evidence suggests that there is a one-to-one connection between the foveal cones and single corresponding fibres of the optic nerve; but in other regions it seems probable that sixty or more rods may connect with one fibre. The rods in the periphery become comparatively numerous, exceeding the cones in the proportion of 10 : 1. It is said that the thin ends of the cones contract and thicken when stimulated by light.

The distance between the centre of the optic disc and the fovea is about 4·0 mm. The "pole" varies somewhat in different eyes, but is usually a little to the nasal side of the fovea, perhaps 1·25 mm.

The rods have the peculiarity of secreting a purple fluid known as the visual purple or rhodopsin; spectroscopic observations show that the region of maximum absorption in the spectrum is at wavelength ·50μ in the green. This substance is bleached by light (see below, p. 158), and is considered to play an important part in the visual process. It is not definitely known whether a similar substance occurs in small quantity *in* the rod-like cones of the fovea or whether, as suggested by Edridge-Green, the rhodopsin diffuses among them from the surrounding regions of the retina.

The pigment layer which forms the outer parts of the retina contains closely-packed cells of hexagonal section containing dark brown pigment; these have numerous fine "processes" or extensions passing up amongst the rods and cones. In amphibian eyes, stimulation of the retina by light causes an elongation of these processes, and this action probably plays an extremely important part in the *adaptation* of the retina to different degrees of light intensity. A similar action may take place in the human retina, but has not been conclusively proved. It is estimated that there are altogether about four million cones and more than one hundred million rods.

The nerves from each eye, having passed through an aperture at the back of the orbit, meet in the *chiasma* at the base of the brain, and the fibres from the nasal side of each retina cross over at this point to the opposite part of the brain, while those from the temporal side exhibit no such crossing. This phenomenon is known as *decussation*. Each optic nerve contains approximately one million recognizable fibres which are probably capable of conveying separate impulses. It is noteworthy that the number of fibres is much less than the receptor elements.

Optical Properties of the Eye. The axis of symmetry passing from the anterior pole in the cornea intersects the retina at a point close to the nasal boundary of the macula.

The determination of the radii of curvature, separations of surfaces, and refractive indices of the media of the human eye as they exist during life is a matter of considerable difficulty, since only limited observations are possible on the living organ, and important changes may be encountered in an eye which is opened up after death. Evidence on any point has to be collected from various sources.

The variations of refractive index in the crystalline lens present some difficulties, but attempts have been made to represent its performance by the action of a theoretical lens composed of an outer portion of refractive index 1·386 and an inner core (double convex) of refractive index 1·406. The data given by Gullstrand in his Appendix to the English translation of Helmholtz's *Physiological Optics* show the constants of a "schematic" eye which would closely represent the optical working of an average real human eye with completely relaxed accommodation. The data for a simpler scheme also due to Gullstrand have been given in Chapter II.

Schematic Eye
Refractive Indices

Cornea	1·376
Aqueous and vitreous humours	1·336
Lens (outer part)	1·386
Core of lens	1·406

Positions, measured in mm. along the axis from the anterior pole

Anterior surface of cornea	0
Posterior ,, ,, ,,	0·5
Anterior ,, ,, lens	3·6
,, ,, ,, core	4·146
Posterior ,, ,, ,,	6·565
,, ,, ,, lens	7·2

Radii of Curvature in mm.

Anterior surface of cornea	7·7
Posterior ,, ,, ,,	6·8
Anterior ,, ,, lens	10·0
,, ,, ,, core	7·911
Posterior ,, ,, ,,	− 5·76
,, ,, ,, lens	− 6·0

Under these conditions, the equivalent optical system of the complete eye can be calculated, with the following results—

Complete System of Eye

Refracting power	58·64 diopters
Position of first principal point	1·348 mm. from anterior pole
,, ,, second principal point	1·602 ,, ,, ,, ,,
,, ,, first focal point	− 15·707 ,, ,, ,, ,,
,, ,, second focal point	24·387 ,, ,, ,, ,,
First focal length	− 17·055 mm.
Second focal length	22·785 ,,
Position of *fovea centralis*	24·0 mm. from anterior pole
Axial "refraction" (see Chapter IX)	1·0 diopter

The second focal length being 22·785 mm., the distance from the second nodal point to the second principal focus will be obtained by dividing 22·785 by 1·336, giving 17·055 (i.e. the distance of the first focal length). Thus, the second nodal point will be situated at 7·332 mm. from the anterior pole; the distance for the first nodal point is 7·078 mm. Under the above conditions the image of an infinitely distant object would be formed just behind the retina; slightly increased accommodation would be needed to obtain a sharp focus.

Owing to the closeness of the two principal and the two nodal points, it is sufficient for general purposes to consider each pair as one point, and a simplified schematic eye or "reduced" eye (due to Laurance) is shown in Fig. 87. The distances, in millimetres, are: $AP = 2\cdot2$, $PF = -15$, $PF' = 20$, $AN = 7\cdot2$, $NF' = 15$, $AF' = 22\cdot2$ $AF = -12\cdot8$. The "round numbers" for PF and PF' adopted in this scheme are sufficiently accurate for most purposes, and are convenient for quick calculations. In a normal eye viewing infinitely distant objects, the retinal point B' will coincide with the second principal focus F'.

A simple scheme, adapted by Emsley from Listing's proposal, takes as the starting point an eye having one refracting surface, of power 60 D; separating air from a medium for which $n = 4/3$. The radius of this equivalent surface is $5\cdot55$ mm.; $f = -16\cdot65$ mm. and $f' = 22\cdot22$ mm. The equivalent surface is taken

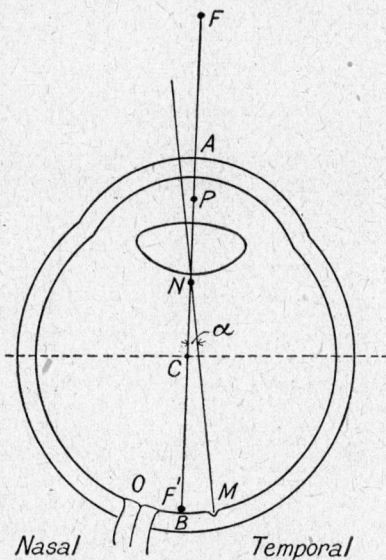

FIG. 87. REDUCED EYE

2 mm. back from the cornea. The total axial length of the Gullstrand reduced eye, quoted in Chapter II, was $24\cdot17$ mm., and the figures just given correspond closely to the focal lengths, etc., there calculated.

The *visual axis* may be considered to pass from the fovea through the nodal point to the fixation point. It makes an angle (the "angle α") of about 5° to 6° with the optic axis; the direction is such that if the right eye "fixes" the centre of a clock face normal to the line of sight, the optic axis is deviated approximately in the four o'clock direction. The visual axis does not, therefore, pass out through the true centre of the cornea, or the anterior pole, but on the nasal side and slightly upwards. The angle between visual and optical axes may vary with the anatomical construction of the eye.

The *pupillary axis* of the eye is the line passing through the centre of curvature of the corneal surface and the centre of the pupil. The *optic axis* is conceived as the central axis of symmetry of the globe, and passing through the centre of the cornea, but it cannot be located with the same experimental certainty as the pupillary axis if the two do not coincide. The angle κ (kappa) is the angle between the pupillary and visual axes.

Another angle denoted by γ (gamma) has been defined as the angle between the optic axis and the *"line of fixation"* joining the centre of rotation of the eyeball to the object viewed by the eye.

Energy and Light. Quantitative Units. When energy radiated in wave-lengths between approximately $\cdot 4\mu$ and $\cdot 7\mu$ reaches the retina of the eye, a sensation of "light" is produced. In the measurement of quantities of light, as distinct from quantities of energy, the valuation must take account of the sensation produced.

The "standard candle" unit (once represented by a candle fulfilling a certain specification, but now fixed by standardized electric lamps) is the unit source of light having unit "luminous intensity"; the quantity of light radiated by this unit source into unit solid angle is the unit quantity of light, called the *Lumen*.

The unit of illumination is the *foot-candle*; it represents the illumination given by unit source at a distance of 1 ft. (Another unit sometimes used is the metre-candle.)

The *brightness* in a given direction of a surface emitting light is the quotient of the luminous intensity (candle-power) measured in that direction, by the area of this surface projected on a plane perpendicular to the direction considered. The practical expression will be in "candles per square foot" or per square metre, etc.

The properties of radiating surfaces are of considerable importance in photometry. A "uniformly diffusing" surface is such that if the candle-power of an element of the surface in the normal direction is J, the candle-power in a direction at an angle θ to the normal will be J cos θ. This property is a close approximation to the truth in the case of most self-luminous smooth surfaces (such as of red-hot or white-hot objects). It is also nearly true of many "matt" reflecting surfaces such as those of blotting-paper, chalk, etc., and it may be shown that if the above condition is fulfilled, the surface will "look" equally bright when viewed from any direction.

The sensation of "brightness" can be differentiated from that of colour, and it is possible to make reasonably consistent photometric matches between white and coloured fields. Hence, it is possible to establish a photometric unit of brightness for any coloured light by comparison with a standard which may approximate to white.

Another unit of brightness sometimes employed is that of a perfectly reflecting and diffusing surface on which the normal illumination is one foot-candle; the brightness of a surface is often given thus in "equivalent foot-candles."

Still another practical unit is the "Lambert," i.e. the brightness of a perfectly diffusing surface which reflects or radiates one lumen per square centimetre. The thousandth part of this unit, the milli-lambert, is more convenient. If the relation between the foot-candle and the milli-lambert be computed (allowing for the change of units of length) it will be found that 1 equivalent foot-candle = 1·076 milli-lamberts = 3·426 candles per square metre = 0·3183 candles per square foot.

The Perception of Light. In order that a sensation of light may be perceived at all, the stimulation of the retina must be of sufficient intensity and duration. The luminous surface employed as the

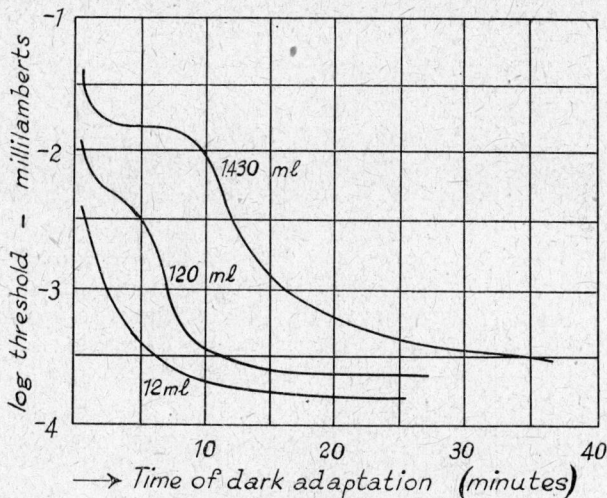

FIG. 88. PROGRESS OF DARK ADAPTATION

visual object may be called the stimulus source. It has been shown by Ricco[3] and others that, with steady illumination for the macular region of the retina, the condition that a luminous sensation may just be perceived is that the total quantity of light (proportional to area of source *times* brightness) must reach a definite value; this law holds for sources subtending angles up to nearly one degree (50′ to be more exact). Hence, the brightness required for a small circular disc would be inversely proportional to the square of the diameter. These experiments were confirmed by the present writer,[4] who also found that for disc objects subtending angles above 1° (up to 4°) the threshold brightness is approximately inversely proportional to the diameter of the disc.

The "threshold brightness" found in such a way with a source of constant size varies, however, with the portion of the retina used and the "state of adaptation" of the eye. It is found that the regions just outside the fovea (the "parafoveal" region) are more

sensitive to light, a maximum sensitiveness being reached at about
5° to 6°. As the eye is kept free from light, or adapted to a lower
degree of illumination, the sensitiveness rapidly increases; the
"threshold" thus falls for upwards of an hour, but most rapidly in
the first few minutes.

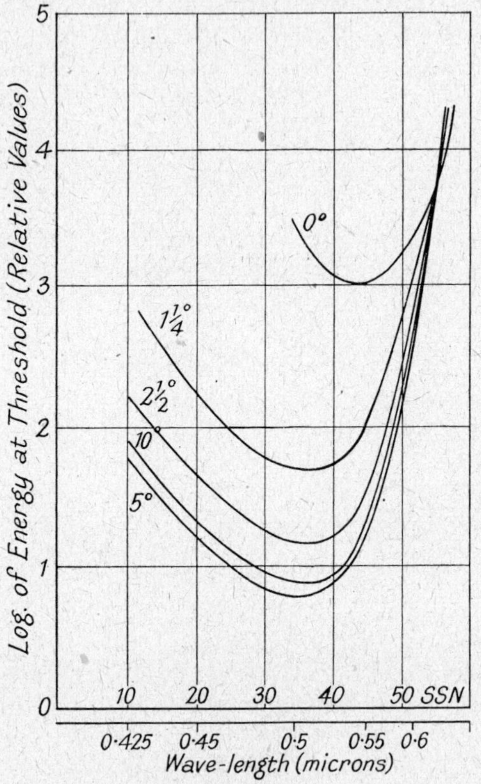

FIG. 89

Fig. 88 shows the variation of the threshold with time as the
"light-adapted" eye is subjected to re-adaptation to darkness.
The curves represent typical results due to Winsor and Clark.[5]
The initial steady states of adaptation are indicated against the
curves. In adapting from a high brightness level, it is considered
that the tendency to a slowing-down of the recovery after about
2 to 8 minutes is characteristic of vision mediated mainly by the
cones, and that the much greater lowering experienced after a longer
time interval is due to the recovery of the rod receptors, which,

according to the "duplicity theory" of von Kries, are supposed to be mainly responsible for vision at low levels of illumination.

It is on this process of adaptation that we depend for the capacity of the eye to function comfortably as it does, over a range of relative brightness values of the order of a million to one.

Fig. 89 shows the variation of the threshold energy with wave-length. The ordinates represent the logarithms of the energy. The experiments were made by Abney and Watson, using parts of the retina at various angular distances from the fovea, and it is interesting to see that the wave-length for minimum threshold energy is shorter away from the fovea. It will be seen that the greatest sensitiveness was found at 5° from the fovea.

As far as foveal vision is concerned, the initial sensation, as the stimulus intensity rises through the threshold value, is said to be "colourless" for all spectral colours except the red. There is thus in general an interval in which no hue is apparent (the "photo-chromatic interval") which is greatest for the shorter wave-lengths.

The Visibility of Radiation. It was mentioned above that it is possible by various means to make photometric matches between white and coloured fields, and thus to establish a photometric scale for light of any colour.

When the eye views a "continuous" spectrum of some suitable source, a band of coloured light is seen which has maximum brightness in some intermediate part and sinking gradually to zero on each side. Physical means enable an observer to measure the relative quantity of energy for different regions of the spectrum, and photometric experiments determine the relative brightness of the corresponding parts of the spectral band.

The "visibility" of the radiation is defined as the quotient of the brightness by the energy, and this is a function of great importance in colorimetry and photometry.

The visibility curve has been determined for a great number of observers with normal vision, and the mean result,[8] now accepted as a standard, is shown in Fig. 90. (See Table, p. 159.)

The results are modified when the visibility curve is re-determined for lower degrees of brightness,[9] say, below 0·1 foot-candle. The maximum of the visibility curve is moved towards the shorter wave-lengths. This means that if a red and a blue field have the same brightness when the intensity is great, the blue will appear the brighter when the energy reaching the eye from each source is reduced in the same proportion for each. This is known as the Purkinje[10] effect.

The chief change occurs between external field brightness of about

1 equivalent foot-candle (when the peak of the visibility curve is at about 0·555μ) and about ·001 foot-candles,* when the peak has moved to about 0·505μ, much farther towards the blue.

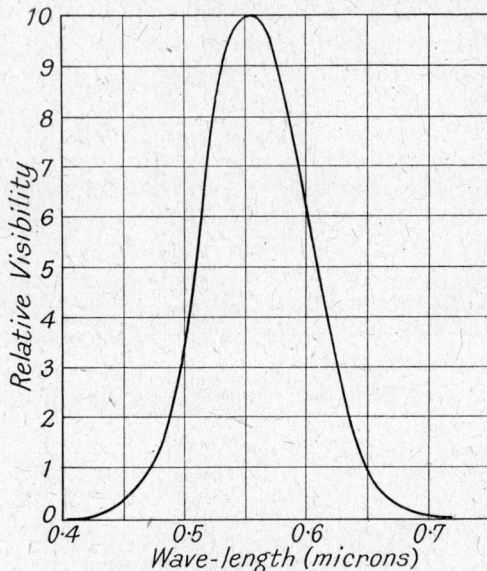

FIG. 90. ADOPTED "VISIBILITY" CURVE FOR NORMAL EYE

It is interesting and suggestive that the human scotopic† luminosity curves for the spectrum corresponds closely to the rates of bleaching effected by the dispersed radiation in visual purple from the frog (Trendelenburg[11]).

* When experiments on retinal sensitiveness are made, the data given should be sufficient to determine the *retinal* illumination. The results are sometimes reduced to those which would be obtained with a standard pupillary aperture of 1 sq. mm. In this case, the unit of retinal illumination is the "photon," i.e. the illumination of the retina produced when the brightness of the object observed is 1 candle per square metre and the aperture of the pupil 1 square millimetre. However, for ordinary purposes, it is useful to know the apparent external brightness levels at which the visual changes occur. White paper illuminated by sunlight may have a brightness of about 1,000 apparent foot-candles or higher. Indoor day illumination may be of the order of 100 foot-candles, while good reading illumination by artificial light may be about 4–10 foot candles. Fair-sized print can be read, although with difficulty, at 0·05 foot-candles. At this stage the pupillary aperture may be of the order of 50 sq. mm. The calculation of the *effective* retinal illumination cannot properly be made without taking into account the Stiles-Crawford effect. See p. 141, and also Vol. II.

† Scotopic = referring to conditions of weak illumination.

TABLE
VISIBILITY OF RADIATION

Wavelength in μ	Visibility	Wavelength in μ	Visibility
0·400	0·0004	0·600	0·631
·41	·0012	·61	·503
·42	·0040	·62	·381
·43	·0116	·63	·265
·44	·023	·64	·175
·45	·038	·65	·107
·46	·060	·66	·061
·47	·091	·67	·032
·48	·139	·68	·017
·49	·208	·69	·0082
·50	·323	·70	·0041
·51	·503	·71	·0021
·52	·710	·72	·00105
·53	·862	·73	·00052
·54	·954	·74	·00025
·55	·995	·75	·00012
·56	·995	·76	·00006
·57	·952		
·58	·870		
·59	·757		

The Perception of Form. Visual Acuity. Taking the distance from the double nodal point to the retina as 15 mm., we find that an intercept of 1 mm. on the retinal surface subtends an angle of 3° 48′, say, 4° approximately, at the nodal point. From the properties of the nodal point we see that an object which subtends about 4° in the field of vision will give a retinal image of length 1 mm. The estimated diameter of a foveal cone, ·002 mm., subtends an angle of ·002/15 radians, or 28 seconds of arc.

The possible fineness of the detail of a retinal image must be dependent, as with any optical system, on the factors, *inter alia*, of the aperture ratio of the system and the wave-length of light, although there may, of course, be reasons why the optical system fails to realize the theoretical possibilities. Assuming an aperture of the pupil of 4 mm. diameter, an average size, and a focal distance of 21 mm., assuming also an optical system without aberration, the radius of the Airy disc may be calculated by formula (321), written in the form

$$h' = 0·61 \frac{\lambda_0}{n'} \frac{f'}{y}$$

When $\lambda_0 = 0·5\mu$, $n' = 1·34$, $y = 2$, and $f' = 21$ mm., we find $h' = ·0025$ mm. This length would subtend an angle of 34″ of arc approximately. A 2 mm. pupil produces a disc with a radius subtending 68″ of arc. Now, from our experience of image formation it is certain that the centres of two independent Airy discs can only approach each other just a little closer than the length of the radius before the possibility of resolution ceases. The presence of moderate spherical aberration does not prevent the formation of an image disc which approximates closely to the Airy disc (in fact, even slightly smaller concentrations may be obtained[12]), but it is necessary to consider both the presence of irregularities in the lens, and the chromatic aberrations of the eye (which is *not* chromatically corrected), in order to judge whether the limiting factor is the wave-nature of light or the defects of the system.

The irregularities of the lens and the edge of the pupil are doubtless the cause of the radiating streaks which are characteristic of the

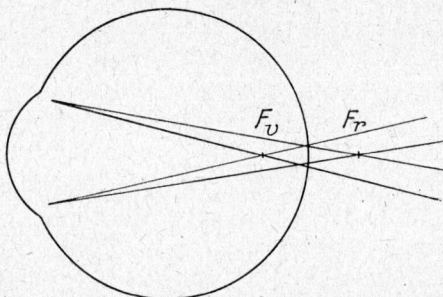

Fig. 91

usual appearance of a star, and it is only necessary to screen a part of the pupil when looking at the bars of a window (with bright sky behind them) to become aware of chromatic effects in the visual image.

It has been calculated that the chromatic aberrations of the eye are practically the same as those of a single spherical refracting surface with the refractive index of water, having a radius of 5·125 mm. (Listing reduced eye.[13]) Assuming the proper refractive indices for water for the extremes of the spectrum, violet and red, the positions of the corresponding foci, given incident parallel light and a 4 mm. pupillary diameter, are separated by approximately 0·43 mm. Assuming that the retina is placed at the position where the patch of confusion of the rays is least (Fig. 91), the diameter of the latter can be calculated to be 0·04 mm., which is twenty times the diameter of a cone. The visible concentration of light is, however, very much more compact. There are the following facts to remember. First, the high relative luminosity of the brightest parts of the spectrum, as compared with the end regions; secondly, that the relatively lower dispersion in the longer wave-lengths draws the red focus closer to that for brightest light than the violet focus, and also that there is a physical depth of focus (see p. 140) which is about 0·04 mm. with a 4 mm. pupil. Although it is only one-tenth of the geometrical axial chromatic aberration, this focal depth or range will include a great deal of the spectrum in the region of brightest light. A concentration comparable with the Airy disc is valid for the depth of focus. Subjectively, the concentration of the image is very great, and the faint purple border which must be present in the retinal image is apparently suppressed in ordinary vision.

It is interesting to note in passing that the length (70μ) of the foveal cones is of the same approximate magnitude as the physical depth of focus (about 40μ). This suggests that the origin of the stimulus of light may occur anywhere in the length of the organ. Stiles and Crawford[14] have shown that light passing through the marginal regions of the lens, and passing somewhat obliquely through the retinal layers, is less efficient in stimulating the sensation of sight than light which passes through the centre of the lens and is incident normally.

Spherical aberration, and irregular aberrations arising, perhaps, from the lack of homogeneity in the crystalline lens, produce some effect on acuity, but any attempt at obtaining measurements of such aberration meets with considerable difficulty.[15] The main method is the subjective examination of "out of focus" images of small sources of light and their variation with accommodation. The presence of such aberration may be responsible for the diminution in acuity which occurs when the diameter of the pupil increases above 5 mm. Lister and Cobb found a practically constant acuity between 5 mm. and 3 mm., but a decrease for diameters above or below this range. The retinal illumination was kept constant in Cobb's experiments.

The work of Gullstrand has indicated that the anterior surface of the cornea is usually to be regarded as aspherical. The spherical aberration of the system is likely to be of the zonal type, in which the axial focus of some intermediate zone falls closest to the lens. The marginal focus may lie a little beyond the zonal focus according to the pupillary aperture.

The considerable magnitude of the zonal errors is illustrated by the 0·7 diopter difference (under-correction) between the paraxial zone and a zone of 2 mm. radius, which is indicated by the observations of Ames and Proctor.

Hooke first pointed out in 1671 that the resolving power of a normal eye for such an object as a double star is just about one minute of arc. Thus, in spite of chromatic and monochromatic aberrations, the optimum acuity of the eye is not far removed from the limits imposed by the nature of light, for pupillary diameters of 3 to 4 mm. The decrease in acuity for smaller pupillary diameters must be ascribed to the lower physical resolving power of the optical system.

It is remarkable that the fineness of the mosaic of retinal receptors in the fovea is of the order required to do justice to the resolving power of the optical system of the eye for two close point objects. It has been, in fact, held that the visual condition for "resolution" must be the presence of a relatively unstimulated cone between two others in which more energy is received. Hence, the closest approach for the centres of two images would correspond, on this supposition, to the double cone diameter, subtending about 56 seconds of arc in the visual field, and this was imagined to set a limit to the possible acuity of vision. Experiments suggest that there are individuals who attain a resolution a little better than this limit. The remarkable facts of contour acuity need further explanation.

The realization of this optimum acuity of vision is, of course, entirely dependent on the capacity of the retinal receiving apparatus. A great deal of experimental work on the influence of *illumination* on visual acuity has been performed, with illumination increasing from very low values. There is a rapid rise in acuity up to about 5 equivalent foot-candles when viewing a black-and-white test chart; the rate of increase then diminishes. Lythgoe and others have shown, however, that, provided the acuity is measured with a large visual field adapted to the same brightness level, it increases continually with brightness up to and beyond 1000 ft. candles. This extreme dependence on brightness makes it very difficult to detect experimentally any considerable difference in acuity when using white or monochromatic light, in spite of the improvement in optical definition on the retina, which must be expected in the latter case. For this reason any attempts to improve acuity by the use of colour filters for spectacles usually fail.

In such work it is necessary to allow time for the *adaptation* of the eye to any given condition of illumination. If an eye adapted to, say, 0·1 foot-candle is suddenly exposed to 1,000 times this brightness, there is at first a sensation of discomfort and glare, with practically a total loss of fine discrimination in vision. This, however, rapidly passes away and the eye begins again to function normally, delicate details of form and contrast coming again into view.

Of course, an overwhelming intensity of light may result in permanent physical damage to the retina; experiments at a very high brightness level are subject to difficulty and uncertainty on this account.

Measures of Acuity. The simplest measure of "acuity" or sharpness of vision from the theoretical standpoint is the minimum angular separation which permits of resolution for two point objects. As mentioned above, the value for the normal eye is approximately 1 minute of arc. Other criteria sometimes discussed are: the minimum dimensions for seeing a line or point, and the *minimum separabile* for lines or sets of lines arranged as a grating.

Another criterion of acuity is the minimum distinguishable change of contour, which concerns the power to distinguish the displacement between two parts of a line, as in reading a vernier where the apparent continuity of vernier and scale divisions must be examined. This is called the "contour" or "vernier" acuity.

The minimum dimensions for a distinguishable line or point are quite indeterminate if the object is self-luminous, and mainly depend on the amount of light radiated by the object, which must simply exceed the threshold of vision valid for the case in question. The object may, however, be exhibited black on a white ground or vice versa, as by using objects of paper. Aubert[16] found that a square of white paper on a black ground could be seen when the side of the square subtended 18 seconds of arc. For a black square on a white ground, the angle had to exceed 35 seconds. With all such objects, the contrast between the parts of the field to be distinguished is of the first importance. A grating may consist of opaque black wires seen against a light ground, thus producing a maximum contrast. The lines may then be distinguished under a much smaller angle than with a grating in which the lines are grey on white.

Irregularities of the eye such as axial astigmatism are likely greatly to affect the measurements of acuity of the unaided eye, according to the nature and position of the object.

The "page of type" naturally employed as a test object in selecting spectacles must have suggested the employment of a graduated series of test letters. Donders suggested to Dyer and Snellen that the 1 minute subtense characteristic of the *minimum separabile* for points should form the basis of construction of test letters, and in 1862 Snellen's optotypes were published. In these a number of rows of letters are printed. Each letter in one row has a diameter subtending 5 minutes of arc at a certain distance (marked on the chart against the row), and the stroke or limb of the letter has a width subtending 1 minute; the spaces between the adjacent limbs of each letter also subtend 1 minute. It is considered that a person of normal vision should be able to read the letters of any row at the distance marked above it. A chart showing figures in a similar way is illustrated in Fig. 92, this chart being one published by Zeiss. Fig. 93 shows the details of the construction of a typical test-chart "letter."

Vision is usually tested at 6 metres or about 20 ft. The types are provided for distances of 2 metres to 60 metres. Imagining that a patient being tested at 6 metres can just read line No. 12 (readable by the normal eye at 12 metres), the visual acuity thus found for the patient would be expressed as $V = \dfrac{6}{12}$.

Tested in this way, many persons of good eyesight will find an "acuity" greater than $\dfrac{6}{6}$.

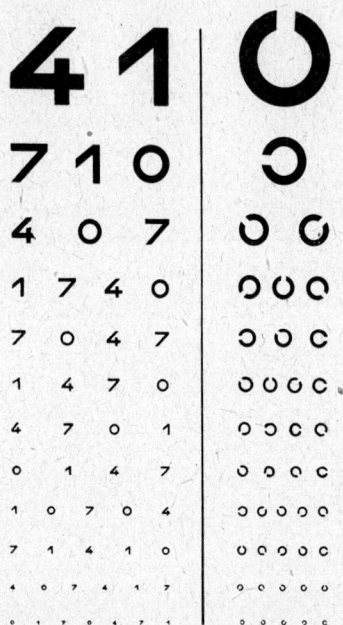

FIG. 92. TEST CHART
Zeiss.

The chart illustrated in Fig. 92 is one-quarter of the size of a normal chart for use at 5 metres. Hence it would be used at 1·25 metres to obtain the correct angular subtense of the letters. Only part of the chart is reproduced; the bottom line is labelled 0·5.

(10 m.)

These types have been arranged by A. Hegner on the basis of data due to Hess, and the originals are published by Messrs. Carl Zeiss.

The conditions of the test need some care in arrangement; the illumination should be adequate, i.e. above 5 foot-candles, and glare must be avoided. No reflection from a "shiny" surface can be tolerated. If the results of tests made at successive times are to be comparable, the illumination must be equal in both cases. Hence, artificial light is usually employed.

It is almost invariably found that some letters are read more easily than others, and, though this may even be a convenience when using the chart for finding the power, etc., of spectacles to correct eyesight, it is confusing when a reliable measure of visual acuity is required. The "broken ring" of Landolt[17] (see Fig. 92) aims at providing a test less variable than that of the letters. The ring has a diametrical subtense of 5 minutes at the standard distance, while the line and the gap have each a subtense of 1 minute. The observer must be able to recognize the position of the gap in any relative position. Although the measurement of acuity by such a "broken ring" or "broken square" may be rendered more difficult

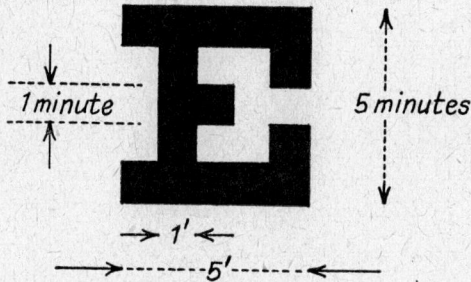

FIG. 93. TO ILLUSTRATE THE PRINCIPLE OF CONSTRUCTION
OF A TYPICAL TEST CHART LETTER
Subtending 5 minutes at the standard distance: the width of the stroke subtends 1 minute.

in the presence of uncorrected visual astigmatism, a greater consistency can be obtained in tests with such standardized objects.

A recent test chart, due to Emsley, avoids the use of open letters like L, T, V, etc., and only retains those in which lines and spaces can be standardized to one-minute angular subtense.

Vernier or Contour Acuity. The investigation of the causes underlying the 1 minute value found for the *minimum separabile* naturally includes the answering of the question: "What is the least retinal image displacement which gives a mental impression of a change of position of the object?" The sense of vision is endowed in the language of physiology, with a specially sensitive "local sign."

The question of the space image in binocular vision and the general question of the perception of "direction" are too complex to be discussed at present, but the perception of relative position is very important; it is much more delicate than the resolving power of the eye for close double images would seem to suggest.

Wülfing[18] and many others have examined the contour or vernier acuity of the eye in experiments in which human subjects of normal vision are asked to place the separated parts of a line (Fig. 94) in exact alignment. The lines may be drawn on two cards, one movable relatively to the other along the line of separation. Such experiments show that the minimum separation detectable by unaided vision is as low as 10–12 seconds of arc, and with practice the lines can be adjusted by many persons within a probable error perhaps as small as 3 or 4 seconds.

The experiments of Langlands[19] show that there is distinct ability to make a good judgment of relative position with similar objects, even with flash illuminations of extremely short duration (Spark $< 10^{-3}$ second), but the accuracy improves as the duration of the illumination rises above about $\frac{1}{10}$th second. These experiments were carried out on "binocular acuity" depending on the perception of depth through the stereoscopic sense.

No finally satisfactory explanation of the extraordinarily great acuity of the human eye in observations of this type has yet been

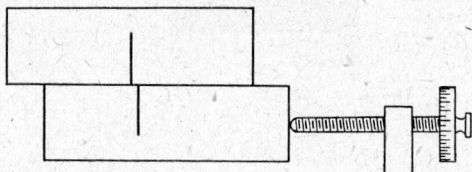

FIG. 94. DIAGRAM OF APPARATUS FOR INVESTIGATING CONTOUR ACUITY

suggested. One of the best-known theories was advanced by Hering, and the class of argument which he put forward is illustrated by Fig. 95. In (a) we see the retinal mosaic on which an imaginary image with a broken line of separation between light and dark portions is shown. It is assumed that any one cone or row of cones has its own "local sign," i.e. the passage of stimulation from one cone or row of cones to another causes a definite apparent displacement of the image. In the upper portion the row n of the cones is stimulated, but in the lower portion no cone in this row receives light. Hence, a break in the line would be perceived, even though the actual discontinuity might be small in comparison with the diameter of a cone. In part (b) the image has been slightly shifted and no discontinuity would be perceived; hence, we see why slight retinal movements might be helpful in discrimination; Hering's discussion covered other cases. A review of modern ideas of the theory is given by Walls.[20]

The experiments of Hartridge,[21] however, would indicate that a very high order of accuracy in "coincidence" settings of the above type is possible not only when the lines (the parts of which are to be brought into alignment) are sharp or bounded by sharp edges, but also when they are very diffuse as they must be in fact owing to the physical spreading of the image. Hartridge conducted his experiments with apparatus which presented a spectrum divided into two parts by a line of separation perpendicular to the spectrum lines themselves; the diffuse lines were, actually, absorption bands. The setting consisted in making a consistent alignment of the two halves of a "band." The question of acuity of vision as regards form is therefore intimately connected with the capacity of the retina to register fine differences of stimulation or simultaneous contrast between contiguous regions, and is probably connected

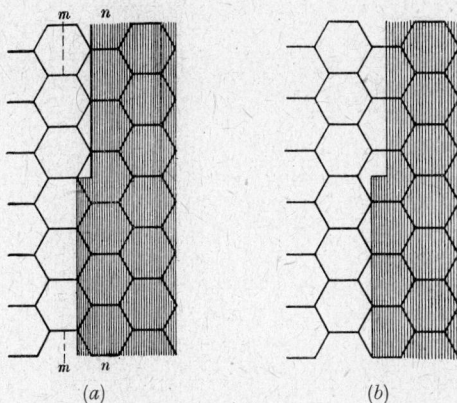

FIG. 95. TO ILLUSTRATE HERING'S THEORY OF THE RETINA

with "fine-grained" effects of induction and inhibition. Many of the phenomena both of acuity and contrast perception can be accounted for by theories[27] of photochemical action in the retina.

Perception of Movement. A similar delicacy exists in the perception of the minimum displacement in the perception of movement. Such movements may be slow, regular movements to and fro, of time-period about $\frac{1}{2}$ second. Volkman,[22] Stern,[23] and others have made measurements which indicate, as an average, a possibility of recognition of a displacement of 10 seconds of arc or even less. Such conditions assume the presence of a fixed reference object in the field.

When the movement is continuous, the minimum angular velocity in the visual field which allows of a perception of movement is 1 to 2 minutes of arc per second.

Peripheral Vision. The power of the visual apparatus to impart the mental impression of a sharply-defined "point" image rapidly diminishes as the image moves away from the fovea, and the power to discriminate the independence of two close images rapidly falls. Fig. 96 shows the visual acuity and its variation at various angles in the visual field (Wertheim[24]); at 5° from the fovea it falls to one-third of the maximum. Similarly, the power of the retina to register "displacement" or "movement" diminishes from the fovea outwards, as shown by Ruppert.[25] The results of his experiment showed, however, that the acuity for separation diminishes relatively more

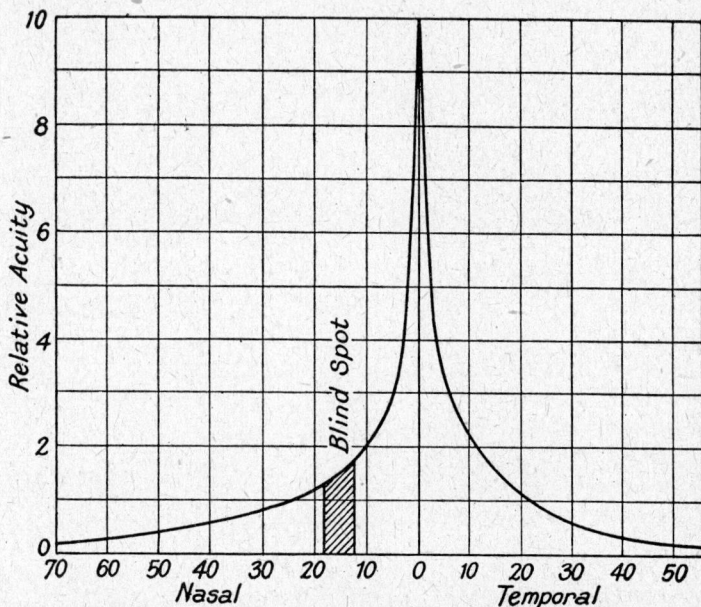

FIG. 96. VARIATION OF ACUITY WITH ANGULAR DISTANCE FROM THE FOVEA

rapidly than the sensitiveness to movement. Sensitiveness to movement is equivalent to a high sensitiveness to changes of illumination; the sensitiveness to flicker in the dark-adapted eye is greater in the outer regions of the retina than at the centre. In some respects, the retinal periphery must be regarded as specially adapted for the perception of movement. The lack of discrimination of form away from the fovea can be associated with the arborization of the nerve fibres referred to above, through which several rods and cones may transmit impulses to a single bi-polar cell, while several bi-polar cells may connect to a single ganglion cell. Hence, two separated images on the retina may give rise to a single visual impression.

Perception of Contrast. It is not difficult to present to the eye a photometric field of two equal portions in which the relative "brightness" can be quantitatively adjusted. If the brightness of one part is B and the other B + dB, where dB is the least *perceptible* difference in brightness, then the fraction

$$d\text{B}/\text{B}$$

(often called the "Fechner fraction") can be measured under various conditions. In experiments on direct vision, the size of the matching field is restricted to 2°, so that the image may fall within the area

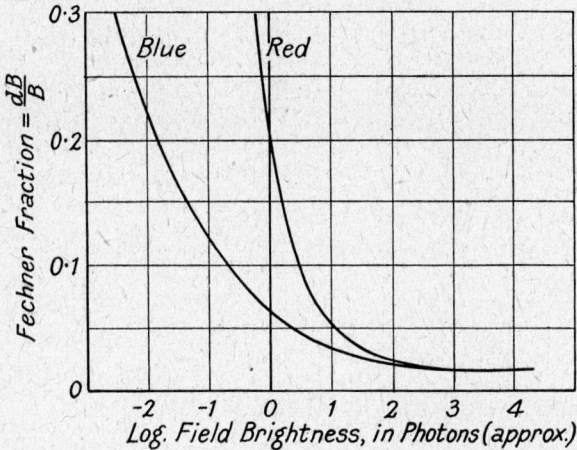

FIG. 97

of the retina which is more or less uniformly pigmented. Measurements of this type have been made by König and Brodhun,[26] Hecht,[27] and others, and tables of their results show that for monochromatic or white stimuli the value of the fraction is approximately uniform over a wide range of absolute brightnesses corresponding to those encountered in ordinary vision, but its value rises greatly when the retinal illumination sinks below 30 photons or thereabouts (external field brightness of the order of one-fifth equivalent foot-candles).

König and Brodhun's results for orange-red (0·605μ) and violet (0·43μ) are shown in Fig. 97. There is some little doubt as to the effective value of the unit of brightness employed,* but it will be seen that the Fechner fraction is plotted as ordinate against the logarithm of the field brightness. The eye is more sensitive to

* König and Brodhun used an "artificial pupil" for observation, so that the values of the field brightness are truly proportional to the retinal illumination.

contrast changes in the shorter wave-length regions for equal apparent field-brightness under conditions of low illumination.

Photometric Scales. Addition of Luminosities. Given monochromatic light of a single wave-length, the photometric measure of quantity of light is proportional to the energy. Let e_1, e_2, e_3, etc., be the relative energy of the monochromatic components of a mixed radiation, and v_1, v_2, v_3, their visibility coefficients, then the photometric "quantity of light" will be proportional to

$$e_1v_1 + e_2v_2 + e_3v_3 = F, \text{ say.}$$

The additive property of the "luminosities," e_1v_1, e_2v_2, etc., is a very important one; it has been established by the work of Abney and Ives. Luminosity, in fact, appears as an experience, regarding any stimulus, of a unique and separable character.

If now the relative energy of all the components is increased in the same ratio, K, say, the quantity of light in the photometric sense will now be

$$K(e_1v_1 + e_2v_2 + e_3v_3) = KF.$$

If the *relative* amounts of energy of the components in the mixed radiation vary, the quantity of *light* will no longer be proportional to the total energy. The photometric scale is only related to the energy scale for light of constant composition.

Weber's "law" states that the least perceptible increase of the stimulation of a sensation is proportional to the intensity of the original stimulus. Mathematically—

$$d\mathrm{I}/\mathrm{I} = \text{constant.}$$

König and Brodhun's results have shown how far this law is obeyed.

If it may be assumed that the just perceptible steps, ds, of sensation are equal steps in the quantity of the sensation (Fechner[28]), then (at least over wide ranges of intensity)

$$ds = K\frac{d\mathrm{I}}{\mathrm{I}}$$

and in order to obtain a measure of the increase of sensation resulting from an increase of the stimulus from I_o to I, we integrate, thus obtaining

$$s - s_o = K \log\left(\frac{\mathrm{I}}{\mathrm{I}_o}\right)$$

for the range in which K may be considered constant.

It is to some degree a matter of speculation as to whether this represents a true scale of sensation, but there is no doubt that the sensation scale of brightness is very different from the practical photometric scale. To illustrate this, it is possible to prepare a series of grey papers which have reflection coefficients increasing in arithmetic progression from 0·1 to 0·9, say. The higher steps, i.e. between 0·7 and 0·8, and 0·8 and 0·9, appear exceedingly small differences of contrast as compared with the steps 0·1 to 0·2, 0·2 and 0·3. On the other hand, a series with the reflection coefficients increasing in geometric progression appears to possess practically equal steps of contrast.

Colour Vision. The briefest summary of a few outstanding phenomena of colour vision must suffice for the present purpose. Colour is a sensation. The colour variables are those of hue, brightness, and saturation. Hue is a property of colour which varies with changes in the frequency of the stimulating light, but colours may retain the same hue while containing a greater or less admixture of white. The smaller the white constituent, the greater the "saturation."

Now we may illuminate one side of a photometric field by any colour we please, and the other by an *additive* mixture of three spectral colours, such as red, green, and blue, in their pure condition. (An "additive" mixture would be secured, in one way, if the same screen were illuminated by red, green, and blue lanterns.) Then it is a most remarkable fact that by a variation of the relative proportions of these three "primaries" in the mixture, we can secure all possible changes of hue, and we can further match most colours which can be put into the other field (with the exception of certain ranges of the most highly-saturated colours). If the brightness of the test colour and of the three primaries can be varied in known numerical proportions, then the amount of the primaries necessary to match any test colour can be found. A "colour equation" results—

$$mC = \alpha R + \beta G + \gamma B$$

where m is the amount of the test colour C, and α, β, γ, are the amounts of red, green, and blue respectively, measured on some convenient scale established for each colour on a photometric basis. One possible scale is that of "luminosity," see p. 170. A suitable adjustment of the primaries enables us to match a definite amount of a *white* test colour.

Let it be supposed that we are now given a colour C_1, which is too saturated to be matched by a mixture of the three primaries alone. Then we can secure a match in one of two ways: either by adding a small amount of one of the primaries to it, so that its saturation is reduced and we obtain a match represented by

$$m_1C_1 + \beta_1 G = \alpha_1 R + \gamma_1 B,$$

or we can reduce the saturation of the test colour by mixing it with white, thus getting an equation of the type

$$m_2C_1 + n_2W = \alpha_2R + \beta_2G + \gamma_2B$$

This can be combined with the equation for white

$$n_2W = \alpha_3R + \beta_3G + \gamma_3B$$

so that in either case we can obtain an *equation* representing the test colour, no matter what its saturation.

(The primaries may be, theoretically, any three different colours, but in order directly to match a wide range of colours, it is necessary to have them as pure or fully saturated as possible, and spaced as far as possible from each other in the spectrum; thus red, green, and blue, or red, green, and violet, are usually selected.)

These remarkable experimental facts led Thomas Young[29] to suggest that a visual colour sensation was, in general, a mixture of three primary sensations. This is an enormous simplification of the theory of colour vision. Springing directly from the experimental work of Newton and expressed thus by Young, the question was taken up and put on a sound experimental and theoretical basis by Maxwell and Helmholtz. In recent years a tri-chromatic system has been adopted as the basis of an adequate international system[30] of colour specification and measurement.

While there must be at least three "primary" sensations, there may be more; but the weight of evidence derived from subjective observation still points to three. Modern work based on the trichromatic theory is described by W. D. Wright.[31]

Whether or not the "trichromatic" theory is in harmony with all the phenomena of colour vision is still undecided. The "hue" sense must be regarded as a part only of the visual process. Moreover, no satisfactory anatomical evidence of any triply differentiated structure of the retinal or cortical visual apparatus has yet been adduced; thus the relative parts played by this trichromatic apparatus (supposing its existence in any form) and by the remainder of the visual equipment are hard to differentiate. In recent years, R. Granit[32] has developed a technique whereby the electrical response of individual retinal receptors to the various wave-lengths of the spectrum can be investigated. He claims to distinguish *more* than three specific types.

Colour Blindness. Various individuals differ in the amounts of the three primaries, red, green, and blue, which they require to effect colour matches, especially in the blue end of the spectrum, and many such variations are attributable to variations in the amount of macular pigmentation. Others are found, however, who can match any spectral hue with two primaries only, red and blue, or green and blue. Such often cannot distinguish the hues of red and green, and they may sometimes be blind to some range at the extreme red end of the spectrum. They are called "dichromats." Other individuals, again, are totally unable to perceive any "hue," their sensations being of relative brightness and darkness only. Their "spectral luminosity" measurements correspond to those effected in normal vision under scotopic conditions. Recent work on colour blindness ([31]) is also described by W. D. Wright.

Field of Vision for Colours. Under normal conditions for normal sight, the power of distinguishing hue is confined to certain regions of the retina surrounding the fovea. Green may be indistinguishable beyond a zone from 20° to 30° from the centre, but blue and red may have larger fields. With increased intensities, however, the limits of the hue perceiving areas are greatly extended.

König noticed that the colour vision in the fovea itself is dichromatic, a discovery which was often overlooked, but which has been confirmed and extended by recent experiments. The later work is associated with renewed research in the physiology of the retinal receptors.

Time Relations in Vision. When a dark adapted retina is suddenly stimulated by exposure of the eye to a field of steady brightness, the sensation rapidly rises to a maximum which is the sooner reached the greater the intensity of the stimulus. The sensation thereafter sinks somewhat until a fairly steady state is reached for a time at least. (Long-continued stimulation of the retina may result in a state of abnormal visual action, in which the field of vision disappears.) The chief investigators have been Exner,[33] Broca and Sulzer, and Schouten.[34] The main features of the results of Broca and Sulzer are indicated in Fig. 98, from which it will be seen that the blue stimulus causes a sharp rise of sensation to a maximum not shown in the diagram, but which is at least five times the final value. The action is least marked with the green stimulus. The maximum is reached in under one-seventh of a second. Confirmatory evidence has recently been derived from electrical measurements of nerve impulse records by Hartline and Graham, and others.

On the other hand, the sensation does not immediately disappear when the stimulus is removed, but takes a finite time to sink below the limit of perception.

The effect of the finite rates of growth and decay of sensation when the stimulus is suddenly applied or removed, enables the eye to "integrate" the brightness of a rapidly-varying source, provided that the total cycle of variation is regular and of sufficiently great frequency. If I is the apparent photometric brightness and t the total period of the complete cycle, while i is the actual photometric brightness,

$$I t = \int_o^t i dt$$

Put into words, the principle states that the impression produced by a light undergoing rapid regular periodic variations of sufficiently

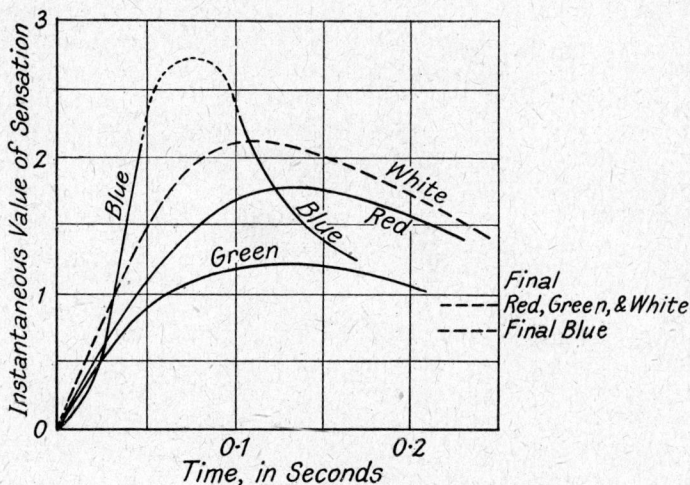

FIG. 98

great frequency, is as if the light emitted during each period were distributed uniformly throughout the duration of the period.

This law, which rests on the work of Talbot[35] and Plateau,[36] and has been abundantly verified by Abney and others, shows that the apparent intensity of light transmitted by a sector disc (Fig. 99) in rapid rotation is proportional to the angular opening.* Such a disc transmits a "flickering" light; the flicker, however, is only seen at low frequencies. Porter[37] and Ives[38] showed that for various monochromatic lights the critical frequency at which flicker disappears is a linear function of the logarithm of the photometric brightness of the field. It is interesting that the function may suddenly change at certain brightness levels, although remaining linear.

* The use of too small an angular opening for the sector should be avoided, as it may lead to inaccuracy.

In the flicker photometer, advantage is taken of the fact that "flicker" occurs at slow speeds of alternation between any two successions of brightness or colour in the field. However, even when the alternate fields differ in hue, the critical frequency of flicker is a minimum when their apparent photometric brightness is equal. Hence, by adopting a suitable frequency, the flicker may be made to disappear by adjusting the brightness of one of the pair.

FIG. 99. ADJUSTABLE SECTOR

Spatial Induction. The retina is by no means a system of independent receptors, for stimulation of one area may profoundly affect the sensitiveness and the action of another part. The most familiar examples of such actions are found in the familiar phenomena of simultaneous contrast both in brightness and colour. A succession of uniform strips of grey, increasing in darkness from one to the other, give the impression of "flutings" owing to the subjective accentuation of contrast at each boundary. The surprising effects of colour contrast cannot be discussed here.

The retina seems to function best in general when the average brightness level of the whole is near that of the immediate field under observation. Thus Jones[39] found that a kinema picture, a relatively small field surrounded ordinarily by complete darkness, can be better seen if a certain amount of light reaches the periphery of the field. Cobb[40] has investigated the effects on foveal vision produced

by stimulation of the peripheral parts of the retina, and has shown
that with intensities of the surround field increasing from "darkness" the contrast sensitivity is at first improved, but becomes
impaired as the surround intensity rises above that of the central
field. Similar experiments by Emerson and Martin[41] investigated
these phenomena with monochromatic light. The first increase of
sensitiveness (giving a lower contrast "limen") is followed by a
decrease, but more quickly in the longer wave-lengths. The experiments were made at wave-lengths 0.68, 0.67, 0.56, and 0.48μ. In
the case of 0.48μ, the brightness of the surround may be increased
to nearly three times that of the central field before a decrease of
sensitiveness (as compared with the sensitiveness for an entirely
dark surround) manifests itself.

Experiments of this kind, and direct trials with instruments,
point to the great importance of providing large fields of view in
observational instruments, such as "night glasses" intended for
use under conditions of extremely low illumination. On the other
hand, they suggest that under some circumstances it may be desir-
able to be able to reduce the size of the field.

The phenomenon of "glare" is sufficiently common to be familiar
to all. Many attempts have been made to study it systematically.
Nutting, Blanchard, and Reeves conducted experiments in which
the retina was sensitized to a definite field brightness before flashing
on a much brighter field. The intensity of the bright field was
increased by trial until it appeared uncomfortably bright when first
seen. The three observers agreed very well in their estimates, and
found that for a brightness F of the sensitizing field the lower limit
of "glare" G is represented by the equation

$$G = 1,700 \ F^{0.32}$$

In addition to work involving such introspective estimations as
the above, the effect of a "glaring" stimulus in the field can be
studied in relation to the acuity of vision for form and contrast in
other parts of the field. A review of such work has been given by
Stiles.[42]

The question has been studied in relation to the size of the field
of view of observational instruments by the writer with T. C.
Richards.[43] It was found that in the case of night glasses the largest
possible visual field is almost invariably required for best effects
in very weak illumination. Under these conditions, a small object
not discernible against the background in the centre of a small field
may come into view easily when the size of the stimulated retinal
area is increased. On the other hand, it is frequently the case that

the object observed in the central part of the visual field of a telescope in daylight is darker than its bright surroundings. Such conditions were studied by statistical methods of observation, and it has been shown that an improvement in the speed and accuracy of observation could then be obtained by a diminution in the size of the field, which removes the excessive stimulation of the peripheral regions of the retina.

A partial explanation of these various effects is to be found in the variation of the "adaptation level" of the retina due to the various stimuli present in the visual field. Thus, with the telescope field bright in the peripheral portions and dark in the centre, the adaptation level of the central region of the retina is too high and the comparatively weak central stimulus fails to secure the necessary sensitiveness; on the other hand, with a bright central field in surrounding darkness there may be some effect of "glare," because the adaptation level is too low, due to the relatively unstimulated peripheral portions of the retina. However, the relative "adaptation level" is not the only factor in the full explanation of these effects, especially those concerned with feeble stimuli; Nutting[44] has shown, for example, that the increase in size of a weak sensitizing field actually lowers the foveal threshold. This evidently involves an action of another type which might, following the one theory, be concerned with the stimulation of the output of visual purple, effecting a higher sensitization. According to Edridge Green, the rods of the retina are solely concerned with the production of visual purple, which acts as the photo-sensitive substance when diffused among the cones; the latter organs pick up the visual impulse. This, however, is in opposition to the duplicity theory of von Kries.

An important investigation on the effects of various factors, including contrast, on visual thresholds, and its implication in regard to visual instruments, is due to Arnulf. (See a paper by Fabry.[45])

After-images or Successive Induction. The time relations in vision hitherto mentioned have included the rate of adaptation to darkness and the rate of growth of sensation subsequent to the commencement of stimulation. Certain phenomena of some importance occur on the removal of a stimulation. If the retina, moderately dark adapted, is exposed for, say, 1 second to stimulation by a bright field, the immediate impression is followed by an image resembling the original in colour and form. If the original stimulus is strong, the hue may change through red, green, and blue phases, even if the original was white. Meanwhile the image gradually loses its form. Such changes have been described by MacDougall[46] and others. The above are the phenomena of the "positive" after-image.

If the eye is turned to a grey field immediately after the first short stimulation, a "negative" after-image is observed which is at first of a hue complementary to the original stimulus. With white stimuli, coloured negative after-images are observed which again exhibit various phases of hue.

Physical Character of Visual Process. The aim in much recent research on vision has been to progress beyond the empirical and descriptive character of the earlier work.

The activity of any single nerve fibre is associated with the occurrence of electrical action currents, each of fixed amount and very short duration (perhaps about 0·0015 sec.). An increase in the stimulation increases the *frequency* of these pulses, but not their intensity; the nerve is either active or inactive ("all or none principle"). This has been shown to be true for the nerve currents of the visual nerve by Adrian[47] and many followers.

The occurrence of the sensation of light must depend on the initial absorption of energy (probably by the visual purple or other medium in the retina, and a consequent photo-electric emission from the molecules of the absorber). Any "pulse," once started along any nerve fibre path, must find a free channel to a higher level in the nervous system of the visual process, and the mutual arborization above and below the synaptic layers may offer alternative pathways, as well as the possibility of collecting "pulses" from a group of receptors into one ganglion cell. The greater the number of pulses, the greater the chance that a higher number will find free channels; these are not necessarily available, for pulses may be blocked or "inhibited" at some synapsis for a variety of reasons.

Both these layers have features in common with the structures of the central nervous system, of which they may be considered outlying parts. Duke Elder says: "We must regard one or both of the synaptic layers as a sheet of nervous material capable of acting as a whole and capable of being reciprocally influenced."

The quantum-like activity of the conducting paths may be affected by temporary physiological causes, as well as by the activity of neighbouring channels; this would be connected with many of the phenomena of spatial induction; sensation is not a fixed function of the stimulation. For such reasons, photometric matches are likely to be distributed, according to an approximately Gaussian error curve $\{y = \exp(-ax^2)\}$, about some level near that of equality; and the standard deviation is likely to vary with the physical condition of the observer.

In the case of the determination of visual thresholds, it is thought by some that the quantum nature of light (see p. 234) is responsible for the greater part of the experimental scatter of results. The minimum green light energy, which must enter the eye to stimulate the sensation of vision, is about 50 quanta, of which it is estimated that only about one-tenth can be absorbed by the visual purple. According to quantum theory, any apparatus designed (on strict photometric principles) to flash N light quanta to the retina would, in fact, do so only as an average number; individual flashes would contribute numbers of quanta varying about N with a standard deviation of $\sqrt{N}$. Thus, if N quanta represents the true threshold, successive single flashes might fail to give a sensation as many times as they succeed. If the experimental curve representing the percentage of successful stimulations against the nominal amount of the energy be plotted, the threshold can be regarded as the energy for which 50 per cent of successes are recorded. The curve rises very slowly at first; then more steeply; eventually the slope diminishes until the curve tends to become horizontal. It is like a very open "S," and resembles the "characteristic curve" of density against energy in photographic action. On such lines Hecht, Shlaer, and Pirenne[48] account for the scatter of observations on the visual parafoveal threshold, since it would be expected from the scatter of the quantum numbers about the number supposed to be delivered. Other workers have criticized the theory as not allowing for the possible physiological scatter.

Statistical averages must clearly enter into the discussion of many other quantitative aspects of vision. For example, the area summation in threshold observations (Ricco[3]) is probably due mainly to retinal interaction. However, suppose that interaction were absent, and that a group of stimuli equal in area and brightness act on the retina, the chance p of detecting one of them being independent of the presence or absence of the others. Then, if n stimuli act together, the chance of *missing* any one of them is $(1 - p)$, and, further, the chance of missing all of them is $(1 - p)^n$. So thus the chance of *not missing* all of them is $1 - (1 - p)^n$. Hence, the larger the group of patches, the greater the probability that at least *some* visual sensation will result. Such considerations probably enter into the lowering of the threshold when the total subtense of the stimulated area of the retina exceeds about one degree.

The phenomena of visual acuity and its variation with brightness have received much thought. Low visual acuity at threshold levels is characteristic of rod vision with extensive retinal interaction. As the intensity increases, the cone vision of the fovea becomes possible, but the curve of variation of visual acuity tends to follow an "S" shape similar to the form previously discussed.

A theory advanced by Hecht supposes that the retina contains a population of cones with varying thresholds, so that as more and more come into action with increasing stimulation by light, the effective retinal mosaic interval becomes smaller and smaller. When the complexity of the visual process is remembered, however, alternative possibilities will present themselves.

A more recent theory of intensity discrimination, also due to Hecht, supposes that the sensitive substance in the retina is broken down by photo-chemical action to form certain products which can be recombined by natural processes. Therefore under steady conditions a balance is set up which can, however, be upset by any change $\triangle I$ in the illumination I. In order that the change may be perceived by the brain, the rate of change of concentration of the photo-products on the addition $\triangle I$ must, according to the theory, be independent of the value of I.

This theory is capable of explaining many of the phenomena of contrast discrimination, and acuity, when it is supposed that there is a constant involuntary movement of the retinal image over the sensitive elements. However, the definition of the optical system, and the retinal structure, have important effects on acuity which have not yet finally been brought into their true relation with the above ideas.

Polyak,[49] in his recent treatise on *The Retina*, blames physiologists for the inadequacy of existing studies, and has himself carried out much fresh investigation. The results of some of his measurements have been used in revising this chapter.

A useful review of contemporary research is due to Stiles.[50]

REFERENCES

1. Blanchard: *Phys. Rev.*, 11, 81 (1918).
2. Fincham: *Trans. Opt. Soc.* XXX (1928–29).
3. Ricco: *Ann. di. Ottal.*, VI (1897).
4. Martin: Department of Scientific and Industrial Research, *Bulletin No.* 3.
5. Winsor and Clark: *Nat. Acad. Sci.*, 22 (1936).
6. Abney and Watson: *Phil. Trans. Roy. Soc. A.*, 216, 91 (1915).
7. Abney: *Researches in Colour Vision*, Chapter XII.
8. *Receuil des Travaux de la Commission Internationale de l'Eclairage*, 6, 348 (1924).
9. König: *Gesammelte Abh. zur Physiol. Optik*, p. 144 (Leipzig, 1903).
10. Purkinje: *Magazin f. d. gesammte Heilkunde, Berlin*, 20, 199 (1825).
11. Trendelenburg: *Centralbl. f. Physiol.*, XVII (1904).
12. Conrady: *Monthly Notices, R.A.S.*, June, 1919.
13. Helmholtz: *Physiol. Optics.*, English translation, Vol. I, p. 176.
14. Stiles and Crawford: *Proc. Roy. Soc. B.*, 122 (1937).

15. Ames and Proctor: *Jour. Opt. Soc. Amer.*, 5, 22 (1921).
16. Aubert: *Physiologie der Netzhaut*, Breslau, 1865.
17. Landolt, E.: *Ann. d'Ocul*, 75, 207 (1876).
18. Wülfing: *Zeit. f. Biol.*, XXIX, 189 (1892).
19. Langlands: Medical Research Council, Special Report Series, No. 133.
20. Walls: *Jour. Opt. Soc. Amer.*, 33, 487 (1943).
21. Hartridge: *Phil. Mag.* XLVI 49 (1923).
22. Volkman: *Physiol. Untersuchungen im Gebiete der Optik* (Leipzig), 1863.
23. Stern: *Zeit. f. Psychol.*, VII, 321 (1894).
24. Wertheim: *Zeit. f. Psychol.*, VII, 177 (1894).
25. Ruppert: *Zeit. f. Sinnesphysiol.*, XLII, 409 (1908).
26. König and Brodhun: *Sitz. Akad. Berlin*, July 26, 1888.
27. Hecht, Peskin, and Patt: *Jour. Gen. Physiol.*, 22, 7 (1938).
28. Fechner: *Leipzig Berichte*, 4, 455 (1859).
29. Young: *Phil. Trans.*, 92, 12 (1802).
30. Smith and Guild: *Trans. Opt. Soc.*, 33, 73 (1931–32).
31. W. D. Wright: *Investigations in Colour Vision* (Kimpton, London, 1946).
32. R. Granit: *Nature*, 151, 11 (1943).
33. Exner: *Sitz. d. Wiener Akad.*, LVIII, 2, 601 (1868).
34. Schouten: *Visuelle meeting van Adaptatie*, Schoutens & Jens, Utrecht, 1937.
35. Talbot: *Phil. Mag.* 5, 327 (1834).
36. Plateau: *Acad. Roy. des Sciences, Brussels, Bull.* 2, 52 (1835).
37. Porter: *Proc. Roy. Soc.*, 63, 347 (1898).
38. Ives: *Phil. Mag.*, 24, 352 (1912).
39. Jones: *Comm. No.* 135, Research Lab., Eastman Kodak Co.
40. Cobb: *Jour. Exp. Psychol.*, 1, 419, 540 (1916).
41. Emerson and Martin: *Proc. Roy. Soc. A.*, 108, 483 (1925).
42. Stiles: *Reports on Progress, Physical Soc.*, III, 310 (1936).
43. Martin and Richards: *Trans. Opt. Soc.*, 30, 22 (1928–29).
44. Nutting: *Trans. Ill. Eng. Soc. Amer.*, XI, 4 (1916).
45. Fabry, *Proc. Phys. Soc.*, 48, 747 (1936).
46. McDougall: *X.N.S.*, 235, (1901).
47. Adrian: *Jour. Physiol.*, 61, 465 (1926).
48. Hecht, Schlaer, Pirenne: *J. Gen. Physiol.* 25, 819 (1942).
49. Polyak: *The Retina*, University of Chicago (1941).
50. Stiles: *Proc. Phys. Soc.*, 56, 356 (1944).

CHAPTER VI

PHYSICAL OPTICS

Polarization. The early beginnings of the wave-theory of light were developed with the idea that the displacements or vibrations in the medium were performed in the direction of propagation, in a manner analogous to the case of sound waves in air. The explanation of the phenomena of polarization and double refraction, some of which are dealt with below, can only be given satisfactorily under the assumption that the displacements, whatever their nature, are transverse, or perpendicular to the direction of propagation.

For the systematic and theoretical discussion of this subject, reference must be made to works on physical optics. The present

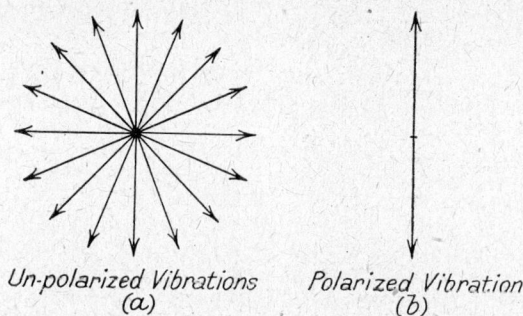

Un-polarized Vibrations　　Polarized Vibration
(a)　　　　　　　　　　(b)

FIG. 100

account will be confined to a recapitulation of the main facts of importance in applied optics.

The vibrations in ordinary unpolarized light take place in all directions perpendicular to the direction of propagation. Figs. 100 (a) and 100 (b) suggest the vibration directions in (a) ordinary unpolarized light, (b) plane polarized light, the direction of propagation being perpendicular to the plane of the paper. In the case of ordinary light, the intensity of the components is constant for all directions of vibration, but in "plane polarized" light all the displacements are parallel to one direction.

The simplest way of producing plane polarized light is by oblique reflection at a plane surface of a refracting medium, such as glass or water. The angle of incidence has to bear a certain relation to the refractive index of the medium, which follows from the general equations governing the reflection coefficients of polarized light at a plane reflecting surface.

Imagine a "parallel" beam of polarized light to be incident at an angle i on a plane reflecting surface, and let the angle of refraction be i'. The refractive indices above and below the surface are unity and n' respectively. Let it be supposed that the vibrations of the light take place at right angles to the plane containing any ray and the normal to the surface.*

The development of the electro-magnetic theory has taught us that the "vibration direction" just mentioned may be regarded as that of the electric forces in the wave-front. (The electric forces are accompanied by corresponding magnetic forces perpendicular both to the electric forces and to the direction of propagation, but these need not be considered in the simple account to be introduced here.)

Then, for light polarized in the above sense, the ratio of the amplitude A_1' in the reflected light to the amplitude of the incident light A_1 is given by

$$A_1' = - A_1 \frac{\sin (i - i')}{\sin (i + i')} \qquad . \qquad . \qquad . \quad (601)$$

The corresponding equation for the *intensity* of the reflected light I_1', as compared with the incident, is

$$I_1' = I_1 \frac{\sin^2 (i - i')}{\sin^2 (i + i')} \qquad . \qquad . \qquad . \quad (602)$$

When the light is so polarized that its vibration directions are in the plane of incidence containing a ray and the normal, then the formulae are

$$A_2' = - A_2 \frac{\tan (i - i')}{\tan (i + i')} \qquad . \qquad . \qquad . \quad (603)$$

$$I_2' = I_2 \frac{\tan^2 (i - i')}{\tan^2 (i + i')} \qquad . \qquad . \qquad . \quad (604)$$

When ordinary light is reflected, it is regarded as containing components which are not polarized in either of the above ways, but we may regard any arbitrary displacement OA, Fig. 101, as being the resultant of two displacements OB and OC in directions at right angles. An argument of this kind leads to the assumption that the incident unpolarized light can be regarded as the resultant of two sets of components of equal total intensity, polarized in

* The light is then said to be polarized in the "plane of incidence," a rather unfortunate convention. The "plane of polarization" was originally defined as the particular plane of incidence in which the polarized light suffers maximum reflection, so the convention was established before the development of the electro-magnetic theory.

mutually perpendicular directions, and exhibiting all possible variations of relative phase. This will be more fully understood when
circular and elliptical polarization has been explained. Hence, the
total intensity of the reflected energy is

$$I_1' + I_2' = \frac{I}{2}\left\{\frac{\sin^2 (i - i')}{\sin^2 (i + i')} + \frac{\tan^2 (i - i')}{\tan^2 (i + i')}\right\} \qquad . \qquad (605)$$

where I is the intensity of the incident unpolarized light.

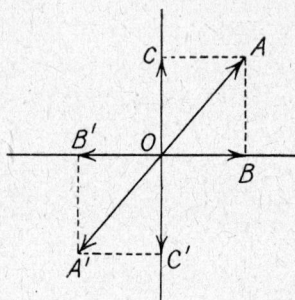

FIG. 101

A closer examination of equation
(602) for the case when $n' > n$ will
show that with increasing values of i,
the value of I_1' steadily increases up
to a value of I_1 when $i = 90°$, since
whatever the value of i' (less than $90°$),

$$\sin (90° - i') = \sin (90° + i')$$

and hence the factor of I_1 is unity.
We also see that

$$\frac{\tan^2 (i - i')}{\tan^2 (i + i')}$$

will be unity when $i = 90°$, but the value of I_2' does not regularly
increase with increasing angles of incidence owing to the rapid
increase of the denominator, which passes through an infinite value
when $(i + i') = 90°$.

Since (if the first medium is air) in this case

$$\sin i = n' \sin i'$$
$$= n' \sin (90° - i)$$
$$= n' \cos i$$

we see that the second term in the equation for the total intensity
is zero, when $\tan i = n'$. In this case we have plane polarized light
only reflected, in which the vibrations are perpendicular to the plane
of incidence. This is applied in the simple reflecting polariscope.
For ordinary glass, $i = 57°$ approx. (See p. 207.)

For perpendicular incidence the reflection factor is independent
of the plane of polarization of the light, and therefore holds for
unpolarized light also. It is

$$I_R = I \frac{(n' - n)^2}{(n' + n)^2} \qquad . \qquad . \qquad . \qquad (606)$$

Fig. 102 shows the variation of intensity of the two components
of the reflected light for glass of refractive index 1·5, the curve

drawn as a dotted line indicating the mean of the two. There is a relative phase change of $\pi/2$ for the vibrations parallel to the plane of incidence (lower full-line curve in Fig. 102) on passing through the angle for zero intensity.

Fig. 103 shows, in the same way, the variation of intensity of the

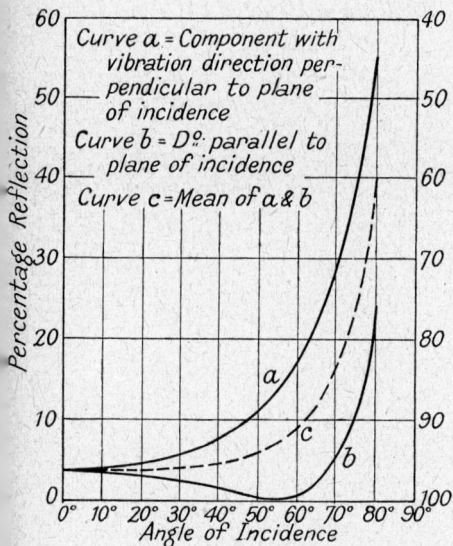

FIG. 102. REFLECTION FROM SURFACE OF GLASS

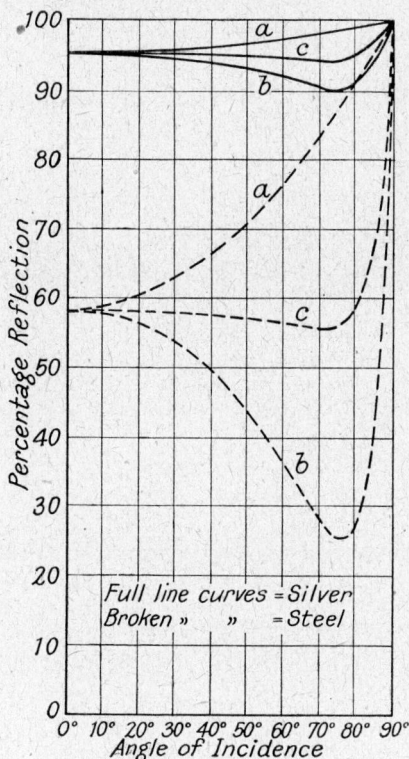

FIG. 103. REFLECTION FROM SILVER AND STEEL

two polarized components in the case of silver and steel. The figure is from results given by von Rohr. There is evidently no possibility of producing plane polarized light by reflection from such surfaces.

Interference Caused by Successive Partial Reflections. Successive reflection of light from two close parallel or nearly parallel surfaces produces two close images of the same small source. In such a case, interference effects can be observed by the eye even when the source of light is very broad.

Consider two parallel reflecting surfaces bounding a layer of refractive index n'. The refractive index of the medium outside the layer is n. Let OA, Fig. 104, be the incident ray which suffers partial reflection at A and at B, the final parallel directions of the reflected rays being AD and CE. Drawing CD perpendicular to these emergent rays and imagining them brought to a common focus P by some optical system (which might be the eye), it is assumed that the relative difference of path with which the disturbances meet in P will be that which they already possess at C and D.

The optical path difference is

$$\delta = n'(AB + BC) - nAD$$

$$= \frac{2n't}{\cos i'} - 2nt \cdot \tan i' \sin i$$

$$= 2t \left\{ \frac{n' - n \sin i' \sin i}{\cos i'} \right\}$$

$$= \frac{2tn'}{\cos i'} \{1 - \sin^2 i'\}$$

$$= 2n't \cos i' \quad . \quad . \quad (607)$$

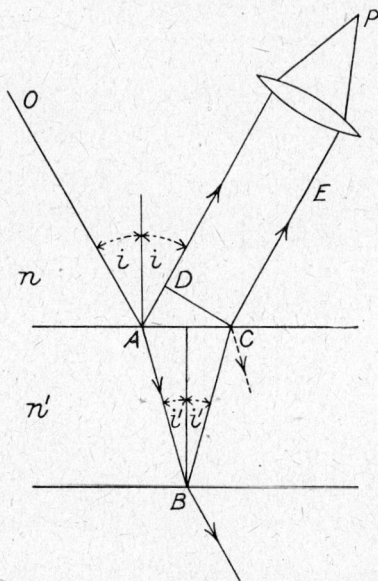

FIG. 104

It is found that reflection at a denser medium introduces a phase advance of π in the reflected light. Hence, the total path difference arising on reflection will be equivalent to

$$\delta_1 = 2n't \cos i' - \frac{\lambda}{2}$$

If the thickness is zero there will be destructive interference; this also occurs when $2n't \cos i'$ happens to be equal to any whole number (m) of wave-lengths, i.e.

$$2n't \cos i' = m\lambda$$

Interference of this kind can be observed with a telescope under conditions of very great path differences if the two surfaces are *accurately* parallel, and homogeneous light (say, the green light from a mercury lamp) is employed.

In the case of a very thin film, such as a soap bubble, the eye receives a diverging cone of rays, filling the pupil, from any small elementary area of the film. If BC, Fig. 105, is the broad source of light, there will be a definite area of this which contributes light to the image of the film element, but the relative retardation of the

different pairs of interfering disturbances will be very nearly equal
if the angles of incidence and reflection do not differ greatly. It
may be noted that if the eye is focused on a point P of the film
(Fig. 106), the paths of the two disturbances may be different from
that shown in Fig. 104, but the change of the calculated path
difference will be negligible if the film is of the order of thinness

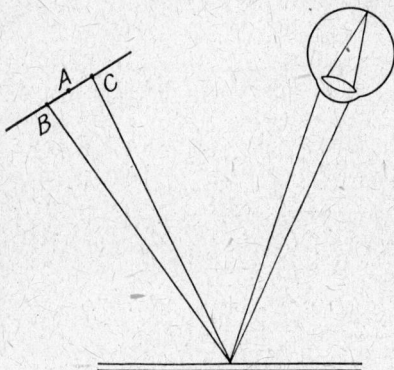

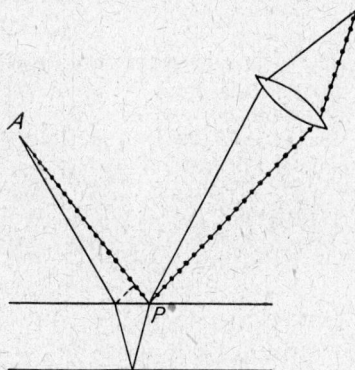

FIG. 105   FIG. 106

which causes the interference colours to appear. In Fig. 106, the
path of one disturbance is distinguished by a dotted line.

The conditions for "destructive" interference might, for example,
be fulfilled for green light $\lambda = \cdot555\mu$, say. Neighbouring wave-
lengths would be subject to more or less reduction of intensity, but
the red, $\lambda = \cdot65\mu$, and the violet, $\lambda = \cdot45\mu$, would be clearly much

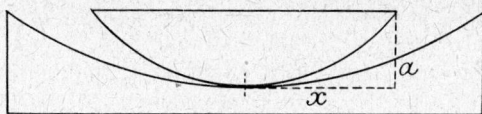

FIG. 107

less reduced. The reflected light would therefore exhibit a purple
coloration owing to the excess of red and violet.

The colour exhibited by the film at any point is thus a function
of the thickness and the angle of incidence.

When the thin film interferences are formed in the space near the
contact of a plane and a spherical surface, the appearances have a
circular symmetry. They were, as previously mentioned, described
by Newton.

Let x be the radius of a circular zone, concentric with the point of contact of two spherical surfaces, Fig. 107. The spherometer formula for the sagitta "a" of the surface of radius r is

$$a = r - (r^2 - x^2)^{\frac{1}{2}}$$

Developing by the binomial theorem—

$$a = \frac{x^2}{2r} + \frac{x^4}{8r^3} + \text{etc.}$$

The region in which interferences are observed will often be very close to the point of contact, where x is small in comparison with r. The second term $\frac{x^4}{8r^3}$ and higher terms can then be neglected.

The separation of two curved surfaces can therefore be written approximately,

$$S = \frac{x^2}{2}\left(\frac{1}{r_1} - \frac{1}{r_2}\right)$$

In the case where light suffers double reflection under practically normal incidence, as will usually be the case when Newton's rings are observed, the retardation in the air film will be

$$2S = x^2\left(\frac{1}{r_1} - \frac{1}{r_2}\right)$$

which will be equal to o, λ, 2λ, etc., for the centre dark spot and successive dark rings.

In measuring the radius of a shallow convex curve by Newton's rings method, the contact between the curve and a flat glass surface is illuminated with the aid of a "vertical illuminator" plate in the measuring microscope. The microscope is focused on the ring system, and the diameter of the first and any other convenient ring measured. Mercury green light is the best illuminant. Let x_1 be the radius of the first ring and x_{21} that of the 21st ring, then

$$r = \frac{x_{21}^2 - x_1^2}{20\lambda}$$

(N.B. For mercury green line, $\lambda = \cdot0005461$ mm.)

Colours of the Rings. When the interferences are observed with white light, colours appear in the rings, of which only a few are visible. The optical path differences in the film increase more rapidly for the shorter wave-lengths which are the soonest restored, and the soonest again extinguished if we think of zones of increasing radius. The order of appearance of the colours is given in a table by Quincke (p. 210).

Amplitude Reflection Coefficients. The amplitude reflection and transmission coefficients are of importance in the fuller theory of interferences in thin films. In the case of nearly normal incidence both equations 601 and 603 reduce for practical purposes to

$$A_1' = - A_1(i - i')/(i + i')$$

and since $ni = n'i'$ under the same conditions,

$$A_1' = - A_1(n' - n)/(n' + n)$$

If $n' > n$, the reflected and incident amplitudes have opposite signs, corresponding to the expected phase change of π on reflection. For a reversed direction of the light we have to interchange n and n' in the last formula; then if $n' > n$ no phase change is indicated.

In theoretical discussions it is shown that if "parallel" light is incident normally on a reflecting surface with a step-up of refractive index from n to n', then if $r = (n' - n)/(n' + n)$ the amplitude transmission coefficient is $1 - r$; for a reversed direction of the light the amplitude transmission coefficient is $1 + r$. (This does *not* mean that the *energy* is increased; there is a drop in refractive index.)

Reflection from a Thin Film. Fig. 108 represents multiple reflections and transmissions at the two surfaces of a thin film, the angles of incidence being exaggerated to distinguish components 2, 5, 8, 11, etc. Let the

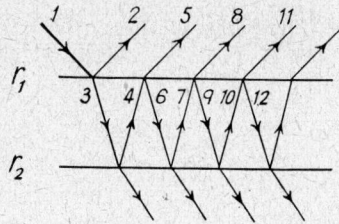

FIG. 108

retardation $(2\pi/\lambda)$ $(2n't)$ of the normal ray reflected once at the back surface be called δ; then taking into account the above amplitude coefficients we can assign the following vibration expressions to the above components; let the numerical values of the amplitude reflection coefficients be r_1 and r_2, at the upper and lower surfaces respectively; and let us first consider a case similar to that of a film having a higher refractive index than the media on each side, so that the first reflection only will show a change of phase, but not subsequent ones.

$$\begin{aligned}
\text{Total amplitude*} &= - Ar_1 + A(1 - r_1^2)r_2 \exp. i\delta \\
\text{(reflected)} &\quad + A(1 - r_1^2)r_2^2 r_1 \exp. 2i\delta \\
&\quad + A(1 - r_1^2)r_2^3 r_1^2 \exp. 3i\delta \\
&\quad + \text{etc.}
\end{aligned}$$

The terms on the right-hand side constitute a geometric series. On taking the sum for our infinite number of terms we obtain as r_1 and r_2 are < 1,

$$\text{Total amplitude} = - Ar_1 + \frac{A(1 - r_1^2)r_2 \exp. i\delta}{1 - r_1 r_2 \exp. i\delta}$$

$$= - \frac{A(r_1 - r_2 \exp. i\delta)}{1 - r_1 r_2 \exp. i\delta} \qquad . \qquad . \qquad . \quad (608)$$

If the film is of negligible thickness, $\delta \to 0$ and $\exp. i\delta \to 1$. Thus, if

---

* The symbols i on the right-hand side of this equation denote, of course, $(-1)^{\frac{1}{2}}$; do not confuse it with the angle of incidence.

$r_1 = r_2$, which is the case for a film with air on each side, the total reflection is zero, i.e. the film appears perfectly black and reflects no light. In general the reflection will be annulled if $\delta = 2\pi p$, where p is an integer. The thickness of the film will then be $p\lambda/2n'$, and successive integral values of p may (if the film is thick) correspond to a number of wave-lengths in the visible spectrum. Hence, if white light is incident, the spectrum of the reflected light will exhibit dark bands. The colour is complementary to the sum of the missing components. If there is a great number of bands the light will appear white.

In the general case the relative intensity is obtained by multiplying the right-hand side of (608) by the complex conjugate, obtaining

$$\text{Relative intensity} = A^2 \left\{ \frac{r_1^2 - 2r_1r_2 \cos \delta + r_2^2}{1 - 2r_1r_2 \cos \delta + r_1^2r_2^2} \right\} \qquad . \quad (609)$$

If r_1 and r_2 are not zero the numerator in the bracket is represented by the hypotenuse of a triangle with sides r_1, r_2, enclosing an angle δ. It cannot vanish unless $r_1 = r_2$ and δ is zero or some multiple of 2π.

Thin Films on Glass. In the case of certain thin films on glass the incident light encounters an increase of refractive index, with the consequent change of phase, at both surfaces. This is represented in (609) if r_2 is made numerically negative. If the refractive indices of air, film, and glass are n_1, n_2, n_3, respectively, we therefore put

$$r_1 = \frac{n_2 - n_1}{n_2 + n_1}, \text{ and } r_2 = -\left(\frac{n_3 - n_2}{n_3 + n_2} \right)$$

Thus when $\delta = \pi$, or some odd multiple thereof, (609) gives

$$\text{Relative intensity} = A^2 \left(\frac{r_1 + r_2}{1 + r_1r_2} \right)^2$$

and inserting the above values of r_1, r_2, we find

$$\text{Relative intensity} = A^2 \left(\frac{n_2^2 - n_1n_3}{n_2^2 + n_1n_3} \right)^2$$

Thus the total reflected intensity will vanish if

$$n_2 = (n_1n_3)^{\frac{1}{2}}$$

and if $\qquad\qquad \delta = (2\pi/\lambda)(2n_2t) = (2p + 1)\pi$

i.e. if $\qquad\qquad t = \lambda/4n_2$

or some odd multiple of this thickness. It can easily be verified that the value of n_2 just given will make $r_2 = -r_1$. Again, if $\delta = 2p\pi$, that is when $t = p\lambda/2n_2$,

$$\text{Relative intensity} = A^2 \left(\frac{r_1 - r_2}{1 - r_1r_2} \right)^2 = A^2 \left(\frac{n_3 - n_1}{n_3 + n_1} \right)^2,$$

so that the reflected light, which will be at its maximum, will be equal to that reflected from the air-glass surface without the film. It can be shown that when $r_2 = -r_1$, the transmitted intensity will be such that

$$\text{Relative transmitted intensity} = A^2 \frac{(1 - R)^2}{1 + 2R \cos \delta + R^2},$$

where $R = r_1^2$. Therefore when $\delta = \pi$ or some odd multiple, all the light (of the wave-length for which the condition holds) will be transmitted and will travel onwards with the incident light. A discussion of the technical aspects of the use of thin films will be found on p. 266.

Double Refraction. In 1669 Erasmus Bartholinus discovered that near objects seen through a crystal of Iceland spar or calcite appear doubled. The doubling is not noticeable when a very distant object is so viewed;* the *actual* separation of the two images is constant and is therefore not observable when they are at a great distance.

A rhomb of calcite is shown in Fig. 109. The three edges OA, OB, OC make equal angles with each other in the sense that $\widehat{AOB}$ = $\widehat{BOC}$ = $\widehat{COA}$. We can imagine a line entering the rhomb symmetrically through O, so that it makes equal angles with the three edges; this line gives the direction of the "optic axis."

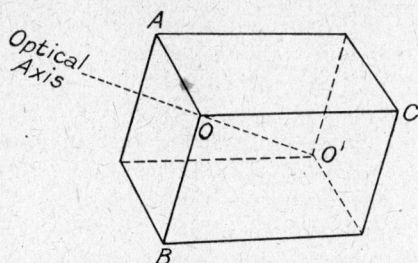

FIG. 109. RHOMB OF CALCITE   FIG. 110

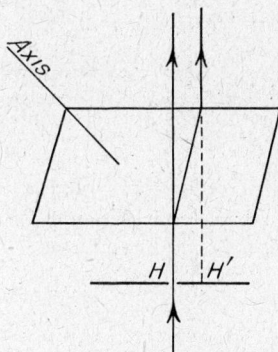

If the rhomb of spar is put down on a card pierced by a small hole, the two images formed by "double refraction" are seen to be so situated that the line joining them is apparently parallel to this "optic axis," no matter how the rhomb is placed on the card. If the rhomb is rotated about the direction of view, one image remains stationary, while the other moves round it so as to fulfil the above condition. Experiment with a piece of spar soon shows that the double refraction of the light must be in the sense indicated in Fig. 110. One image appears in the original direction, the other displaced with respect to the crystal as indicated, so that the light has suffered a deviation away from the normal in passing through the crystal. Since the *actual* separation of the images appears constant, no matter what the distance of the object, it is inferred that the two parts into which the original ray is divided become parallel on emergence.

* Several textbooks of light fall into the error of stating that a distant object appears doubled, but this cannot be the case if a natural rhomb with parallel bounding faces is used for the observation.

Interesting experiments may be carried out by supporting a piece of black glass above the rhomb and observing the light, after it has been reflected from the glass at the polarizing angle, for various positions of the calcite. In this way it is not difficult to show that the light from the two images is plane polarized in perpendicular directions. That from the stationary image (called the *ordinary* image) is "polarized in the plane which passes through the two images," which means that the electric forces in the wavefront are perpendicular to that plane, while the light from the rotating image, called the *extraordinary* image, is polarized in the direction perpendicular to the first.

By cutting and polishing faces perpendicular to the axis of a rhomb of calcite, it may be shown that double refraction of this kind does not take place when the light traverses the crystal in the direction of the axis.

Types of Crystals. Through the experiments of Laüe, Friedrich, Knipping, and others, carried out since 1911, it has been established that (as was indeed previously suspected) the external form of crystals is a consequence of their atomic structure. This is a regular arrangement of the atoms, in three dimensions, known as a space-lattice. The ordinary molecules lose their identities, the constituent atoms all filling definite places in a continuous arrangement, which is an indefinite repetition of a fundamental elementary structure, such as is illustrated in Fig. 111, which represents potassium chloride. The black dots are the chlorine atoms and the white are the potassium.

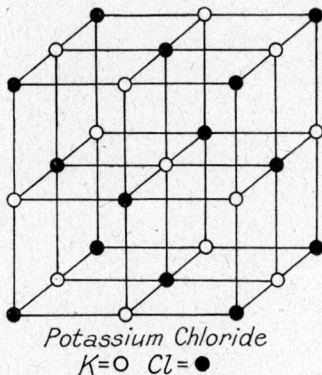

Potassium Chloride
$K = \bigcirc$ $Cl = \bullet$

Fig. 111

It will be realized that there are various planes which are relatively rich in atoms; these represent the possible crystal faces and cleavage planes. The regular structure is capable of producing diffraction effects in X-rays, which are radiations analogous to light, but of much shorter wave-length. Just as the number of lines in a diffraction grating can be calculated from the angle of diffraction of light, so the relative spacing of the atoms in a crystal are inferred from the X-ray spectra.

The classes of crystals are usually defined in relation to the "crystallographic axes," which are to some extent a matter of geometrical convention, but which are most easily employed to express the symmetry and arrangement of the crystal faces if the selected axes are parallel to the edges of the ultimate "cells," of which the structure is composed. Of the seven main classifications

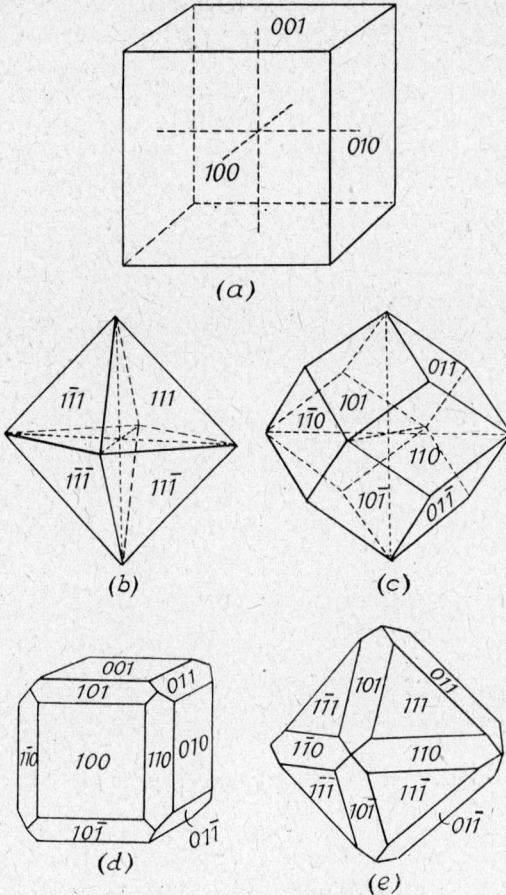

FIG. 112. CRYSTAL FORMS OF THE CUBIC SYSTEM

(a) Cube (fluor-spar, rock salt)
(b) Octahedron (magnetite, spinel)
(c) Rhombdodecahedron (garnet)
(d) Faces characteristic of cube and rhombdodecahedron appearing in the same crystal as in fluor-spar.
(e) Rhombdodecahedral and octahedral faces appearing as in magnetite.

of crystals, there are six in which the unit cells are parallelopipeds with various relative lengths of edges and various angles between the edges.

The relative lengths of the edges are determined by important parameters, which govern the inclinations of the faces of the crystal. The "law of rational intercepts" due to Haüy, states that any face of a crystal makes intercepts on the axes, which may be expressed as rational multiples of the parameters.

Thus, in the table given below, in which the relation of the main classifications are set out, the axes for the cubic system may be imagined parallel to the ordinary axes of Cartesian co-ordinates. Since the parameters, a, b, and c, are equal, we may expect faces with equal intercepts on all three axes. Other faces may have unit distance of intercept for one axis and infinite distances for the other two, and so on. These various faces may be developed together in one crystal, as shown in Fig. 112. In the table, D.R. stands for "doubly refracting."

Angles between Edges of Unit Cell	Relative Lengths of Edges of Unit Cell	Classification (Crystallographic)	Optical Classification
Three edges at right angles .	$a = b = c$	Cubic	Not doubly refracting
,, ,, ,, ,, .	$a = b \quad c$	Tetragonal	D.R. Uniaxial
,, ,, ,, ,, .	$a \quad b \quad c$	Orthorhombic	,, Biaxial
Two ,, ,, ,, .	$a \quad b \quad c$	Monoclinic	,, Biaxial
None of edges at right angles .	$a \quad b \quad c$	Triclinic	,, Biaxial
,, ,, ,, ,,	$a = b = c$	Rhombic*	,, Uniaxial
		Hexagonal*	,, Uniaxial

In other cases than the cubic, the parameters may be unequal. Thus, gypsum is a monoclinic crystal, in which $a : b : c = 0.690 : 1 : 0.42$. In all types of crystals there may arise faces in which the intercepts are of the type pa, qb, rc, where p, q, and r may be simple integers of low value or may be infinite. Thus we might have a face $1a$, $2b$, ∞c. In the Millerian system the indices are proportional to the *reciprocals of the intercepts*. If the intercepts are $1a$, $2b$, ∞c, the Millerian indices would be $(2, 1, 0)$. We may form the reciprocals and multiply the numbers by the least common denominator. Thus $(2a, 3b, 4c)$ becomes $(6, 4, 3)$, which is usually written $(6\ 4\ 3)$ without parameters or commas between the numbers. If an intercept is on the negative prolongation of an axis through the origin, the intercept figure is distinguished by a bar over the figure, thus: $\bar{3}$.

Theory of Double Refraction. Calcite or Iceland spar and quartz, or rock-crystal can be referred to the hexagonal type of crystallization, in which there are three equal horizontal axes at 120° apart

---

* The rhombic system may be looked upon as a group of the hexagonal type from the crystallographic standpoint, but the rhombic unit parallelopiped is such that the angles between the edges at two opposite corners are equal. In the hexagonal system there is no unit parallelopiped.

and one vertical axis for which the parameter is different. Fig. 113 shows the position of axes 1, 2, and 3 for a cleavage rhombohedron of calcite, and a quartz crystal with prism and pyramid faces. It will be understood that the direction of the vertical axis is a unique direction in a particular sense; it is the optic axis of the crystal. Thus the term "uniaxial" applies to this unique direction and has no reference to the usual crystallographic axes, which are four in number.

If a disturbance travels outwards from a centre in an isotropic medium (in which the optical properties in all directions are uniform),

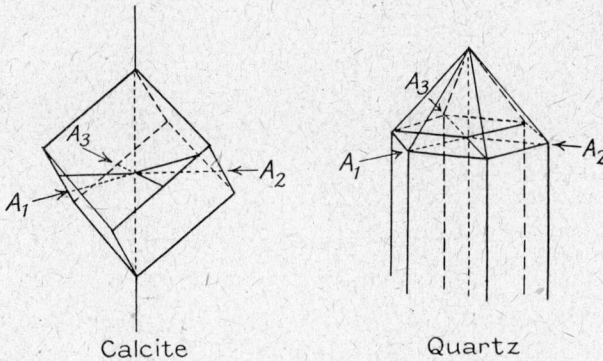

Calcite   Quartz

FIG. 113

the wave-front takes the form of a sphere. Huygens found that in uniaxial crystals, such as calcite, the wave-front travels outwards in two sheets; one is a sphere and the other an ellipsoid of revolution. The axis of symmetry is the optic axis, and the two surfaces touch each other only in the two points on this axis. In Iceland spar the sphere lies within the ellipsoid; this is the characteristic of *negative* uniaxial crystals. In quartz the ellipsoid lies within the sphere, and this is characteristic of positive uniaxial crystals. Huygens' construction, applied to the problem of finding the two directions of refraction for a beam, explains the deviation of the extraordinary ray from the normal shown in Fig. 110; for suppose in Fig. 114 that the optic axis is in the plane of the diagram, and let parallel light fall normally upon the surface of the crystal represented by the line MM'. The disturbances spread in two sheets from M and M', two spheres and two ellipsoids. The envelope of the ellipsoidal wave-fronts in two positions will be the lines EE' and E_1E_1'; the extra-ordinary wave-front for the refracted beam is seen to bear away to the left, while the ordinary beam will be undeviated. (The construction for the ordinary wave-front is not shown in the diagram.)

It will be seen that the velocity of the extraordinary wave-surface normal to itself as compared with the ray velocity is represented by the ratio of WW_1/EE_1 in the figure. *The velocity of the wave produced by the extraordinary ray is not generally the same as the "velocity of the ray" itself.* The "velocity of the ray" is proportional to the radius vector of the ellipsoid in the direction of the ray.

The *vibration directions* are indicated in the figure. A *principal section* of a uniaxial crystal is one which is parallel to the optic axis,

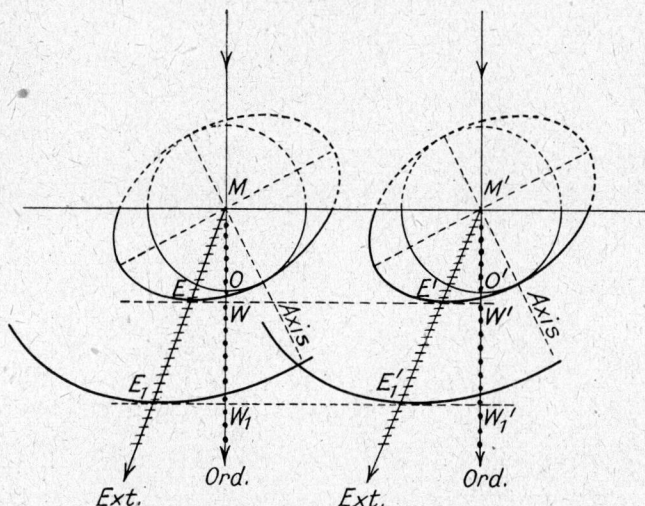

FIG. 114. ILLUSTRATING HUYGENS' CONSTRUCTION FOR THE EXTRAORDINARY WAVE-FRONT AND RAY-DIRECTION

and in the extraordinary ray the vibrations take place in the principal section containing the ray and the axis; in the ordinary ray they are at right angles to this.

The method of construction for various conditions will be understood from the above example, but it may be pointed out that if the optic axis does not lie in the plane of the diagram, the extraordinary ray will in general be deviated above or below the diagram. When the light is normally incident, no change of direction will take place for the extraordinary ray if the optic axis is parallel or perpendicular to the refracting surface. The velocity of propagation for the ordinary and extraordinary rays and wave-fronts is identical only in the direction of the axis.

Ray- and Wave-Velocities. In Fig. 115, let the ellipse represent any principal section of the ellipsoid of extraordinary ray-velocity. The semi-axis $OA = a$ represents the maximum ray-velocity, and

OB $= b$ represents the minimum ray-velocity in the extraordinary wave-front. The vector OP represents the ray-velocity for some intermediate direction, making an angle α with the Y-axis. The

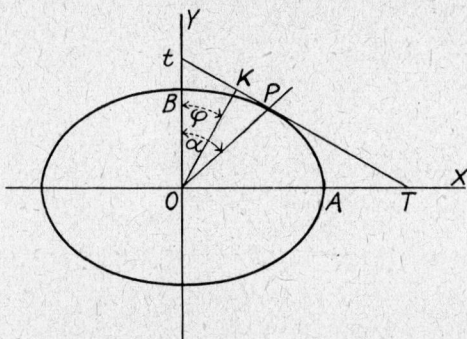

FIG. 115

tangent at this point P represents the wave-front (see Fig. 114). The normal OK represents the wave-velocity on the same scale.

The equation to the ellipse is

$$(x^2/a^2) + (y^2/b^2) = 1$$

If P is the point (x', y'), while OP $= r$,

$$\sin \alpha = \frac{x'}{r}, \cos \alpha = \frac{y'}{r}$$

and, since x' and y' are on the ellipse,

$$\frac{r^2 \sin^2 \alpha}{a^2} + \frac{r^2 \cos^2 \alpha}{b^2} = 1$$

whence

$$r^2 = \frac{a^2 b^2}{b^2 \sin^2 \alpha + a^2 \cos^2 \alpha} \qquad . \qquad . \qquad (610)$$

Again, the tangent at (x', y') is

$$\frac{xx'}{a^2} + \frac{yy'}{b^2} = 1$$

and the intercept on the axes of X and Y are respectively—

$$\text{OT} = a^2/x' \qquad \text{O}t = b^2/y'$$

Let $w = $ OK, then

$$w = \text{O}t \cos \phi = \text{OT} \sin \phi, \text{ where } \widehat{\text{BOK}} = \phi$$

$$w = \frac{b^2}{y'} \cos \phi = \frac{a^2}{x'} \sin \phi.$$

Then, since x' and y' are on the ellipse,

$$\left(\frac{a^2 \sin \phi}{w}\right)^2 \frac{1}{a^2} + \left(\frac{b^2 \cos \phi}{w}\right)^2 \frac{1}{b^2} = 1$$

giving
$$w^2 = a^2 \sin^2 \phi + b^2 \cos^2 \phi \qquad . \qquad . \quad (611)$$

In order to obtain the relation between α and ϕ, note that

$$\tan \alpha = \frac{x'}{y'} = \frac{a^2 \sin \phi}{b^2 \cos \phi} = \frac{a^2}{b^2} \tan \phi \quad . \qquad . \quad (612)$$

Refractive Indices. The maximum and minimum wave-velocities a and b are related to the corresponding "refractive indices" n_a, n_b by the relation

$$a n_a = b n_b = w n = \text{constant } (k, \text{say})$$

Hence, the above formulae can easily be expressed in terms of the refractive indices if required. Thus (611) becomes

$$n^2 = \frac{n_a{}^2 \; n_b{}^2}{n_b{}^2 \sin^2 \phi + n_a{}^2 \cos^2 \phi}$$

and (612) becomes

$$\tan \alpha = \frac{n_b{}^2}{n_a{}^2} \tan \phi.$$

In the case of negative uniaxial crystals, in which the ray-velocity ellipsoid is outside the sphere, the value of n_b coincides with that for the ordinary refractive index; a is greater than b. Hence the ordinary refractive index is the greater.

In quartz, on the other hand, the ellipsoid is within the sphere, and the value of n_a (the lesser) is coincident with the ordinary refractive index.

The conception of the refractive indices of the extraordinary waves is useful in crystal optics, because they enable a convenient calculation of the "optical path" to be made for particular directions of transmission in the crystal. *They cannot, of course, be used in general for the calculation of the directions of the extraordinary ray by the application of the simple law of refraction.*

The determination of the refractive index for the ordinary ray can be carried out on a spectrometer with a 60° prism cut in any way from a uniaxial crystal, but in order to measure the extraordinary index on the spectrometer by ordinary methods, it is necessary to obtain a prism cut with its refracting edge parallel to the crystal axis, or alternatively to have the axis perpendicular to the refracting edge and bisecting the angle between the prism faces.

The condition obtained in the first case is shown in Fig. 116. Applying Huygens' construction to the case in question (shown in

the figure in a section perpendicular to the refracting edge and thus
also perpendicular to the crystal axis), the wave-fronts spread out
in the two sheets, both having circular sections in the plan. The
radius of the extraordinary wave-front section must be taken as
ED/n_e, where n_e is the extraordinary refractive index. It is clear
that in this case the ordinary law of refraction is obeyed. Hence,
the refractive index is calculable from the usual formula

$$n_e = \frac{\sin \frac{1}{2}(A + D)}{\sin \frac{1}{2}A}$$

where A is the angle of the prism and D is the minimum angular
deviation of the beam.

With the axis in these directions, there is evidently a maximum
difference between the directions of the ordinary and extraordinary

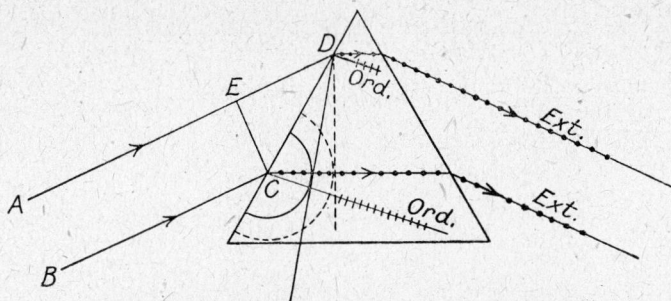

FIG. 116. DETERMINATION OF THE EXTRAORDINARY
REFRACTIVE INDEX

The optic axis of the crystal is perpendicular to the diagram. Note the broken semicircle
and the full-line semicircle which represent Huygens' construction for the extraordinary
and ordinary wave-fronts respectively. The deviation of the ordinary ray is a little
exaggerated for clearness of the diagram.

wave-fronts. The difference is a minimum when the direction of
transmission in a prism can take the direction of the axis; if the
latter is perpendicular to the refracting edge of the prism and
parallel to the base of the equilateral section, the minimum deviation condition will correspond to transmission in the axial direction.
For the recognition of the ordinary and extraordinary beams, see
below.

Another very convenient method of determining the refractive
index of a crystal block is by the total reflection method. Imagine
a crystal block cut with its face perpendicular to the axis, and let
a parallel beam from an isotropic medium pass into the crystal as
indicated in Fig. 117. Let the refractive index of the first medium
be n, and let the ordinary and extraordinary indices of the block
be n_o and n_e respectively.

Two parallel entrant rays, AB and CD, meet the surface in B and D respectively. Dropping a perpendicular BE from B to CD, we know that the time taken for the disturbance to travel from E to D is proportional to $n \cdot$ ED. During this period the disturbances originating from B spread out in two sheets, and reach the points F and G in the surface, where

$$n \cdot ED = n_o BF = n_e BG.$$

When F or G pass beyond the point D, there can be no refracted ray, but all the energy is totally reflected. With varying angles of

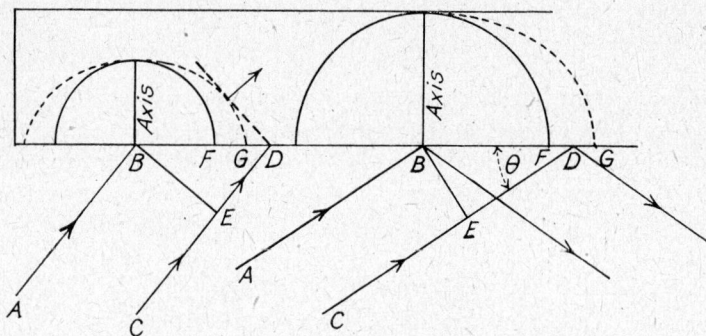

FIG. 117

incidence there is, in fact, a sudden increase in the reflected energy at the "critical angle," for either the ordinary or extraordinary beam. Suppose G coincides with D, then

$$n_e BD = n ED$$

$$n_e/n = \cos \widehat{BDE} = \sin \phi,$$

where ϕ is the angle of incidence.

Alternatively, if a beam be sent along the bounding surface in the crystal block at grazing incidence, no light can emerge into the lower medium except at angles greater than at the critical angle. The equation just quoted shows that n must be greater than n_e, in order that ϕ may have a real value in the case considered.

These phenomena lend themselves to the determination of refractive indices by the crystal refractometer, or total reflectometer (Fig. 118), which, in some instruments, employs a hemispherical block of dense glass with a plane face on the top. The crystal specimen is placed in position with a film of liquid between the crystal and top face; the liquid must have a higher refractive index than the crystal, in order to save total reflection (at the glass-liquid

face) occurring at angles of incidence smaller than that for the
effective critical angle for the crystal; the angle so determined is
that which would be found if the glass and crystal were in actual
optical contact.

If light (*a*, Fig. 118) can be sent into the crystal so that it is
incident at grazing incidence on the bounding surface, the hemispherical surface of the block will produce an image surface in which
the direction of the critical angle is registered by a boundary, on
one side of which all the refracted light is concentrated. If this
method is not practicable, the contact face is illuminated diffusely

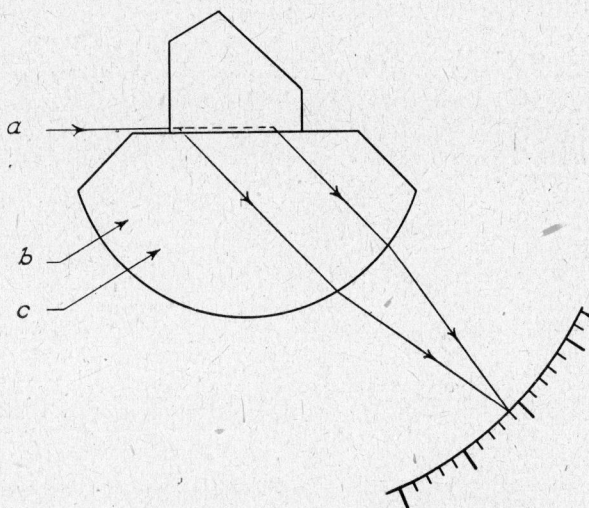

FIG. 118. PRINCIPLE OF THE CRYSTAL REFRACTOMETER

by light (*bb*). The boundary then shows up as a border of contrast
of intensity between the partially and totally reflected light.

Provided that the optic axis is perpendicular to the bounding
face as shown in Fig. 117, there will be a maximum difference
between the critical angles for the extraordinary and ordinary beams.
The angle is decreased if the axis has another direction. It is always
possible to rotate the block on the hemisphere (or rotate the two
together in the instrument) until the crystal axis lies in a plane
perpendicular to the plane of incidence. As this is done, the difference of the angles reaches a maximum, and the ordinary and
extraordinary indices may again be measured.

Direction of Vibrations. The distinction between the ordinary and
extraordinary waves is rendered easy by the recognition of the
direction of vibration of the plane polarized light which they give.

In Fig. 114 we see that the extraordinary ray's vibration direction is in the plane containing the ray and optical axis, while the ordinary ray vibrates in the direction perpendicular to the ray and the axis. Cheshire likened the uniaxial crystal to wood containing a "grain." The elasticity of the medium differs in the grain direction from that found perpendicular thereto; and this would result in a difference of velocities of mechanical wave-motions involving displacements in these respective directions.

The extraordinary ray vibrates in a plane containing the "grain," the ordinary ray *across* the grain. In the axis direction any light propagated must vibrate across the grain; only one velocity is possible. Light propagated perpendicular to the axis, however, may vibrate either across the grain or in a plane containing the grain direction; hence the two velocities for light polarized in these ways.

Polarizing Prisms. Owing to the comparatively wide angular separations of the ordinary and extraordinary rays in calcite, it is possible to remove one of them by total reflection while transmitting the other.

The basis of the Nicol prism is a rhombohedron of calcite about three times as long as it is broad. Fig. 119 represents a section through the shorter diagonals of the end faces. It is slit diagonally, perpendicular to this section, so that the cut makes an angle of about 22° with the edge AB. The natural angles ADC and ABC are about 70° 53'; it is usual to grind the end faces down until the angles are 68° and they are thus at right angles to the plane of the slit. The new faces are polished and the two separated parts are cemented with Canada balsam.

On entering the prism, a ray splits up into the ordinary and extraordinary rays. With increasing angles of incidence on the interior cemented face, we pass from the condition when both rays are transmitted to that when the ordinary ray is incident at 67° 53', and thereafter is totally reflected. The extraordinary ray is still transmitted until its angle of incidence increases to 82° 32'. The external field or angular range for the resulting plane polarized light is 24°.

Different cements may be employed. Canada balsam, balsam of copaiba, linseed oil, and poppy oil are used in various polarizing prisms, and are of assistance in securing the best conditions by choosing a cement of suitable refractive index.

The field of plane polarized light in the untrimmed Nicol, as described above, is not symmetrical about the direction of the central line parallel to the long edges. The field is limited on one side by a blue band[1] with darkness beyond it, and on the other side by a system of fine coloured fringes beyond which the two beams are transmitted, and the light is not polarized; the angular directions of the blue band and the fringes are at about 11° and 3° respectively on each side of the directions parallel to the edge, increased to about 14° and 10° externally. The trimming of the end faces to 68° improves the symmetry. Many efforts have been made to produce prisms with more symmetrical fields; it is in this connection that the use

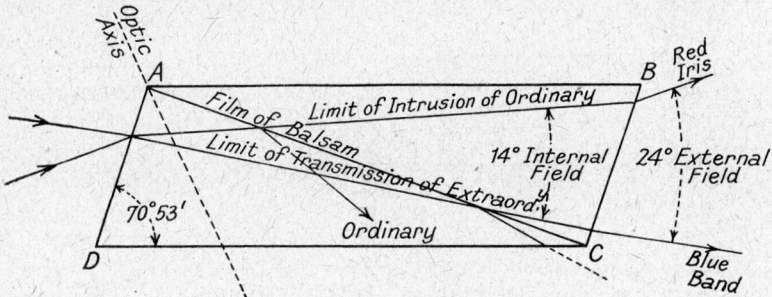

FIG. 119. THE NICOL PRISM

of various liquids is important. The table below gives some useful indices—

		Refractive Indices			Critical Angle
$\lambda(\mu) =$	0·6708	0·5893	0·3962	(0·5893)	
Iceland spar (ordinary ray)	1·6537	1·6586	1·6833	37° 2′ (Spar-air)	
„ „ (extraordinary ray)	1·4842	1·4864	1·4978	42° 16′ „	
Canada balsam	1·523	1·526	1·553	67° 53′ Spar-medium (ord.)	
Linseed oil		1·485		63° 36′ „ „	
Poppy oil		1·463		62° 28′ „ „	
Balsam of Copaiba		1·549		74° 34′ „ „	

The extraordinary refractive indices given in the table above are naturally the minimum values. The actual value of the refractive index and, therefore, the critical angles effective with various media for the extraordinary ray, varies with the direction of transmission with respect to the optic axis. The values can, if required, be calculated from the formulae given above.

There are certain objections to the sloping end faces of the Nicol prism. They diminish the light by reflection and give a lateral displacement to the image of the object unless parallel light is transmitted; there is also some tendency to produce slight "elliptical polarization" of the transmitted light. Hence, in many cases the ends of the "Nicol" are trimmed to be at right angles to the long edges of the prism if the resulting asymmetry of the field can be tolerated.

The Glan-Thompson Prism. This prism is illustrated in Fig. 120, and it will be seen that the end faces are parallel to the optic axis. In one type, the angular breadth of the field for plane polarized light is 41° 50′; the angle between the film and end face is 76° 5′, and the ratio of length to breadth of the prism is 4·16. Linseed oil is used for the cement, with which the extraordinary ray is not totally reflected at any angle of incidence on the film.

The Foucault Prism and Others. Prisms containing a cement such as Canada balsam, do not transmit the ultra-violet. In case a prism is wanted for purposes of ultra-violet polarimetry, the Foucault type, which has a film of air, is employed. The modification due to Hoffman is illustrated in Fig. 121, the air film is at 50° with the axis of vision, and the angular field is between 7° and 8° only.

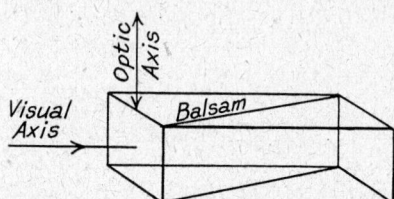

FIG. 120. THE GLAN-THOMPSON PRISM

There are a number of other prisms of some interest which are occasionally encountered. Ahren's prism in three parts, and Feussner's prism are perhaps of greatest interest. In the latter the film of doubly refracting materials is cemented between two wedges of glass. According to Thompson, "The glass and cement ought to have an index of refraction equal to that of the higher of the two indices of the crystal, and the optic axis of the slice ought to be perpendicular to the planes of its faces."

The Lippich prism will be mentioned in the section on "Polarimetry." Papers by S. P. Thompson[2] and W. Grosse[3] may be consulted for comparative details on polarizing prisms.

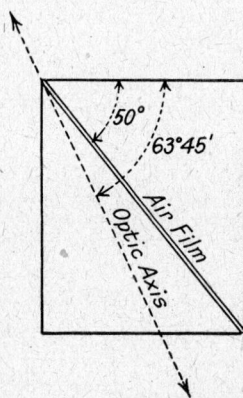

FIG. 121. HOFFMAN'S PRISM

Circular and Elliptical Polarization. The result of the combination of two simple harmonic vibrations is easily and beautifully illustrated by the harmonograph, Fig. 122, in which two pendulums communicate two mutually perpendicular vibrations to a point which marks out on paper, or on a smoked plate, the figure resulting from the two movements. A short time spent with such a fascinating toy will teach far more than can be gathered from description, but even in imagination some of the results may easily be conceived.

In Fig. 123, BB′ marks the path imparted to the pointer by one pendulum, AA′ the other. If both are acting so that the central point of each path would be simultaneously reached on the journey through O to A and B respectively, the result of the joint movement is a journey to C. Thus, if the periodic time is the same in each movement, CC′ represents the new path.

Again, if the movement in the path AA′ has brought the marker to its right-hand extreme position, while the perpendicular movement is passing through its central or zero position towards B, the joint result will be an anti-clockwise circular movement. Change the phase of the BB′ vibration by 180°, so that the movement

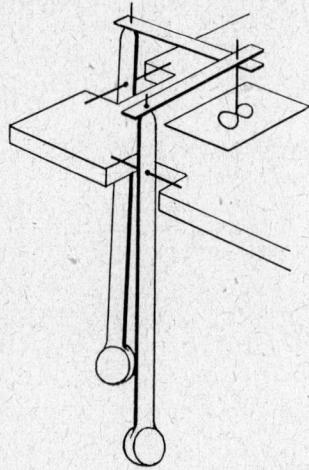

FIG. 122. THE HARMONOGRAPH

through O is towards B′, while the A movement is as before, and it will be clear that a clockwise motion results. The conditions

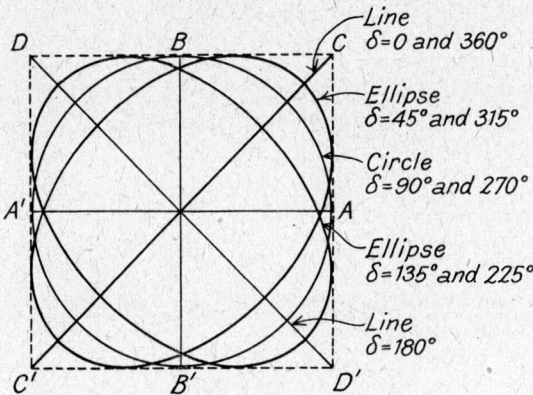

Line
$\delta = 0$ and $360°$

Ellipse
$\delta = 45°$ and $315°$

Circle
$\delta = 90°$ and $270°$

Ellipse
$\delta = 135°$ and $225°$

Line
$\delta = 180°$

FIG. 123

under which we can obtain a linear vibration perpendicular to CC, will also be easily understood.

If the amplitudes are unequal, the vibrations (when the phases have the same relations as in the cases above), will either be along straight lines at different angles, or will be elliptical.

With equal amplitudes, the vibration figure will in general be an ellipse. Particular cases of a straight line will, however, occur if the phase difference δ is $0°$ or $180°$; and a circle if δ is $90°$ or $270°$. A relative change of phase of $180°$ will mean a change of the direction of vibration such as from CC′ to DD′.

If, now, the relative phase of the components is varying, the figure will vary also; with the harmonograph the effect is obtained by making the lengths of the two pendulums differ slightly; the continuous change through linear, elliptical, and circular modes is beautifully represented.

So we may imagine the case with light under certain conditions. Let a ray enter a block of a uniaxial crystal, so that the direction of

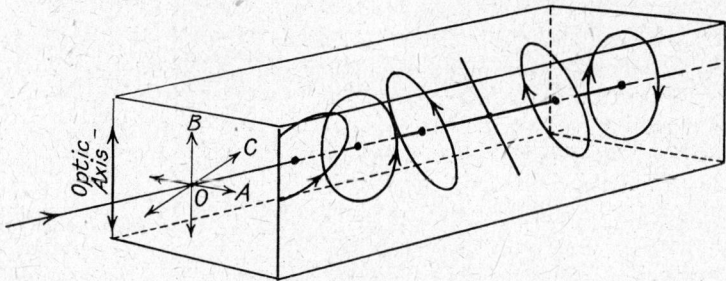

FIG. 124

transmission within the block is perpendicular to the axis. Let the incident light be plane polarized, and let the amplitude and vibration direction be represented by the vector OC shown in perspective in Fig. 124. On entering the crystal the vibration may be regarded as resolved into two components OA and OB, so polarized that OB is parallel and OA perpendicular to the axis. Though there may be no "double refraction" in the sense of a difference of direction, since the components travel along the same line, there will be a difference of velocity and hence a relative change of phase.

Let t be the thickness of the crystal traversed, then the optical path difference p for the ordinary component OA and the extraordinary component OB will be given by

$$p = t(n_o - n_e)$$

and the corresponding difference of phase will be

$$\delta = \frac{2\pi}{\lambda} t(n_o - n_e)$$

Fig. 124 will illustrate how, according to the total thickness of the block, the light on emergence may have the distinctive properties of elliptical, circular, or plane polarization.

Fast and Slow Directions. It is usual to distinguish between the "fast" and "slow" vibration directions of a plate. The "fast" direction is naturally the direction of the vibrations which have the greatest velocity and the lowest refractive index; the "slow" direction is that of the vibrations with the lowest velocity and the highest index. Thus, in quartz the extraordinary refractive index is the higher, which means that the slow direction is that for the ray which vibrates "along the grain." The fast direction in quartz is perpendicular to the grain or optic axis.

In calcite the ordinary refractive index is the higher, and the fast direction is for the ray which vibrates "along the grain" or parallel to the axis.

The Simple Polariscope. The simplest form of polariscope is illustrated in Fig. 125. Diffused light from the sheet of opal glass

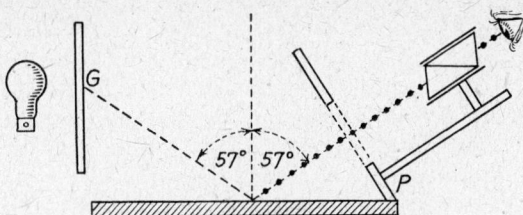

FIG. 125. A SIMPLE POLARISCOPE
Diagrammatic.

is reflected at 57° (see p. 184) from the glass plate. It is usual to black the underside of the sheet to stop light which might get through the plate from below. Although light reflected from the lower surface should also be plane polarized, any strain or imperfections in the glass might induce elliptical polarization in the part of the light thus traversing the thickness of the plate.

The analyser may be any convenient form of Nicol, Glan-Thompson prism, or the like, held in a suitable mount. Naturally, the field becomes quite dark only in one particular portion as the analyser is rotated into the position for the extinction of light; this occurs when the short diagonal of the Nicol (if such is used) is in the plane of incidence. The vibrations of the polarized light are perpendicular to the plane of incidence, while the prism transmits only those parallel to the short diagonal (i.e. the extraordinary ray in which the vibrations are in a plane containing the optic axis of the crystal).

In the general case, let OA (Fig. 126) represent the amplitude and direction of the vibrations in the plane polarized light, and let OB represent the transmission direction of the analyser. The transmitted amplitude is equal to kOA cos θ, where $\theta = \widehat{\text{AOB}}$, and k is a transmission factor for the prism. (There will be reflection and absorption losses.) The intensity of the transmitted light is proportional to $\cos^2 \theta$.

If two polarizing prisms are arranged to transmit the light in turn, they are said to be "crossed" when extinction is secured. Thus we speak of examination "between crossed Nicols," though this apparatus alone is not really a very practically useful form of polariscope.

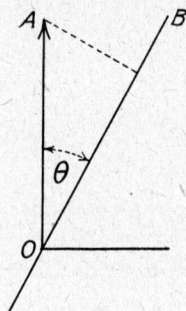

FIG. 126

Crystal Plates in Polarized Light. Consider a plate of a uniaxial crystal cut with its surface parallel to the axis, and let the thickness be such that the retardation between the components is $\lambda/4$, say. If this is placed in plane polarized light so that the vibrations are parallel or perpendicular to the axis, they are transmitted without change from the plane polarized condition, but if the vibration direction (amplitude a) makes an angle θ with the crystal axis, the vibration is resolved into two parts of amplitudes—

$$a \cos \theta, \text{ parallel to the axis, and}$$

$$a \sin \theta, \text{ perpendicular to the axis.}$$

These emerge with a difference of path of $\lambda/4$ or a phase difference of $90°$. This results in an elliptical vibration (in general), since the

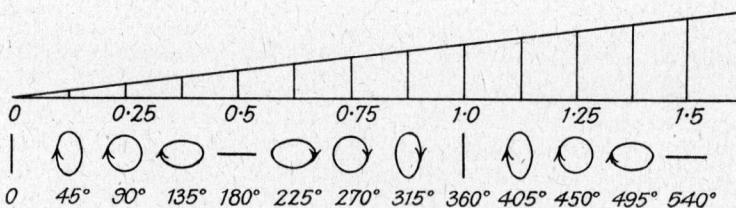

FIG. 127

amplitudes in perpendicular directions are unequal except when $\theta = 45°$, and a circular vibration results.

If the plate is held in the polariscope for observation, the extremes of intensity of the light passing through the analyser as it rotates will be proportional to $a^2 \cos^2 \theta$ and $a^2 \sin^2 \theta$, of which the ratio is $\cot^2 \theta$. The light never totally disappears when elliptical polarization is present, but varies between a maximum and minimum. When the polarization is circular, the intensity remains stationary as the analyser is rotated.

It was shown above that a $\lambda/4$ plate produces circular polarization when held in a plane polarized beam, so that $\theta = 45°$ as above.

With a plate of greater thickness still, elliptical or linear polarization is obtained, and a wedge-shaped piece of crystal cut with its thin edge parallel to the axis and held in the polariscope, so that the axis direction is at 45° to the vibration direction of the polarized light, will exhibit, along its length, all the varieties of polarization as suggested in Fig. 127.

Interference Colours. Such a wedge as described above, when viewed between crossed Nicols with monochromatic light,* shows a regular variation of illumination, having maxima where the retardation is an odd number of half wave-lengths and minima for retardations of integral numbers of whole wave-lengths. The interval between successive maxima decreases, however, with decreasing wave-length, thus producing coloured fringes in the bands obtained with white light.

Let the retardation for violet be p_v wave-lengths, then if t is the thickness of the plate and $\lambda_v =$ the wave-length,

$$p_v \lambda_v = t(n_o - n_e)_v$$

while

$$p_r \lambda_r = t(n_o - n_e)_r$$

is the equation for red. Dividing, we obtain

$$\frac{p_v \lambda_v}{p_r \lambda_r} = \frac{(n_o - n_e)_v}{(n_o - n_e)_r} = v \text{ (say)}$$

If the strength of the double refraction $(n_o - n_e)$ is equal for violet and red, the value of v is unity, and the relative retardation will be inversely proportional to the wave-lengths. The order of the interference colours then follows exactly as in Newton's rings or similar phenomena, but the colour succession is modified somewhat in other cases where v is not unity.

Passing from the "minimum" point of darkness in the wedge at zero retardation and zero thickness to places of greater retardation, the energy grows more rapidly in the shorter wave-lengths than the longer. Bluish-grey tints are the first to appear; these are followed by yellow, orange, and red, etc., in accordance with the table quoted by Quincke.

It will be understood, therefore, that the *colour* is a valuable indication of the relative retardation.

---

* The optic axis in the wedge should be at 45° to the vibration direction of the polarized light, as specified in the previous paragraph.

Imagine now that a separate plate of the same material is held in front of the wedge between "crossed nicols." Let the plate, like the wedge, have its faces parallel to the axis, and let the axis direction in the two be brought into parallelism ("fast on fast"). Evidently the retardation of the plate is now added to that of the wedge. If white light is used, the colour at any part of the wedge is now of a higher order.

Now let the plate be turned through 90° about the direction of the light. The ordinary ray in the wedge becomes the extraordinary ray in the plate, and vice versa; we have the condition of "fast on slow," relative retardation is reversed, the net effect being now the difference of the two.

COLOUR SCALE (adapted from Quincke's Table)

Retardation for "D" Line, $\lambda = 0.589\mu$ (in microns)	Order (retardation in wavelengths)	Interference Colours between Crossed Nicols
0·00	0	Black
·04		Iron-grey
·097		Lavender-grey
·158	$\frac{1}{4}$	Greyish-blue
·218		Clearer grey
·234		Greenish-white
·259		White
·267		Yellowish-white
·281		Straw yellow
·306	$\frac{1}{2}$	Light yellow
·332		Bright yellow
·430		Brownish-yellow
·505	$\frac{3}{4}$	Reddish-orange
·536		Red
·551		Deep red
·565		Purple
·575		Violet (the "sensitive violet")
·589	1	Indigo
·728		Greenish-blue
·826		Light green
·850		Yellow-green
·910	$1\frac{1}{2}$	Yellow
·948		Orange
1·101		Violet-red
1·151		Indigo
1·334		Sea-green
1·426	$2\frac{1}{2}$	Greenish-yellow
1·495		Flesh colour
1·534		Carmine
1·652		Violet-grey
1·682		Greyish-blue
1·711		Dull sea-green
1·744	3	Bluish-green

These effects are seen in the field of the polariscope by a shifting of the coloured bands in the field as the plate is introduced or rotated. If the wedge is furnished with a scale, the shift can be measured, and if the angle of the wedge is found, or calculated from a knowledge of the interval between the dark minima for some homogeneous light for which the extraordinary and ordinary refractive indices are known, the thickness of the plate can be measured. Alternatively, if the thickness of a plate of unknown material is measured, and the double refraction produced is estimated by the shift of the minima in the above manner, the result may be a valuable help in the identification of the substance. This is, in the barest outline, one of the most important of petrographic methods.

The chart of Michel-Levy[4] shows the colours characteristic of different thicknesses of crystal plates of varying bi-refringences, and is a useful adjunct in such work. By methods of this kind, the minerals present in a rock section may be identified.

Babinet's Compensator. Two quartz wedges of equal angle (Fig. 128) may be cut so that the axis directions in the two may be parallel and perpendicular

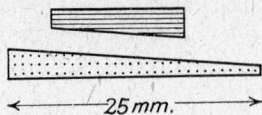

FIG. 128. BABINET COMPENSATOR

respectively to the thin end of the wedge. Together they constitute the equivalent of a plane parallel plate, which produces no ultimate deviation in the direction of the light which is transmitted perpendicular to the plate. When polarized light is transmitted, the ordinary ray in the first becomes the extraordinary in the second, and vice versa, so that if the thicknesses of the two parts traversed by the light are t_1 and t_2, the net relative retardation will be

$$(t_1 - t_2)(n_e - n_o)$$

One wedge can be moved relatively to the other by means of a suitable micrometer screw, the scale and drum of which register the movement very accurately. The position of the central band of zero retardation, found where the wedges have equal thickness, and recognized from the symmetry of the interference colours, can be brought into coincidence with a fixed reference line. With the help of such an instrument, the relative retardation produced by various crystal plates can be readily measured with accuracy by compensating the unknown retardation of the crystal with the measured retardation produced by the instrument.

In case the double refraction differs considerably for different wave-lengths, separate measurements must be made with monochromatic light, as required.

Finding the Slow and Fast Directions. The two directions, parallel and perpendicular to the axis in a uniaxial crystal plate, in which the vibrations of plane polarized light are propagated without change are easily found by examining the plate in a polariscope. Remember that the "vibrations of the light" extinguished by a Nicol analyser are parallel to the longer diagonal of the rhomb end face. R. W. Wood*[5] describes two ingenious methods of finding which of the two directions corresponds to the greatest retardation in a "quarter-wave plate," i.e. one which produces a relative phase difference of 90° between ordinary and extraordinary vibrations and, consequently, circular polarization when held in the proper azimuth in plane polarized light. Once the fast and slow directions of such a plate are known, i.e. the directions in which the refractive indices are smaller and larger respectively, the fast and slow directions of other plates can be found.

One other method of finding these directions is to use a petrological microscope, with polarizer and analyser on a slide which contains some very thin and small quartz crystals, in which the fast direction is perpendicular to the long edges. A thin mica plate placed "fast on fast" over the slide will raise the order of the colour by a maximum amount; the plate is rotated until this occurs, when its fast direction is perpendicular to the long edges of the small crystals. The *exact* angular direction may be checked by examining the same plate in an ordinary polariscope. Another test depending on the examination of the plate in convergent light is explained below.

Quartz. Crystalline quartz belongs to the hexagonal system in which there are three equal "horizontal" axes of symmetry at 120° to each other, and one "vertical" axis. Optically, the crystal may be described as uniaxial in character, but it has certain important characteristics. If polarized light is transmitted along the optical axis, the plane of polarization is rotated, the amount being about 21° 67' per millimetre.

The conventional terminology calls a rotation "right-handed" when it is clockwise to an observer facing the source of light, and vice versa.

Varieties of quartz are known in which the rotation is right-handed and left-handed respectively, and the crystals show characteristic differences. Fig. 129 illustrates the appearances of the crystal faces in the two cases.

---

* It is probable that a number of alternative methods could be devised, such as putting the plate into the path of one of two interfering polarized beams and watching the shift of the fringes as the plate is rotated.

Fresnel explained the rotation effect by supposing that plane polarized light, when traversing the quartz crystal parallel to the axis, is resolved into two circularly polarized beams which are propagated with slightly different velocities. A linear vibration can be looked upon as the result of two circular motions in which the

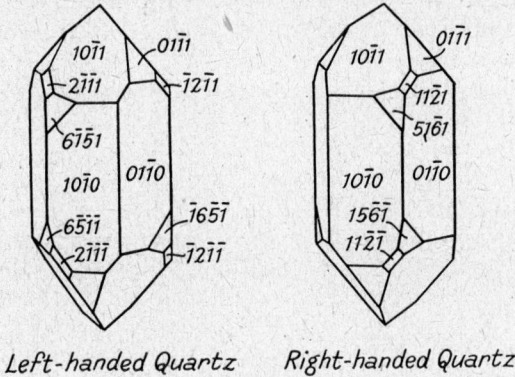

Left-handed Quartz   Right-handed Quartz

FIG. 129

direction of rotation is opposite. If the relative phase is subject to change due to the unequal velocities, the direction of the vibration will change by 90° for every 180° change of phase.

A 60° quartz prism cut with its axis parallel to the base of an equilateral section will clearly show two images of the slit when

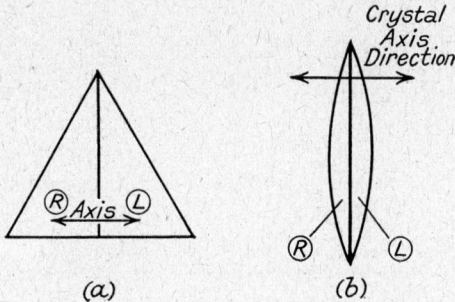

(a)   (b)

FIG. 130

mounted in a spectrometer to give minimum deviation when the light traverses the crystal along the axis.[6] If the images are examined with an analyser held behind the eyepiece, it will be found that they do not vary much in intensity as the analyser is rotated. They might, therefore, be non-polarized or circularly polarized. If, however, the light is transmitted through a $\lambda/4$ plate, it will be understood

from the foregoing work that the passing of light perpendicular
to the axis through a distance sufficient to cause a relative retardation of $\lambda/4$ or a phase difference of 90°, converts a circular vibration
into a linear one. The light becomes plane polarized and can be
extinguished by the analyser, thus showing that the two components
were circularly polarized, in accordance with Fresnel's theory.

Cornu's device for overcoming this doubling is shown in Fig. 130.
The 60° prism is now made in two parts, of right-handed and left-
handed quartz respectively. This type of construction may be
applied to lenses and lens systems. The two parts of a condenser
lens of quartz are right- and left-
handed, and even a Ramsden eyepiece in quartz, in which the lenses
are of equal power, is improved by
making the field lens and eye lens
of the two varieties.

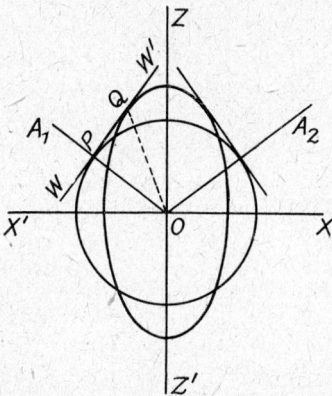

Low-power spectacle lenses are
sometimes constructed from blanks
cut parallel to the axis of quartz
crystal, but it is better for all
lenses in quartz to be "cut perpendicular to the axis," so that
the optical axis of the lens and
the crystallographic optic axis are
parallel. Lenses in quartz are
only satisfactory for purposes in
which the extreme rays only make small angles with the axis,
not more than 5° to 10°; the effects of double refraction become
increasingly apparent at larger angles.

Biaxial Crystals. The term "biaxial" has nothing to do with
crystallographic axes, but simply with "optic axes." If a disturbance starts at a point within a biaxial crystal, the wave-fronts spread
out in two sheets; the section of the surfaces by each of the principal Cartesian planes gives a circle and an ellipse. Such a pair of
sections (XZ plane) are shown in Fig. 131. Now, imagining the wave-
fronts shown in this section to be propagated in a manner similar to
that discussed in previous cases, the velocity of a plane wave parallel
to the tangent at any point Q of the ellipse will be the velocity of
the tangent normal to itself. In the section shown, there is a tangent
common to the ellipsoid and the circle. It is further proved in
textbooks of physical optics that the crossing point of the circle
and ellipse in this section of the two wave-fronts is the lowest point
of a kind of dimple in the outer surface formed by the two sheets

FIG. 131

of the wave-front. An apple resting on a plate may touch the plate at points in a circle round the dimple of the core, and in the same way a tangent surface can be found which touches the outer surface in a circle. The normal to this surface is a direction of single wave-velocity and forms one axis of the biaxial crystal. A_1 and A_2 represent the two axis directions in the section shown in Fig. 131. Imagining the circle to increase in radius relatively to the ellipse, the two axis directions would evidently approach each other and would finally coincide when vertical; if the circle shrinks, both axes will approach the direction of the x axis.

The Monoclinic System. Selenite or Gypsum and Muscovite Mica. Two minerals of importance from the optical point of view crystallize in the monoclinic system, viz. selenite and muscovite (mica). Both of these, but especially mica, have a very marked and perfect cleavage. Skilled hands produce very large, even sheets of mica, by inserting a pin between the lamellae, followed by a piece of

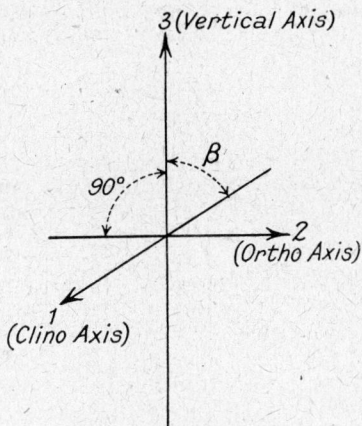

FIG. 132. AXES OF THE MONO-CLINIC SYSTEM

stiff paper with a curved end, which is used to spread the cleavage. Flakes can be obtained so thin as to show interference colours, and plates of muscovite obtained of very uniform thickness which can be used for optical purposes. This is not often the case with selenite; it is extremely difficult to obtain good cleavage plates, but the mineral is very soft and can be easily ground and polished, so that quarter-wave plates, etc., can be constructed from it.

Mica can only just be scratched by the finger-nail, but selenite is easily marked in this way.

In the monoclinic system (Fig. 132) the vertical axis (3) and the horizontal axis (2) are at right angles, but the other (*clino*) axis is not perpendicular to (3), although it is perpendicular to (2). The angle β shown in the figure may have different values in various crystals.

In gypsum or selenite the parameters are $a : b : c = 0.68994 :$ $1 : 0.41241$ and $\beta = 80° 42'$. In muscovite, $a : b : c = 0.57735 :$ $1 : 3.3128$ and $\beta = 89° 54'$. Fig. 133 shows a selenite crystal with "prism" faces f, "hemi-pyramids" l, and "clino-pinacoid" p. The best cleavage is parallel to the clino-pinacoid, which is itself parallel to the plane of symmetry of the crystal containing the clino axis and the vertical axis. This plane of symmetry contains the optic axes of the crystal.

Fig. 134 shows a crystal of muscovite, in which b is the "clino-pinacoid" and c is the "basal pinacoid," while the faces m and o are prism faces. The cleavage in muscovite is parallel to the basal pinacoid, and the cleavage surface is within two degrees of per-pendicularity to the acute bisectrix of the optical axial angle; the optic axes lie (as in selenite) in the plane of symmetry of the mono-clinic crystal. When cleavage plates of muscovite (or selenite) are

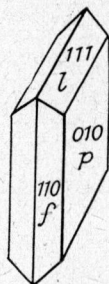

FIG. 133. SELENITE OR GYPSUM

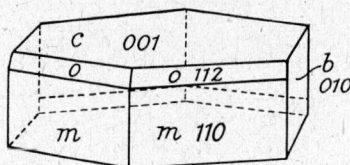

FIG. 134. MUSCOVITE MICA

examined in a polariscope in parallel light, they behave very simi-larly to plates of uniaxial crystal cut parallel to the axis, and the slow direction of vibration for muscovite is at right angles to the line in which the optical axial plane intersects the cleavage surface. Hence, these cleavage plates are very useful for constructing quarter-wave plates, etc. If a sufficiently wide angle transmission can be secured, the directions of the axes can be found by examining the mica plate in convergent light. Then the slow direction is perpen-dicular to the line through the "eyes" (see below).

The effective values of the refractive indices may vary with the specimen of mica employed. In one case their values were 1·603 and 1·595. To calculate the thickness t for a quarter-wave plate,

$$\lambda/4 = t(n_2 - n_1)$$

$$t = \frac{0.589 \times 10^{-3}}{4 \times 0.008} = 0.0184 \text{ mm.}$$

If plates of higher retardation are required, they are often made from selenite, which is more colourless than mica. In the clino-pinacoid cleavage, the maximum difference of refractive indices (measure of bi-refringence) is 0·0095. Hence, for a 1λ retardation plate the thickness required is

$$t = \frac{0·589 \times 10^{-3}}{0·0095} = 0·062 \text{ mm.}$$

In a quartz plate cut parallel to the axis, the bi-refringence is 0·009.

Crystal Plates in Convergent Polarized Light. Fig. 135 is intended to represent a block of uniaxial crystal cut with the axis normal to the surface, and thus parallel to the incident normal ray BA, which may be imagined as the central ray of a bundle of rays diverging from the point B. These rays are all polarized so that the vibrations are vertical, say, while the line BA is horizontal. It is evident that the vibrations entering the plate along the lines CAC′ or DAD′ will

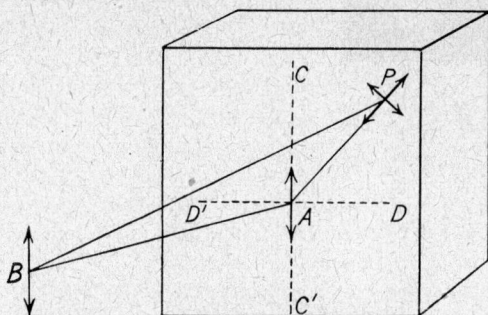

Fig. 135

be transmitted unchanged, since they will be respectively *in* and perpendicular to a principal section of the crystal containing the ray and optic axis.

Consider the oblique ray BP. The vertical vibration will be resolved at P into vibrations parallel and perpendicular to the principal section plane BPA, and these vibrations will be transmitted with differing velocities, emerging therefore with a difference of phase which depends on the angle of obliquity of incidence PBA.

All rays at the same obliquity will have the same retardation; hence, the lines of equal retardation will be circles with centres on the line of symmetry BA. As in other cases, the relative retardation increases most rapidly with the shorter wave-length. If the light transmitted by the plate is passed through an analyser "crossed" with respect to the original polarizer, the appearance obtained is shown in Fig. 136 for the case of monochromatic light. The dark circular fringes mark the zones where the retardation amounts to a whole number of wave-lengths, so that the vibrations in the transmitted light are parallel to their original directions before transmission.

If the light employed is white, the fringes will be coloured in a similar way to that which arises in Newton's rings or the colours in a wedge.

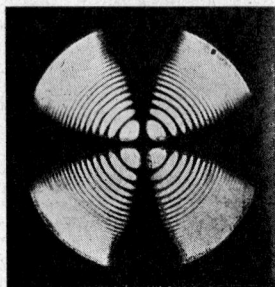

FIG. 136. CALCITE PLATE
CUT PERPENDICULAR TO
THE AXIS
Examined in convergent light
Nicols crossed.

Reference must be made to textbooks of physical optics for the theory of isochromatic surfaces. It is shown that surfaces may be found in crystals for which the retardation is constant (imagining disturbances to originate within the crystal, being propagated in all directions, and subject to resolution into components as explained above). In a uniaxial crystal the surfaces are hyperboloids of revolution, as suggested in Fig. 137, the line of symmetry is the optic axis, and the central point of the whole system is the origin of the light.

If now we have a crystal plate cut parallel to the axis, the dark fringes seen with divergent or convergent light will be hyperbolas. If, again, the axis makes a small angle with the normal to the surface, the section of the system of hyperboloids with the surface will

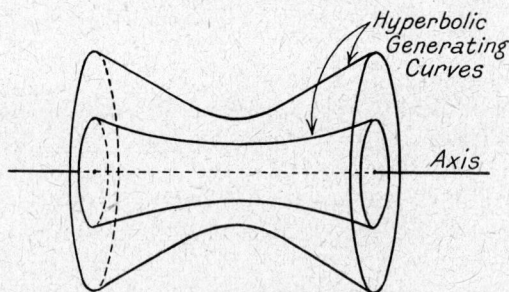

FIG. 137. TWO ISOCHROMATIC SURFACES FOR A UNIAXIAL CRYSTAL

be a system of closed curves, with their centres to one side of the central ray to an extent varying with the obliquity of the surface.

The form of the isochromatic surface in biaxial crystals resembles a jointed tube (Fig. 138), which may intersect a crystal surface in two closed curves. The systems of closed curves corresponding to isochromatic surfaces of different retardations constitute the "eyes" of the interference figure. Fig. 139 shows a characteristic interference figure for a plate of biaxial crystal; the distance between the "eyes" is a measure of the angle between the axes.

In all crystals there will usually also be found curves along which the vibration directions remain constant; these "curves" take the form of a cross with a uniaxial crystal; the arms of the cross are respectively parallel and perpendicular to the vibration direction. In a biaxial crystal these curves (called *isogyres*) have various forms; they are seen in the figure as curved "brushes" narrowing down to pass through the eyes of the interference figure.

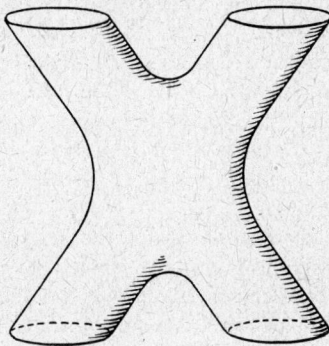

FIG. 138. ISOCHROMATIC SURFACE IN BIAXIAL CRYSTAL

These various phenomena are very simply exhibited by holding the crystal between "crossed" tourmaline crystals or Polaroid plates.

In order to obtain a better rendering of the effects, with a wider angular field also, the crystal plates are mounted in a microscope, and the appearances in the upper focal plane of the objective are viewed with the aid of a "Bertrand lens." Reference will be made to this when dealing with applications of the microscope in Part II of the present book.

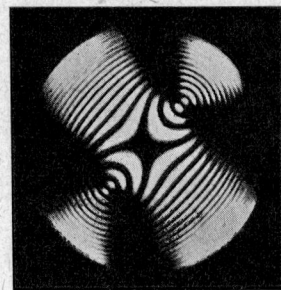

FIG. 139. BIAXIAL CRYSTAL PLATE IN CONVERGENT LIGHT

Section equally inclined to the two optic axes.

If biaxial crystal plates are mounted so that they can be rotated about an axis perpendicular to the direction of view, and are so placed that the two "eyes" are successively brought on to the central crosswire of the microscope, the apparent angle α between the axes (light refracted into air) can be measured with the help of a small divided circle to indicate the rotation. If the mean index of refraction n of the crystal is known, the true angle α_0 between the optic axes may be found from

$$\sin\left(\frac{\alpha_0}{2}\right) = \frac{1}{n}\sin\left(\frac{\alpha}{2}\right)$$

It is sometimes the case that the crystal must be immersed in a suitable liquid in order to get the light to traverse the plate in the direction of the axes.

The tests in convergent polarized light are very useful for determining the character of a crystal. Textbooks of crystallography describe simple tests with a quarter-wave plate to determine whether a uniaxial crystal is positive or negative. In view of the importance of the whole subject in mineralogy, it has undergone a wide development.

Methods involving the use of the polarization microscope are of growing importance in the study of colloids and in biological investigations.

Determination of the Axis Direction. The determination of the axis direction in a crystal of quartz or calcite is comparatively easy if the crystal is undistorted and the various faces can be recognized. Calcite may assume a variety of forms, but its cleavage planes are a definite indication. Quartz or calcite crystals can be mounted on a rotating table so as to rotate about the optic axis; only then can the pyramid faces be brought (by such rotation) into truly parallel directions, so that collimated (or parallel) light reflected from them is brought to the same focus in an observing telescope. The crystal is mounted on the turntable with wax.

Good crystals of quartz usually show lines on the alternate faces, which are perpendicular to the optic axis.

If the crystal is damaged so that the faces cannot be readily distinguished, it is usually cut into a plate for examination in a polariscope. Examination in convergent light quickly reveals whether the crystal is optically "uniaxial" or "biaxial," and indicates the positions of the axis or axes. The direction of the axis of a uniaxial crystal can in general be found by polishing two pairs of opposite parallel faces on the material, and examining with a simple polariscope. (See ref. 7 at end of chapter.)

Very frequently, "twinning" may occur; there may be a plane of division in the material (to casual observation quite homogeneous) on each side of which the axis direction and optical qualities are quite different. Such parts must be avoided for optical purposes and they are readily recognized with the polariscope. The writer has met with "pebble" spectacles (of quartz) which gave the greatest discomfort to the wearer through twinning of the crystal in the lens.

Pleochroism. Certain doubly refracting crystals exhibit marked differences of absorption for light vibrations occurring in different directions. One of the best-known examples is *tourmaline*. In this crystal the ordinary ray, vibrating perpendicular to the crystal axis, is absorbed in a comparatively thin layer, while the extra-ordinary ray is still transmitted. The "green" frequencies show the least absorption in the "extraordinary" components. A "pair of tourmalines," therefore, constitutes a simple polarizer and analyser; they are often convenient for examining the interference figures of crystal plates, and distinguishing between uniaxial and biaxial crystals.

Other crystals showing pleochroism are *iolite, ruby,* and certain forms of *biotite.*

New Polarizing Materials. An artificially produced crystal, *sulphate of iodo-quinine,* prepared by Herapath[8] in 1852, and named "Herapathite" after him, was found to have extremely marked pleochroism; an extremely small thickness of the material will suffice to absorb vibrations parallel to one direction. A special technical method has been found by E. H. Land for the preparation of films of transparent media containing microscopic crystals (of such properties) in suspension, all arranged with their principal axes mutually parallel. The suspension is sufficiently dense to polarize almost completely the light transmitted by the film. In a recent form of this material (*Polaroid*) the pleochroic crystals are said to be produced by a special physical process from the plastic medium in which they are embedded, no compound of iodine being used.

A sheet of such a material performs all the functions of a polarizer or analyser, with efficiency adequate for ordinary purposes of observation, i.e. microscopy, etc.; but in some preparations there is a small residual transmission when the plates are crossed, so that their use in measuring instruments, polarimeters, etc., cannot be recommended.

Sodium Nitrate. In reference to the preparation of large halide crystals (p. 251), a similar technique has been applied to produce large single crystals of *sodium nitrate.* This material is doubly re-fracting, and can be used to replace *calcite* in the manufacture of polarizing prisms. Like calcite, its crystalline form is the Holo-symmetrical class of the Rhombohedral division, and the angles between the cleavage faces are 78° 30', as against the 74° 55' of calcite.

Polarimetry. The power of quartz in rotating the plane of polar-ization of light traversing the crystal in an axial direction is also possessed by other "optically active" substances, and even by certain solutions. Thus, cane sugar solution produces a rotation which is naturally independent of the direction of transmission through the liquid, but is very closely proportional to the weight of the active material dissolved in unit volume of the solution. The rotation increases the shorter the wave-length of light (rotary dispersion), and varies to some extent with temperature, but the phenomenon provides a ready means of ascertaining the strength of sugar solutions by simple optical observations and is, therefore, of great importance in industry.

In the polarimeter, observations are usually made with monochromatic light (Mercury green $\lambda = 0.546\mu$ is now used in preference to sodium light), but in industrial instruments, known as *saccharimeters*, white light may be employed. This is possible because

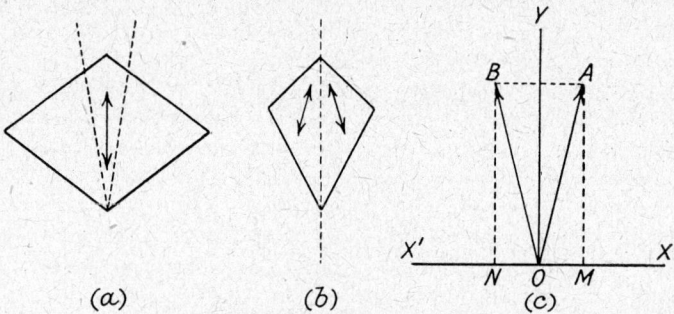

(a)   (b)   (c)

FIG. 140

instead of measuring the angle of rotation of the polarized light directly it is *compensated* by a wedge of quartz, from which graduated compensatory rotations can be obtained. Since the rotary dispersions of sugar solutions and of quartz are not greatly different, the colour phenomena are not troublesome, and the only precaution required is the use of a yellow filter to shorten the spectral range of the light.

The earliest form of polarimeter employed simply a polarizing prism, a tube with flat ends to hold the solution, and an analyser. The analyser could be set into the extinction position before the tube was introduced; the analyser had to be turned through a certain angle to restore the extinction with the tube in place. (The conventional terminology due to Biot calls a clockwise rotation *seen when facing the source of light* a positive or right-handed rotation, and vice versa.)

This simple device fails because the extinction is so far complete for positions of the analyser *near* the real extinction position that the transmitted light cannot be readily recognized, especially as stray light is difficult to eliminate entirely. This led to the invention of instruments in which the "end-point device" gave a field in which the two halves yielded light polarized in slightly different directions. Fig. 140 (a) shows an end view of an ordinary "Nicol," with the transmission vibration directions parallel to the shorter diagonal. This can be cut in two and the parts within the dotted lines removed; the outer parts are then brought together, as shown in Fig. 140 (b), so that the light transmitted by the two parts will vibrate in inclined directions. Let these directions and amplitudes be represented by the vectors OA, OB in Fig. 140 (c), then the amplitudes of the vibrations transmitted by an analyser, for which the transmission direction is parallel to the X axis, will be represented

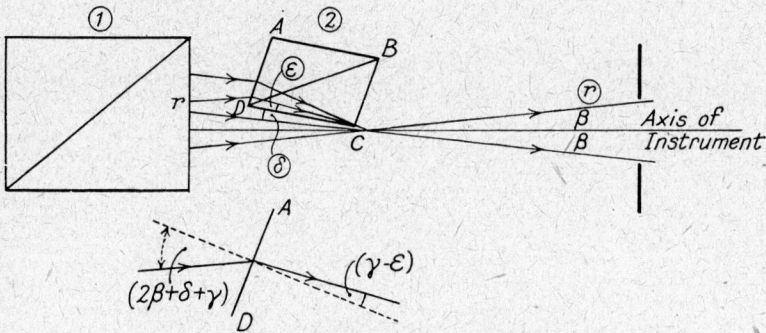

FIG. 141. OPTICAL PRINCIPLES OF LIPPICH END-POINT
Note that the convergence and bending of the rays on entering the auxiliary prism, and also the tilt of the prism are exaggerated for the sake of a clear figure.

by the projected lengths OM, ON. These are equal for one position of the analyser not far from the extinction point of both, but far enough to obtain a field of sufficient brightness. It is easily shown that this mode of setting is much more sensitive. The rotary action of the "sugar solution" is, of course, to rotate each vibration by the same extent, so that the rotation can be measured as before.

The above end-point device, known as the Jellet-Cornu prism, is not now often encountered, a device due to Lippich being more commonly employed. In this device the polarizer, a square-ended prism (1), Fig. 141, which may be of the Glan-Thompson type, is followed by a second smaller polarizing prism, which, in the simplest form, covers one-half the aperture. The polarizing direction of the second is inclined at a small finite angle to that of the first. Hence, of the vibrations from the first prism which enter the second one, it is only the parts resolved in the vibration direction of the second which are transmitted in one-half of the field; the field is thus divided as with the Jellet-Cornu device.

The observer sights upon the edge of the small prism dividing the field in two parts, and it is necessary so to place it that the whole field is illuminated without a gap. In the first place the prism edge at C must be ground perfectly sharp. If the semi-aperture of the cone of light diverging from C and entering the entrance pupil of the observing system is β, it must be possible to displace a convergent cone of the same angular semi-aperture, which enters the face AD of the second prism, and bring its focus to C, as suggested in the figure. A little consideration will show that cones transmitted by AD which try to come to a focus below C will be totally reflected at DC, and that there will be no dark or bright gap in the field.

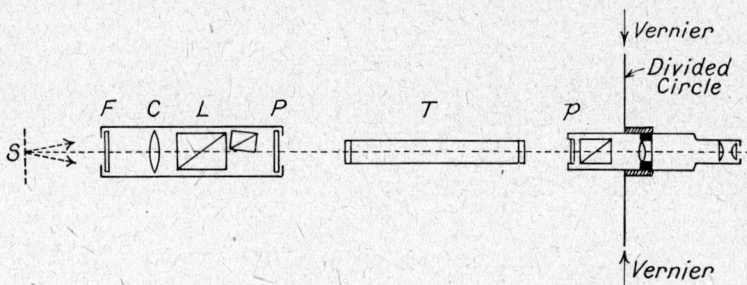

FIG. 142. OPTICAL DIAGRAM OF LIPPICH-TYPE POLARIMETER

Referring to the figure, the angle made by DC with the axis of the instrument is $\beta + \delta$. Let the ray shown by r make an angle of ε with the face DC after refraction, and let the angle $\widehat{ADC} = 90° - \gamma$. Then the angle of incidence of the ray r is $2\beta + \delta + \gamma$ and its angle of refraction will be $(\gamma - \varepsilon)$. If the law of refraction held, we should have (since the angles are small) $2\beta + \delta + \gamma = n(\gamma - \varepsilon)$ or, say, $2\beta + \delta + \gamma = 1 \cdot 5 (\gamma - \varepsilon)$, giving at once

$$\gamma = 4\beta + 3\varepsilon + 2\delta$$

Now, ε and δ may be made quite small, say, about 10′, so that if the last two terms add to 1° and β is, say, 0·5°, the angle of the prism would have to be 87° or thereabouts.

Such rhombs in glass are of fairly frequent use in optical instruments. However, in this case the prism is of spar and doubly refracting. If it is one of the Glan-Thompson type (slightly modified), the optic axis will be perpendicular to the plane of the diagram, so that the ordinary law of refraction will be obeyed as the extraordinary wave-front section will be circular. If, however, another form of prism should be used the extraordinary ray, which is the one transmitted by the prism, may not obey the usual law of refraction, and care must therefore be taken to make sure that the rays can follow the required course.

Fig. 142 shows a diagram of the optical system of the Lippich type polarimeter. In recent forms of the instrument the field has three parts, two auxiliary prisms being used as suggested. An image of the source of light is projected by the lens C into the entrance pupil of the observing telescope. In the figure, S is the source of light, L the Lippich end-point, F a colour filter for use with sodium light, T is the tube for holding the solution, and P and p are windows for protection of the prisms.

Saccharimeters usually possess end-point devices similar to those used in polarimeters, but as mentioned above, they employ wedges to compensate the rotation instead of measuring it directly. Further details of such instruments will be found in the present writer's book on *Optical Measuring Instruments*, while details of technical methods will be found in the Bureau of Standards' useful paper on "Polarimetry" (*Circular No.* 44).

REFERENCES

1. S. P. Thompson: *Proc. Phys. Soc.* 2 (1877).
2. S. P. Thompson: *Proc. Opt. Convention*, p. 216 (1905).
3. W. Grosse: *Zeit. f. Inst.* X, 445 (1890).
4. Michel Lévy et A. Lacroix: "*Les Mineraux des Roches*," Paris, 1888. (See also Johannsen: *Petrographic Methods*, New York, 1918.)
5. R. W. Wood: *Physical Optics*, p. 329.
6. Cornu: *Comptes Rendues*, 92, 13th June (1881); *Journal de Physique* 1, 2e serie, 157 (1882).
(Cornu reaches the conclusion that the two refractive indices for the axis direction have the "ordinary" refractive index as their mean.)
7. J. Walker: *Phil. Mag.*, July, 1909, p. 195. Other unpublished methods of getting quartz to axis to high accuracy are in use by technicians.
8. W. B. Herepath: *Phil. Mag.* 3, 161 (1852).

CHAPTER VII

THE PROPERTIES OF RADIATION IN REGARD TO MATTER

THE study and measurement of radiation is now such a vast field that reference must be made to books and papers on Physical Optics* for an adequate discussion of the subject, but there are many phenomena of importance to the student of applied optics, and a brief account of the underlying principles may be of service.

For most purposes, "light" (using the term in its broadest meaning) may be regarded as an electro-magnetic vibratory disturbance

Wave-length (in microns)	Wave-number (reciprocal of wave-length expressed in cm.)	Characteristic of Radiation
(Approx.) ·00001	10^{10} to 10^8	Gamma rays (from radium).
·00001 to ·005	10^9 to 10^7	Röntgen or X-rays of varying "hardness."
0·1 to 0·2	10^5 to 5×10^4	Extreme ultra-violet region explored by Schumann.
0·12	8·4 ,,	Short wave-length limit of transmission of fluorite.
0·185	5·9 ,,	Short wave limit for quartz. Air becomes relatively opaque for shorter waves.
0·2 to 0·39	5·0 to 2·54 ,,	Ordinary ultra-violet region. Chemically and physiologically active radiation.
0·39 to 0·77	2·54 to 1·3 ,,	Visible radiation.
0·39 to 0·43	2·54 to 2·32 ,,	Violet.
0·43 to 0·47	2·32 to 2·13 ,,	Blue.
0·47 to 0·5	2·13 to 2·00 ,,	Blue-green.
0·5 to 0·53	2·00 to 1·89 ,,	Green.
0·53 to 0·56	1·89 to 1·79 ,,	Yellow-green.
0·56 to 0·59	1·79 to 1·69 ,,	Yellow.
0·59 to 0·62	1·69 to 1·61 ,,	Orange.
0·62 to 0·77	1·61 to 1·30 ,,	Red.
0·77 to 1·0	1·30 to 1·00 ,,	Near infra-red. Can be explored by photography.
1·0 to 20	1·00 to 0·05 ,,	Infra-red or "heat" radiations. Spectrum explored by thermo-pile or bolometer.
20 to 500	$0·05 \times 10^4$ to 20	Radiations also studied by special thermometric methods.
500 to 10^{10} or beyond.	20 to 10^{-6}	Waves detected by electrical methods.

* *Physical Optics,* by R. W. Wood (Macmillan), may be suggested for a comprehensive survey.

capable of being propagated through space from its sources in hot bodies, electrical discharges, etc., and having observable properties dependent largely on its frequency. Though the frequency is the more fundamental characteristic, the properties are usually described in relation to the wave-length in air, which is conveniently expressed either in relation to the micron, 10^{-3} mm. (symbol μ); the milli-micron, 10^{-6} mm. ($m\mu$); or the Angstrom, 10^{-7} mm. (A).

The table on p. 226 surveys the range of observed radiation. The "ultra-violet" comprises wave-lengths shorter than about 0.39μ down to a (terminologically uncertain) boundary beyond which the radiation would be termed X-rays; the "infrared" comprises a region of wave-lengths longer than about 0.77μ down to the range of "electric waves." The production of spectra by prisms or gratings, and the measurement of refractive index and wavelength, etc., is thoroughly described in most textbooks on "Light."

The distribution of energy in the spectrum of a hot body giving a continuous spectrum is a function of the tempera-ture. In the ideal case the

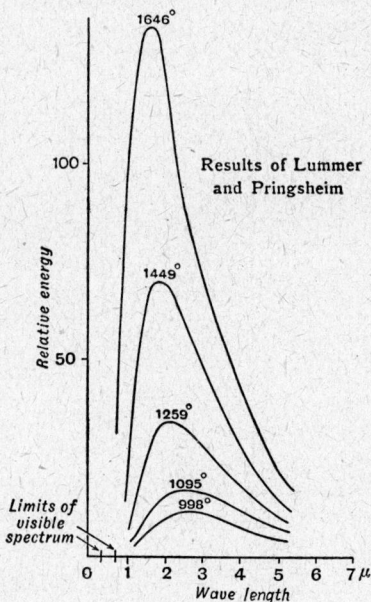

FIG 143

total emission of energy is proportional to the fourth power of the absolute temperature; the ideally efficient radiator (the "black body" of radiation theory; charcoal comes fairly close to the ideal) has an energy distribution at various temperatures represented by Fig. 143. It will be noticed that the visible spectrum occupies a comparatively restricted region in the diagram; most of the energy of hot bodies at the temperatures shown is found in the long-wave heat radiations. As the temperature rises, the maximum energy is found at shorter and shorter wave-lengths. In applied optics, the distribution of energy for various sources is of some importance, and Fig. 144 gives curves for various natural and artificial sources of light. The sun's radiation corresponds roughly to that of a "black body" at 5000° C., a temperature unattainable in practical sources of artificial light; the light from a blue sky has an even greater *relative* energy in the violet end of the spectrum.

Planck has given an expression for the distribution of energy in the spectrum of a black body—

$$E = c_1 \left[\lambda^5 \left\{ \exp\left(\frac{c_2}{\lambda T}\right) - 1 \right\} \right]^{-1}$$

where c_1 and c_2 are constants, e is the natural base of logarithms, and

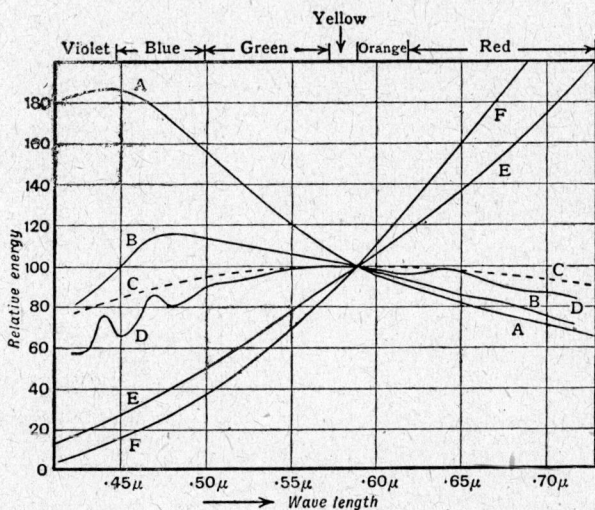

FIG. 144. ENERGY DISTRIBUTION IN THE SPECTRA OF VARIOUS ILLUMINANTS

A. Blue sky.
B. High sun (data from Smithsonian Institution).
C. Black body at 5000° C.
D. Low sun (Smithsonian).
E. Gas-filled tungsten lamp.
F. Acetylene flame.

T is the absolute temperature. For the region of the visible spectrum and shorter wave-lengths, the formula of Wien

$$E = c_1 \left(\lambda^5 \exp \frac{c_2}{\lambda T} \right)^{-1}$$

is sufficiently accurate.

The Constitution of Matter. The usual "picture" of the atom, still of value though modified by more recent wave-mechanical theories, envisages a very small but relatively massive *nucleus* carrying a positive electrical charge around which revolve discrete groups of "electrons" in "shells" characterised by corresponding levels of energy. The electrons are small charges of negative electricity, and the positive and negative charges balance in a neutral atom. The mass of an electron is only $1/1846$ of the mass of a hydrogen nucleus. While the "radius" of an atom (including the shells of electrons) is of the order of 10^{-7} mm. (so that the wave-length of visible light is 5,000 times larger), the radius of the nucleus is of the order of 10^{-12} mm., and that of an electron about the same; but the interpretation of the idea of size in such cases has a complexity which cannot be discussed here. Born gives the following comparison: "If we imagine a drop of water to be expanded to the size of the earth, and all the atoms in it also enlarged in the same proportion, an atom will have a diameter of a few metres. The diameter of the nucleus, however, will be only something like $1/100$ mm."

A *molecule* consists of a group of nuclei, each of which may be surrounded by "shells" of revolving electrons, but certain electrons may be shared by two or more nuclei; thus in this and other ways the whole system is held in a stable configuration. If the centroid of the positive charges does not coincide with that of the negative charges, the system is said to be a "dipole." The distances between the centroids may further be subject to oscillatory movement, or the molecule may rotate (as in the case of gases), as the result of the influence of the electro-magnetic vibrations of light from which it may thus acquire energy. It may lose energy again by acting as the source of similar radiation.

A *crystal* consists of groups of atoms, arranged in a recurring pattern known as a lattice (see p. 192), so that, in fact, the identity of the separate molecules is merged in the larger grouping. Although there can (in general) be no independent rotation of the molecules, such crystal systems are capable of various characteristic electrical and other vibrations, involving spatial regions of the material large in comparison with the nuclear separations.

As against a crystal, a refracting substance like glass consists of groups of molecules which are again held together by interlocking electrostatic forces, but in which no completely systematic arrangement of the atoms is found. It would appear that, in glass, specially strong linkages bind the silicon and oxygen atoms together. When the other atoms (calcium, lead, etc.) are removed by chemical reagents, a skeleton structure of silica is often left, still of a non-crystalline character. In the case of a "homogeneous" substance, the structural irregularities are small in comparison with the wave-length of light, so that the average properties in elements of volume comparable in size with the wave-length do not differ from place to place. A structure of this kind will appear structureless in its action on light.

There may be substances, like imperfectly fused quartz, which contain small crystalline aggregates fused into a vitreous (glass-like) matrix. Many translucent substances, such as hair, horn, etc., have a structure in which very large complex molecules, often easily deformable, are grouped in a fairly regular way, so that the materials exhibit many characteristics of a crystal. Increase of temperature of a solid substance involves increased movement of the inter-molecular linking electrons, so that the liquid and gaseous stages correspond respectively to the partial and complete breakdown of the cohesive forces. Provided, however, that the above statistical condition of homogeneity is satisfied, the substance will exhibit no visible structure.

Outline of the Theory of Dispersion, etc. The main facts of reflection, refraction, and dispersion were accounted for satisfactorily in the classical theories, which owed much of their development to mechanical analogies; the more recent "quantum-mechanical" theories have modified the older account in some ways without destroying its pictorial value, and a verbal sketch of it may be of assistance. The ordinary account applies to gases with independently vibrating molecules; the cases of liquids and solids need some modification of the treatment.

When the electro-magnetic wave traverses a material medium, it sets the dipoles into "forced vibrations," having the same period as the wave. If this frequency is a small fraction of the fixed natural period of the dipole oscillators, the phase lag will be negligible, provided the damping* is negligible. If damping is present, it can be shown that the phase lag will increase as the wave frequency increases; it will reach a lag of 90° when the oscillator frequency is reached and resonant vibration takes place; and the lag will further increase towards 180° with increasing wave frequency. On the other hand, if damping is consistently negligible, the lag shows a tendency to a more *abrupt* change from 0° to 180°, if the increasing wave frequency passes through the oscillator frequency.

The vibration of the dipoles now gives rise to secondary waves, which are propagated in all directions; the resultant at any point is the sum of the "original wave" displacement *plus* the sum of the secondary displacements. So far as certain internal high-frequency modes of oscillation are concerned, they can often occur without inter-molecular vibrations; but if resonant vibration is approached,

---

* "Damping" is the term given to the loss of energy of a vibration through such causes as friction in the case of mechanical oscillations or resistance in electrical oscillations, etc., so that the amplitude diminishes.

the disturbances will become very large, and energy is absorbed, usually to be converted into heat.

If there is a plane wave of intensity I, and the loss of energy in a thickness dx of the medium is dI, then

$$dI/I = -\alpha dx \qquad . \qquad . \qquad . \qquad (701)$$

where α is the coefficient of loss. An integration of this equation for a thickness x of the material gives

$$I = I_o \exp(-\alpha x) \qquad . \qquad . \qquad (702)$$

where I_o is the initial and I the final intensity. There is a sense in which distinction should be made between "scattering" and

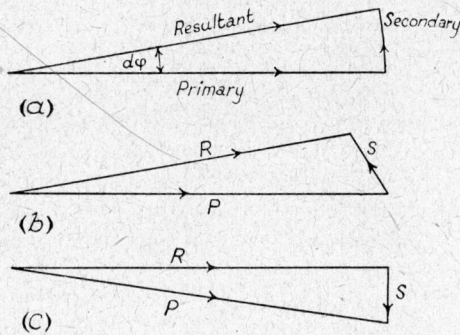

FIG. 145

genuine "absorption" in which energy is lost in heat, but a similar exponential law applies to the energy of the transmitted beam in both cases.

Now referring to Huygens' principle, it will be remembered that if the secondary wavelets originate at an infinity of points on a plane wave surface of uniform amplitude, there is no resultant lateral scattering. Thus, if there is no lateral scattering and no dissipation of energy into heat, etc., all the energy travels onward in the resultant wave system (the absence of a back wave is explained in the full mathematical theory); however, the secondary waves from the oscillators in a thin layer parallel to the wave surface have a resultant at any point, which has a phase corresponding to a path length greater by $\lambda/4$ than the original wave (see p. 87). Thus the theory formulates the relative amplitude and phase of a secondary resultant from a very thin layer of thickness dx, containing N oscillators per unit volume. The amplitude of the secondary waves will be proportional to the sum of the waves from the first Fresnel zone (area $\pi c\lambda$), where c is the distance of the point from the thin layer. Consequently, if the amplitude of the primary wave is P, that of the secondary will be $KP\lambda Ndx$, where K is a constant. The phase angle of the secondary is $90°$; consequently the resultant has a phase lag $d\phi$ given by

$$d\phi = KP\lambda Ndx/P = K\lambda Ndx$$

Fig. 145 (a) represents the relevant phase and amplitude diagram. The retardation of the resultant wave in terms of refractive index (n) is given by

$$(2\pi/\lambda)\ (n - 1)dx = K\lambda Ndx,$$

so that $$n - 1 = K\lambda^2 N/2\pi\ .\qquad.\qquad.\qquad(703)$$

This expression shows at once that if the pressure of a gas is increased, the number of molecules per unit volume being proportional to the pressure (p), then

$$n - 1 = cp\quad.\qquad.\qquad.\qquad.\qquad(704)$$

where n is the refractive index and c is a constant.

If the substance is not homogeneous, some of the energy is lost in scattering; this corresponds to a damping of the oscillators, and the full theory shows that the absorption coefficient is then proportional to N. To show the dependence on λ, Lord Rayleigh[1] found that scattering coefficient α is given by

$$\alpha = \text{constant} \times (n - 1)^2 N^{-1} \lambda^{-4}\quad.\qquad.\qquad(705)$$

The use of this equation to explain selective effects in scattering, e.g. the blue colour of the sky, is explained in books on Light. It is to be pointed out as important that scattering only occurs in the presence of inhomogeneity of the medium or variations of the amplitude in the wave front.

A substance which is homogeneous to ordinary light may be deficient in the ultra-violet region; for example, a poor specimen of fused quartz may be a poor ultra-violet transmitter as compared with a well-fused and homogeneous sample if it loses energy by scattering of the shorter waves.

The theory shows that if the secondary vibration is damped, its phase will lag further behind that of the primary wave. The phase angle of the secondary component now exceeds $90°$; see Fig. 145 (b). This gives a resultant R, which is less than the primary wave; the lost energy has been scattered. It needs a fuller analysis to show the effect of the natural period of the oscillators on the amplitude of the forced vibrations; but it is understandable that if the wave frequency approaches the natural oscillator frequency, the amplitude tends to increase greatly, and therewith the lag of the phase of the resultant, i.e. the refractive index, will tend to increase. But if the frequency of the wave exceeds that of the oscillators, the phase angle of the secondary increases to 180° (as remarked above), so that we may now find a resultant with an apparent lead of phase, Fig. 145 (c). The refractive index would be now less than unity, and this agrees with the observed properties of many materials; see the remarks below in the refractive index of glass, etc., for X-rays.

There are many reservations in adapting such a theory to solids or liquids, where the oscillators are not independent, but similar considerations appear. Fig. 146 represents the general form of a typical dispersion curve for a substance having absorption bands corresponding to natural oscillator frequencies ν_0 and ν_1. Theory leads to an equation of the type represented by the curve, i.e.

$$n^2 - 1 = \frac{A}{\nu_0^2 - \nu^2} + \frac{B}{\nu_1^2 - \nu^2} \qquad . \qquad (706)$$

The more familiar transparent substances have "absorption bands" which lie beyond the limits of the visible spectrum, and these correspond to the presence of oscillators with corresponding frequencies. If the "light" frequency differs greatly from these, it suffers little absorption. Naturally the exact limits of high transmission depend enormously on the thickness of the specimen, but (to take a few examples) thin optical glass transmits between about $0 \cdot 31 \mu$ and $3 \cdot 0 \mu$; quartz between $0 \cdot 185 \mu$ and $4 \cdot 5 \mu$; fluorite between $0 \cdot 12 \mu$ and $9 \cdot 0 \mu$; sodium chloride between $0 \cdot 172 \mu$ and 20μ; potassium chloride between $0 \cdot 181 \mu$ and $25 \cdot 0 \mu$. All these have very strong absorption bands in the far ultra-violet, and when the radiations of still higher frequency (soft X-rays of wave-lengths about $0 \cdot 01 \mu$) are found to be transmitted, they show a refractive index a little *lower* than unity; thus they suffer total reflection when incident at very high angles on air-glass surfaces. This is useful in X-ray spectroscopy, using concave gratings ruled on glass. The oxygen of the air becomes opaque (at atmospheric pressure) to wave-lengths shorter than about $0 \cdot 185 \mu$, though nitrogen will transmit still further into the ultra-violet. The ozone in the upper atmosphere protects the earth's surface from the immense ultra-violet energy of the sun's radiation.

Metals contain electrons which are much more free to move than those in other substances, and this is associated with their high electrical and thermal conductivity. The electro-magnetic theory gives a reasonably satisfactory explanation, on this basis, of the usual metallic characteristics of high reflectivity and *very* high absorption coefficients; but selective effects are very marked,

and there is a wide range of refractive indices; for example, Drude[2]
gives the values 2·06 for platinum and 0·005 for sodium; the whole
subject is a theoretical and practical field of great complexity.
The selective reflection of gold and copper in the visible spectrum
is well known. Silver, which reflects over 90 per cent throughout
the visible spectrum, has a band of relative transparency near
0·316μ, where the reflection coefficient is only 4·2 per cent.

As far as surface reflection is concerned, there will be no scattering
if the surface irregularities are sufficiently small in comparison with
the wave-length of light; but the reflection coefficient of a well-
polished surface is a property of the substance and the frequency
of the light, and cannot be improved beyond a certain limit by any
amount of polishing. Polish adequate for visible light may be
unsatisfactory for the ultra-violet.

Quantum Phenomena. The classical theory of dispersion, scattering, etc., based on the wave-treatment, is reasonably satisfactory,
but it does not explain many of the well-known phenomena of
emission and absorption spectra. In an attempt to improve on the
older theory of the distribution of energy in the spectrum of a
perfect radiator, Planck assumed that radiation is emitted and
absorbed in finite amounts known as *quanta*. The modern term
*photon** means a discrete "packet" of radiation, of which the energy
ε is proportional to the associated electro-magnetic frequency v.
Thus $\varepsilon = hv$, where h is "Planck's constant." According to the
wave-mechanical theory, the photons are analogous to wave-groups.
The relative statistical probability of their appearance at any point in
space can be considered in terms of the intensity of a theoretical
wave motion.

A photon in collision with an atom may give up the whole or a
part of its energy; sometimes it may capture energy from the atom,
or again it may be deflected without change of energy (elastic
scattering). If it loses or gains energy, it will manifest a lower or
higher frequency respectively. Thus light scattered in certain media
will give faint spectrum lines differing in frequency (by an amount
depending on the energy interchange) from the exciting light. This
is known as the "Raman effect"[3]; and is very "faint" in ordinary
circumstances. It is without much present significance in the theory
of instruments.

As for the atom in collision with a photon, an electron may be
raised to a "level" of higher energy than its normal one, or even
ejected entirely; in the latter case the atom is "ionized." If the
electron in the higher energy level in an excited atom falls back to

* Note the conflicting usage in physiological optics, p. 158.

a lower level, the ejected energy leaves the atom in the form of a photon having the corresponding characteristic frequency, according to the above relation. The possible energy levels are characteristic of the particular nucleus; hence the possibilities of energy exchange are limited, and this broadly accounts for the appearance of characteristic "lines" in the spectrum. Atoms can be excited also by collision with electrons or other atomic particles having sufficient energy, and we can, for example, observe the emission spectrum of atoms excited by electron collisions in a discharge tube. If, on the other hand, we pass a beam of directed white light (containing all frequencies) through the same gas, some of the photons in the beam will have just the right energy to be completely taken up by exciting the atoms as before (and this is the most common kind of energy interchange); but if light is *subsequently* emitted by the atoms (fluorescence) it is radiated in all directions (and is not coherent in the sense of the dispersion theory), so that energy is now lacking in the spectrum of the transmitted beams, and dark lines appear in the spectrum. The dark lines of the solar spectrum were first observed by Wollaston and described in more detail by Fraunhofer. The absorbing gases surround the sun, and the white light is derived from deeper levels beneath the gaseous layer.

Provided we deal with gases at low pressures, both emission and absorption spectra corresponding to the transitions between molecular energy states (vibrational and rotational), or to the atomic energy states, usually give sharp spectrum lines, though usually the lines of molecular spectra are closely grouped into "bands." If, however, the molecules are more closely packed, as by an increase of pressure, there will be energy exchanges between excited and non-excited molecules; this means that some energy will be lost in heat, etc., and will not be re-radiated as light. The liquid and solid states are examples of much closer packing, which affects the possible transitions, so that broad absorption bands with ill-defined limits often result. Very strongly marked selective absorption is generally characteristic of the dyes and pigments. In the case of certain solid dyes (cyanin, for example), the proximity of a fairly sharp absorption band has been shown to be accompanied by variations in refractive index, of the type suggested in Fig. 146. The detailed discussion of dispersion theory on the lines of quantum mechanics is beyond the scope of this discussion, but has been treated by Schrödinger and others.

In Applied Optics the effects of colouring materials in solution are perhaps of most interest. The "dispersion" of the material in the solution may be complete, so that its molecules move among

those of the solvent, and some of them may be separated into
oppositely charged "ions"; or the material may be present in the
form of a "colloid," in which there may be small molecular aggregates or particles (sizes of the order of 0.15μ) in suspension.

If the concentration of the solution is small, the relative numbers
of the alien "colouring" particles among those of the solvent will
be small, and there will be no possibility of the building up of
strong secondary waves from them (using the terms of the older
dispersion theory) capable of much appreciable effect on the general
resultant wave-transmission. Thus, while the absorption effects
may build up to a great degree in a large thickness of the solution,
there will be no considerable associated changes of refractive index

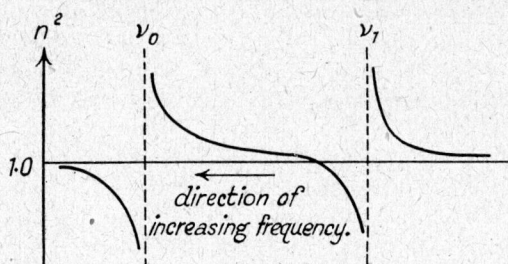

FIG. 146

such as mentioned above (cyanin, etc.). There will be little or no
lateral scattering of light in a homogeneous solution. The absorption coefficient will be proportional to the concentration (Beer's
Law).

The remarks of the last paragraph apply also to colloidal solutions or suspensions. A single colloidal particle will have complex
possibilities with regard to diffraction, reflection, and transmission
of the incident light. While a single very small particle will scatter
light fairly uniformly in all directions, highly complex directional
effects take place with a larger one. The internal absorption may
play a large part. In the case of a solution containing very small
particles of colloidal gold, green light is absorbed (being converted
into heat), and the solution appears purple by transmitted light;
larger gold particles may scatter red-yellow light, and the transmitted light is blue. Garnett[4] showed that many of the colours
produced in glasses by the introduction of metallic oxides are due
to colloidal particles. A comprehensive study of the physics of the
phenomena is due to Mie.[5]

Transformation of Absorbed Radiation. Photo-electricity. As
previously mentioned, the metals contain electrons which are

relatively free to move in the substance, though they cannot usually escape from the surface owing to the barrier of electrical potential in its immediate vicinity. Energy exchanges can take place between photons and free electrons, in which the photon can part with energy (at the expense of frequency), while giving increased velocity (and thus kinetic energy) to the electron. This effect has been observed experimentally by Compton apart from the effects to be described.

Photons can penetrate a short distance under the surface of a metal, where they meet with electrons. If an electron acquires sufficient velocity normal to the surface, it will leap the potential barrier. Thus light must have a certain minimum frequency charac-

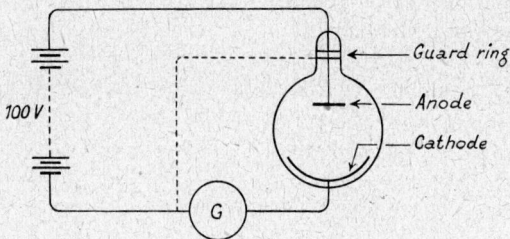

FIG. 147

teristic of any particular metal before it can thus release electrons from it. The potential barriers are low for the alkali metals: cæsium, sodium, potassium, etc., the minimum frequency for the latter two lying in the visible spectrum; it requires ultra-violet frequency to produce the effect with cadmium. X-rays can release photo-electrons from non-metals also.

A photo-electric cell of the bulb type often has the cathode surface (cæsium, etc.) coated as a film on the interior surface, while the anode is an opposing plate (Fig. 147). The cathode and anode are attached respectively to the negative and positive terminals of a battery (100 volts perhaps); contact is made by leads sealed through the glass. The released electrons are attracted to the anode. If the bulb is evacuated, the current is closely proportional to the light energy entering the cell, provided its geometrical mode of incidence is unaltered. On the other hand, gas-filled cells contain small quantities of the rare gases, and the current is magnified by ionization at the expense of the truth of the linear relationship. For further discussion of photo-electric cells, including the modern barrier-layer or rectifier cells, see reference 6.

Thus, under certain conditions, light can lose energy through the release of photo-electrons in addition to the ways already mentioned. Even if electrons are not released, there may be a transfer of an electron from one atom to another within the substance of a material, as, for example, in photo-sensitive substances like silver salts. This may cause a change in chemical properties.

Fluorescence and Phosphorescence. It was mentioned above that atoms and molecules excited by radiation may subsequently re-emit light; the re-emission of the same frequency as the exciting light is known as resonant fluorescence; but the fluorescence often shows great numbers of lines or bands of frequencies differing from the excitation. In most cases the quanta of the fluorescent light have less energy (and lower frequencies) than the exciting light (Stokes' Law), but exceptions are known in cases where the derived quanta owe a part of their energy to a store already "in hand" in the molecule.

A similar re-emission of light takes place from many liquids and solids under certain forms of stimulation, but just as in the case of absorption spectra, the mutual proximity of the radiating elements complicates the effects; the study is still largely in a descriptive stage, though of great technical importance.

Glass coloured by oxide of uranium (canary colour) is well known for the yellow-green fluorescence evoked by wave-lengths shorter than the fluorescent band. Many organic substances fluoresce. For example, the lens and cornea of the human eye are made fluorescent by ultra-violet light, producing a general lavender-coloured illumination of the retina. Hydrocarbon oils fluoresce in the ultra-violet; photographic plates will register "short ultra-violet" light about 0.2μ more readily if coated with a film of paraffin; the fluorescent light of longer wave-length can penetrate the gelatine in which the silver salts are embedded, and thus expose the plate.

Fluorescent materials (e.g. zinc orthosilicate, calcium tungstate, etc.) are coated on the inside of discharge tubes to convert visually useless radiation into visible light, and thus make the modern discharge lamp of high efficiency.[7] Minerals, etc., may be identified by characteristic fluorescence both in the mass and in microscopic sections.

Fluorite (natural calcium fluoride) has often a fluorescence, due to traces of impurities, which can be excited by ultra-violet light. This should be remembered in connection with its technical use, but is not usually a bad drawback.

Phosphorescence only differs from fluorescence in lasting for a relatively long period after the removal of the exciting light. The scientific term "phosphor" is now restricted to certain crystalline substances containing minute traces of metallic impurities, but in the colloquial sense the term "phosphorescent" is applied to substances like calcium sulphide (the basis of Balmain's paint), in which the emission of light continues for some hours with an exponential drop in luminosity. Such effects should be distinguished from luminescence of chemical origin, which may occur from molecular energy adjustments without excitation by light.

REFERENCES

1. Rayleigh: *Collected Works*, Vol. I, p. 87.
2. Drude: *"Optics."*
3. Raman: *Indian Jour. Physics* II, 387, 1928.
4. Garnett: *Phil. Trans. Roy. Soc. A.*, 203, 385.
5. Mie: *Ann. der Phys.*, 35, 377 (1908).
6. Strong: *"Physical Laboratory Practice"* (Blackie).
7. Physical Soc.: *Reports on Progress in Physics*, III, 317 (1936).

CHAPTER VIII

OPTICAL GLASS, AND THE PRODUCTION AND TESTING OF LENS SYSTEMS

ALTHOUGH the art of glass-making has been known since very early historical times (before 2500 B.C. in Egypt), the varieties of "optical" glass obtainable until the second half of the nineteenth century were practically limited to the old types of "crown" and "flint." Typical compositions of these (as manufactured by Guinand about A.D. 1805 and onwards) were—

Crown: 72 per cent silica, 18 per cent potassium oxide, 10 per cent calcium oxide.

Flint: 45 per cent silica, 12 per cent potassium oxide, 43 per cent lead oxide.

In the manufacture of glass for all purposes, the oxides employed were limited to silica, sodium, potassium, calcium, lead, and aluminium.

THE FRAUNHOFER LINES, WITH ADDITIONS

Distinguishing Letter	Wave-length in μ	Line due to	Production in Laboratory	Colour
A′	$\begin{cases}0\cdot76990\\0\cdot76649\end{cases}$	Potassium	Flame	Red
A	0·7594	Oxygen*	——	,,
b	0·70652	Helium	Vacuum tube	,,
B	0·6867	Oxygen*	——	,,
C	0·65628	Hydrogen	Vacuum tube	,,
D†	0·58929	Sodium	Flame	Orange-yellow
d	0·58756	Helium	Vacuum tube	Yellow
e	0·54607	Mercury	Mercury lamp	Green
E	0·5270	Iron and calcium	——	,,
F	0·48613	Hydrogen	Vacuum tube	Blue-green
g	0·43583	Mercury	Mercury lamp	Violet
G′	0·43405	Hydrogen	Vacuum tube	,,
G‡	0·4308	Iron, calcium	——	,,
h	0·40466	Mercury	Mercury lamp	,,
H	0·39685	Calcium	Arc	,,
K	0·39337	Calcium	,,	,,

* Produced by absorption in atmosphere. The wave-length given is really the head of an absorption band which does not make a very good "line" for measurement.

† Mean of D_1 and D_2 (0·58959 and 0·58900 respectively).

‡ A double line; the components can be distinguished under high resolving power.

The dispersion and refraction of glass was studied by Newton (1642–1727), but in his time he had no means of making very exact measurements owing to the difficulty of isolating sufficiently homogeneous light. He reached the erroneous conclusion that the amount of dispersion in any substance was proportional to the refracting power, a circumstance which would have rendered the making of "achromatic" lenses or prisms impossible, as will be understood from the discussion given below.

Fraunhofer's re-discovery* (A.D. 1814) of the dark lines of the solar spectrum, and the consequent facilitation of the measurement of refractive indices, put the whole subject of achromatism on a more exact basis. The "Fraunhofer" lines were called A, B, C, etc.

In modern times, laboratory measurements are usually made with the convenient spectra of hydrogen, helium, and mercury. The Glass list published by Messrs. Chance Bros., Ltd., contains data for the lines b, C, D, d, e, F, g, G', and h of the above table.

Dispersive Power and Constringence. If a single lens has refractive indices n_C, n_d, n_F, the corresponding focal lengths are found from

$$\frac{1}{f_C'} = (n_C - 1)\ \mathbf{R}, \qquad \frac{1}{f_d'} = (n_d - 1)\ \mathbf{R}, \qquad \frac{1}{f_F'} = (n_F - 1)\ \mathbf{R}$$

Hence

$$\frac{1}{f_F'} - \frac{1}{f_C'} = (n_F - n_C)\ \mathbf{R}$$

or

$$\frac{f_C' - f_F'}{f_C' f_F'} = (n_F - n_C)\ \mathbf{R}$$

Since the product $f_F' f_C'$ will not be very different from $(f_d')^2$, the equation becomes a close approximation

$$\frac{f_C' - f_F'}{f_d'} = f_d'\ (n_F - n_C)\ \mathbf{R} = \frac{n_F - n_C}{(n_d - 1)} . \qquad . \quad (801)$$

or

$$\frac{f_d'}{f_C' - f_F'} = \frac{n_d - 1}{n_F - n_C} = V \qquad . \qquad . \qquad . \quad (802)$$

The quantity $\dfrac{(n_F - n_C)}{(n_d - 1)}$ is termed the dispersive power of the medium of the lens. It is seen to determine the ratio of the length of the axial spectrum to the whole focal length. Its reciprocal, which we denote by V (often given as v, following Abbe), is convenient in calculations respecting achromatism. The "V value" is sometimes called the "constringence" of the medium.

* Wollaston had previously observed the dark lines. Fraunhofer's *earliest* accurate measurements of refractive index were, however, made with an ingenious monochromator.

Achromatism. Denoting the properties of two thin lenses by the additional suffixes $_1$ and $_2$, the focal power of the combination of the two when in contact, for the wave-lengths of C and F, will be

$$F_C = (n_{1C} - 1)\, R_1 + (n_{2C} - 1)\, R_2$$
$$F_F = (n_{1F} - 1)\, R_1 + (n_{2F} - 1)\, R_2$$

When the system is achromatized in the usual method, the focal powers of the combination for C and F will be equal. Thus, $F_C = F_F$, which gives

$$R_1\, (n_{1F} - n_{1C}) + R_2\, (n_{2F} - n_{2C}) = 0$$

Introducing the V values for 1 and 2 where

$$V_1 = \frac{(n_{1d} - 1)}{(n_{1F} - n_{1C})}, \text{ and } V_2 = \frac{(n_{2d} - 1)}{(n_{2F} - n_{2C})}$$

we obtain immediately

$$\frac{R_1\, (n_{1d} - 1)}{V_1} + \frac{R_2\, (n_{2d} - 1)}{V_2} = 0$$

giving

$$\frac{F_{1d}}{V_1} + \frac{F_{2d}}{V_2} = 0$$

Since now

$$F_d = F_{1d} + F_{2d}$$

$$F_{1d} = F_d \left(\frac{V_1}{V_1 - V_2} \right) \text{ and } F_{2d} = F_d \left(\frac{V_2}{V_2 - V_1} \right) \quad . \quad (803)$$

These last equations give for the corresponding focal lengths

$$f_{1d}' = f_d' \left(\frac{V_1 - V_2}{V_1} \right) \dots \text{ and } f_{2d}' = f_d' \left(\frac{V_2 - V_1}{V_2} \right) \quad . \quad (803\text{A})$$

NUMERICAL EXAMPLE. Let us choose two glasses from Chance's catalogue to make an achromatic doublet by means of this approximate "thin lens" theory.

Type	n_d	V
Hard crown	1·51899	60·4
Dense flint	1·61021	37·5

Let $f_d = 1$ metre. Then

$$f_{1d}' = 1 \left(\frac{22 \cdot 9}{60 \cdot 4} \right) \qquad\qquad f_{2d}' = 1 \left(\frac{-22 \cdot 9}{37 \cdot 5} \right)$$
$$= 0 \cdot 379 \text{ metres} \qquad\qquad = -0 \cdot 611 \text{ metres}$$

To check $F_{1d} = 2 \cdot 638$ $F_{2d} = -1 \cdot 638$

If the lens 2 is to have a flat back surface—

$$* \quad F_2 = (n_2 - 1)(R_{12} - 0)$$

$$\therefore R_{12} = \frac{-1 \cdot 638}{0 \cdot 6102} = -2 \cdot 68, \text{ or } r_{12} = \frac{-0 \cdot 6102}{1 \cdot 638} = -0 \cdot 3734 \text{ metres.}$$

If the lens is to be a cemented doublet, $R_{21} = R_{12}$

$$F_1 = (n_1 - 1)(R_{11} - R_{21})$$

$$2 \cdot 638 = (0 \cdot 51899)(R_{11} + 2 \cdot 68)$$

$$R_{11} = 2 \cdot 403 \text{ or } r_{11} = 0 \cdot 416 \text{ metres.}$$

It is now desired to calculate the difference of the focal lengths of the combination for some other wave-lengths, say, D and F. We have

$$\frac{1}{f_d'} = (n_{1d} - 1) R_1 + (n_{2d} - 1) R_2$$

$$\frac{1}{f_F'} = (n_{1F} - 1) R_1 + (n_{2F} - 1) R_2$$

Hence, $\quad \dfrac{1}{f_F'} - \dfrac{1}{f_d'} = \dfrac{f_d' - f_F'}{f_F' f_d'} = (n_{1F} - n_{1d}) R_1 + (n_{2F} - n_{2d}) R_2$

and therefore $\quad \dfrac{f_d' - f_F'}{f_F'} = (n_{1F} - n_{1d}) R_1 f_d' + (n_{2F} - n_{2d}) R_2 f_d'$

$$= (n_{1F} - n_{1d}) R_1 f_{1d}' \left(\frac{V_1}{V_1 - V_2} \right) + (n_{2F} - n_{2d}) R_2 f_{2d}' \left(\frac{V_2}{V_2 - V_1} \right)$$

$$= \frac{(n_{1F} - n_{1d})}{(n_{1F} - n_{1C})(V_1 - V_2)} + \frac{(n_{2F} - n_{2d})}{(n_{2F} - n_{2C})(V_2 - V_1)}$$

Now, these partial dispersions, such as $(n_F - n_d)$, can be obtained from the glass lists giving particulars of optical glasses, and sometimes such ratios as $\dfrac{(n_F - n_d)}{(n_F - n_C)}$, i.e. the "relative" partial dispersions, are also given. Calling this ratio β, the equation above becomes

$$\frac{f_d' - f_F'}{f_F'} = \frac{\beta_1 - \beta_2}{V_1 - V_2} \qquad . \qquad . \qquad . \quad (804)$$

With any two glasses, therefore, the difference of the β values determines the difference of the focal lengths of the combination for the "d" focus and the equalized focus of C and F. The glass lists also give the partial dispersions for other pairs of lines, such as b and C, C and d, d and e, e and F, F and g, g and h. Evidently, in order to effect perfect achromatism, the ratio of these differences to the

---

* Note that R_{12} means "the curvature of the first surface of lens 2." The two suffixes relate to the "surface" and the "lens" respectively.

values of $(n_F - n_C)$ should be equal for the glasses chosen. There are always differences in actual practice, but equation (804) above shows that the extent of the differences of focus will be diminished by a large value of the difference $(V_a - V_b)$.

In order to estimate the separation of the foci for d and F in the case of the glasses cited above, we obtain the following additional information from the glass lists for the same crown and flint—

Type	Mean Dispersion	Partial Dispersions and Relative Partial Dispersions		
	C to F	b to C	d to F	F to g
Hard crown	·00859	·00149 (·173)	·00597 (·695)	·00467 (·544)
Dense flint	·01629	·00267 (·164)	·01150 (·706)	·00945 (·580)

From these figures

$$\frac{f_d' - f_F'}{f_F'} = \frac{\beta_1 - \beta_2}{V_1 - V_2} = \frac{0·695 - 0·706}{22·5} = -\frac{1}{2045} \text{ (approx.)}$$

Relative Accuracy of Measurement. There are some practical difficulties in obtaining measurements of these partial and relative dispersions which may be illustrated by a numerical example. It is an attainment of a high order to obtain measurements of refractive index correct to one unit in the fifth decimal.

$$\text{If } n_F = 1·51794$$
$$n_C = 1·50990$$
$$n_F - n_C = 0·00804$$

Thus, with the above accuracy of absolute measurement, the relative accuracy in the difference is 1 or 2 parts in 804. If the original accuracy of absolute measurement was to one in the fourth decimal of refractive index, the error in the "mean dispersion" $(n_F - n_C)$ is more than 1 per cent. The error in the partial dispersion of smaller range, such as $(n_d - n_C)$ and the *relative* partial dispersions, is naturally more serious still. Therefore the estimation of the differences of focus in a doublet lens requires very accurate refractive index determinations.

Historical. The old types of crown and flint when used as achromatic combinations invariably showed a considerable divergence between the focal points for D and G′ and the common focus for

C and F, when achromatism was effected in that sense. The variation is illustrated in Fig. 148, in which curve A shows the variation of axial focusing position for the various wave-lengths in the spectrum (the latter are plotted vertically). The length of this "secondary spectrum," (D to F), may be roughly $\frac{1}{2000}$th part of the whole focal length, and the focus for the bright yellow-green region in the spectrum is nearest the lens.

The earliest attempts to produce glasses which allowed of a reduction of the secondary spectrum by avoidance of the irrationality of dispersion were made by Fraunhofer, working with P. L. Guinand between 1811 and 1813, and alone from 1814 to 1828. Then Harcourt in England carried out experiments between 1834

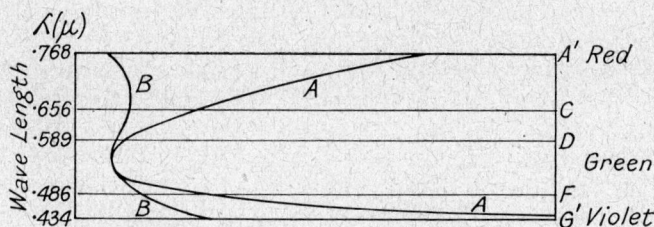

FIG. 148. RELATIVE AXIAL POSITIONS OF FOCI IN AN ACHROMATIC (A) AND APOCHROMATIC (B) SYSTEM

and 1860, and discovered the important effects of boron and barium on dispersive properties when introduced into the composition of glass, but he produced few specimens of practical utility, although an objective made with a disc of his borate glass had a greatly reduced secondary spectrum.

In 1866, Ernst Abbe began his long connection with the firm of Carl Zeiss. "For years," he said, "we combined with sober optics a species of dream optics, in which combinations made of hypothetical glass, existing only in our imagination, were employed to discuss the progress which might be achieved if the glass makers could only be induced to adapt themselves to the advancing requirements of practical optics." Failing to induce others to make the necessary trials, he began his work with Schott in 1880. They made tests of introducing boron, phosphorus, barium, fluorine, and other elements, and the result included new and useful series of boro-silicate crowns, barium crowns, barium flints, borate flints, and the phosphate and borate glasses; in these the character of the dispersion varies from type to type.

The early work resulted in the production of a number of glasses, such as the "phosphate crown" and "borate flint," which, when combined in an achromatic objective, give a double bend in the spectrum as instanced by curve B, Fig. 148. The similar "run of dispersion" has resulted in an extremely small secondary spectrum. Unfortunately, however, some of these glasses were found to be chemically unstable, and their use had to be abandoned. Among the really stable glasses, however, the secondary spectrum can be very greatly reduced by using a glass known as "telescope flint," containing antimony oxide, with a hard crown, although it is necessary to use deeper curves than with the usual "dense flint." Some advantage is thereby lost. Borate flint is often used in preference to telescope flint; it is now made in a fairly stable form.

Before the war of 1914–18, the chief sources of optical glass outside the German firm of Schott & Genossen, Jena, were Messrs. Chance Bros., Ltd., of Smethwick, England, and the Parra Mantois works in France. During that war a great deal of experimental work was carried out, with the result that most of the Jena types were reproduced, and new types originated. Research and development have continued down to the present time, and both in Great Britain and America certain optical firms have manufactured glass for their own uses. It is understood that several American firms are now manufacturing for the market; some recent developments are noted below. Details of the developments in Great Britain since 1918 can be found in various papers in the *Journal of the Society of Glass Technology.*

Effects of Various Elements on the Optical Properties of Glass. The effect of the high lead content in flint glass is to increase both the total relative dispersion (low V values), and the relative dispersion at the blue end of the spectrum. Thus, the V for crown glass containing no lead is about 60, while for dense flint glass it is about 32. The relative partial dispersion for F–g gives a measure of the dispersion at the short-wave end of the visible spectrum. We will call it p. The p value for silicate crown is 0·544, while for dense flint it may be 0·588.

Some of the lead may be replaced by barium—producing a "barium light flint." The V-value may then rise to about 50, while p falls to about 0·551. Barium may be introduced rather than lead into a crown glass to lower the V value to about 55, while p becomes about 0·546. As compared with lead, barium produces a lower refractive index and a much lower dispersion.

Boron introduced into a glass has the important property of lengthening the red end of the spectrum with regard to the blue; borate flint glasses are not very stable, although boro-silicate crowns are satisfactory in this respect. This disability also applies to the use of phosphates in glass; as compared with a silicate glass of the same total dispersion, the phosphate glass has about the same "run" of dispersion, while its refractive indices are higher. This is

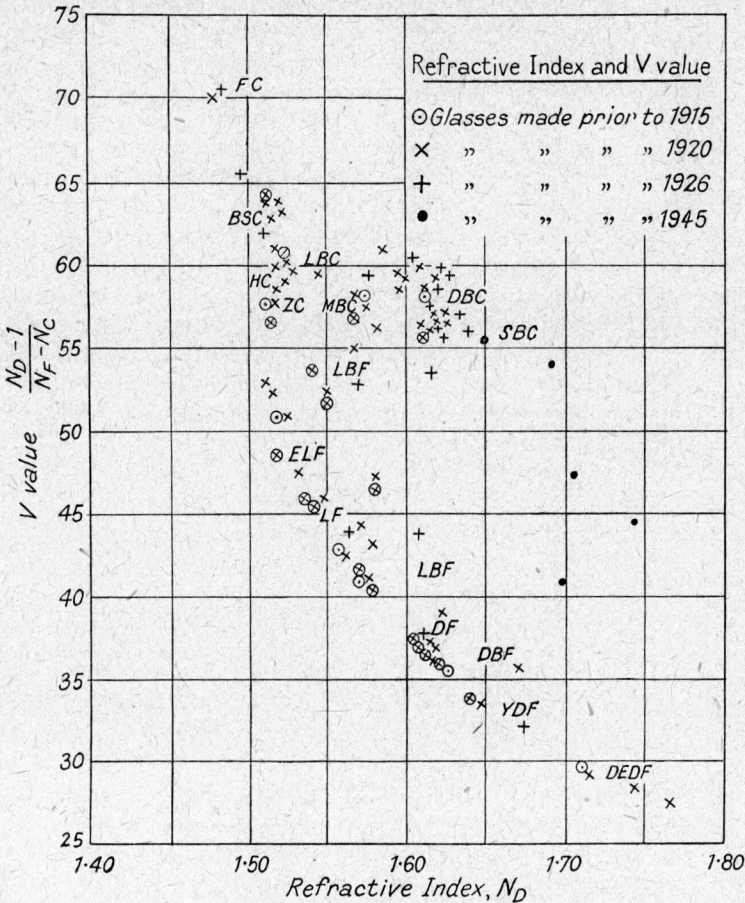

FIG. 149. TYPES OF OPTICAL GLASS
Chance Bros. & Co., Ltd.

a valuable optical effect, but the use of certain phosphate glasses has been largely discontinued for the above reason.

The use of extra potassium and sodium in glass decreases the red end of the spectrum relatively to the blue, to some extent, but potassium can only be used in moderate quantities if the glass is to be chemically stable.

The greatest value of some of the elements, such as zinc, which are introduced, is in connection with the facility they give in the working of the glass. Fluorine can enter into the glass structure either as fluorine or as a fluoride, and it has the property of reducing the V value for a given refractive index (as in Fluor crown), or increasing it (as in fluoride crystals) in the respective cases.

Stability to Weathering. The surfaces of most glasses are attacked to some extent by water with the liberation of free alkali. A well-known test involves the exposure of a freshly broken glass surface to saturated air for seven days at 18° C. On immersing the specimen in an etheric solution of iodeosin for one minute, the latter substance combines with the alkali to form a red precipitate. A control experiment is made with a similar surface unweathered. The effect of the weathering is expressed in terms of the excess in milligrammes of iodesin thus absorbed per sq. metre of the "weathered" surface, over that for the unweathered. The two results give the "weather alkalinity" and the "natural alkalinity" respectively.

Mylius has divided glasses into five groups, according to "weather alkalinity," as follows—

Class	Type	"Weather Alkalinity" mg/m^2	Example
I . .	Very stable	0–5	Silica glass
II . .	Chemical glass	5–10	Pyrex
III . .	Hard glass	10–20	Flints or best crowns
IV . .	Soft glass	20–40	Ordinary crowns
V . .	Poor stability	40–	Certain dense barium crowns, etc.

Optical glasses should have a weather alkalinity of less than 40. Otherwise they should be used under protection. The iodeosin test was introduced as long ago as 1905, and seems to have justified itself as a generally reliable one, but there are certain necessary precautions[1] to be observed. Results are anomalous in some cases, notably with barium glasses.

Lists of optical glasses always give information as to the stability of the various types.

Other tests include an auto-clave test using superheated steam, a solubility test using a powdered sample in contact with various chemical solutions, and an electrical conductivity test. Messrs. Chance Bros. use a "Thermodyne test," which, while not strictly quantitative, enables their glasses to be sorted effectively into six groups. Glasses in group 6 may exhibit heavy general tarnish within a few months. Group 3 (fairly good durability) may show patches of stain within a two-year period, and so on.

Formation of Surface Films on Glass. Glass surfaces in the interior of optical instruments sometimes develop "films" which consist of very minute droplets, and are not continuous like tarnish films, but tend to scatter the light.. Glass of poor durability is specially liable to attack, but trouble may be experienced through the use of unsuitable paints and lubricants in the instrument. The final cleaning of the surfaces is also important in this connection.

Advantages of a Variety in Glass Types. The main advantages of the great variety of glass types are not only found in the possibility of reducing the secondary spectrum in doublet lenses; when more perfect achromatism is required, it is, in fact, usually best obtained by the employment of three or more lenses. Other aberrations, too, can be controlled by the selection of suitable glasses. Thus, a doublet lens can be secured with only a small degree of coma by choosing a medium barium crown to unite with a dense flint.

Very often in designing a complex system, a computer will assume a trial set of glasses for the components. If large aberrations arise at a deeply-curved surface, it may be possible to reduce the curvature by the choice of another glass for one of the lenses, and so gain control over the aberrations in a manner otherwise impossible. In another case a computer may design his system to abolish spherical aberration, etc., making only rough provision for achromatism. He will have fixed the absolute refractive indices of his glasses, and then when the system is practically complete he may work out the dispersions which the glasses should have in order to give proper achromatism. Fig. 149 represents some glasses available from Messrs. Chance Bros., Ltd., in which the refractive index is plotted against the V value. If the computer had one glass of refractive index $1 \cdot 515$, he would have a range of possible V values from 64 to 53 amongst different glasses ranging from boro-silicate crowns through hard crowns and zinc crowns. This choice might easily enable the proper glass to be selected, which would produce achromatism.

The Petzval-Coddington equation for the curvature of field of a thin lens system, consisting of a number of components, is (assume a flat object field)

$$\frac{1}{r} = -\left(\frac{1}{n_1 f_1'} + \frac{1}{n_2 f_2'} + \text{etc.}\right) \text{ or } -\Sigma\left(\frac{1}{n f'}\right)$$

9—(T.5494/5)

It is easily realized that the possible requirement of a flat image field alone calls for a definite relation between the focal lengths and refractive indices of a system; this again illustrates the desirability of having available several possible values of dispersion for one refractive index.

The modern glass list only gives a selection of types. The glass-maker can usually produce intermediate types if they are required.

Optical Glasses of Extreme Properties. In Fig. 149, the more usual types of crown and flint glasses lie close to a mean curve connecting refractive index with "V member," but considerable departures from this locus are seen in glasses containing more or less barium in place of lead. The Eastman Kodak Co. has taken out patents[2] for a series of glasses with low silica content (less than 20 per cent) and containing combinations of zirconium, titanium, tungsten, thorium, lithium, boron, etc. Lanthanum and tantalum have also been used in preparing high index glasses, the former being a constituent in a glass (E.K.2) now produced commercially. It has a refractive index $n_d = 1.74338$ and $V = 45.8$. Refractive indices exceeding 2.0 can be obtained in special melts on a laboratory scale with some of the above materials.

Glasses of optical properties similar to those of E.K.2 are also produced by Messrs. Chance Bros., Ltd., under the names of special barium flints (SBF), with V values below 55, and special barium crowns (SBC) V values > 55. Thus, for example, "SBF 744 447" has a refractive index (n_d) of 1.74416 and V value 44.7. (Note that the code number used by Chance is composed of the three figures after the decimal point in the refractive index and three significant figures of the V value.) Other examples of SBF glasses are 718 477 and 690 547. An example of an SBC is 650 560.

The use of comparatively rare materials makes such glasses expensive to produce; the high proportion of wastage characteristic of melts in clay pots cannot be tolerated, and in most cases they are made with much care in platinum crucibles. The makers find that individual melts will agree in refractive index (n_d) within ± 0.001 and in V value within ± 0.2.

A Schott and Genossen catalogue lists a number of new glasses of general properties similar to the special barium flints; for example, $n_d = 1.6929$, $V = 52.4$. Amongst special glasses (said to differ markedly from ordinary glass in chemical properties) is one with $n_d = 1.9229$, $V = 20.9$. There is also a specially light flint, with $n_d = 1.5236$ and $V = 46.0$; and a phosphate crown $n_d = 1.5038$, $V = 66.7$, with partial dispersions similar to the boro-silicate crown in the table (p. 336).

Other Materials of Optical Interest : Crystals. Various natural and artificial crystals of the cubic system (and, therefore, free from double refraction) are of interest as possible components of optical systems. Refractive index data for some of these will be found at the foot of the table (p. 337). Fluorite has long been used as a valuable component of apochromatic microscope objectives. Certain members of the alum family (e.g. potassium alum $n_D = 1·45601$, $V = 58·4$) have also been used in microscope objectives, cemented between outer lenses of glass. There is a fairly wide range of optical properties in other alums. Sylvine or sylvite (natural potassium chloride) is used in systems for the infra-red, as well as rock salt.

During the last twenty years the technique of preparation of large single crystals of the so-called "alkali halides" has been developed, notably by Stockbarger. (*N.B.* The alkali metals are lithium, sodium, potassium, rubidium, and cæsium. The halide salts are the fluoride, chloride, bromide, and iodide.) The chief examples of present optical interest are lithium fluoride, sodium chloride, and potassium bromide. In some cases, specimens can be made up to 10 in. diameter. Protection of the surfaces is advisable in use. Special precautions have to be taken in grinding and polishing such materials; the avoidance of temperature shock is essential.

Other crystals of some interest are magnesium oxide or *periclase* ($n_D = 1·7378$, $V = 53·5$), and magnesium aluminate or *spinel* ($1·7165$, $V = 59·7$). Spinel is produced for jewellery, but only in small sizes, and small magnesium oxide crystals are a by-product in another process. The surface of magnesium oxide is slowly clouded by the formation of magnesium carbonate in ordinary exposure to air. Fused quartz is now produced in specimens as large as $1\frac{1}{2}$ in. in diameter and of homogeneity adequate for most optical purposes.

Optical Plastics. Important new optical possibilities are offered by "optical plastic materials," of which many very transparent varieties are known, the chief being polymethyl methacrylate (Transpex 1, Perspex, etc.), corresponding optically to crown glass, and polystyrene (Transpex 2, Styron, Distrene, etc.) corresponding to flint. Polycyclohexyl methacrylate (crown) is used in the U.S.A.

Many specimens compete with optical glass in transparency and homogeneity, having a somewhat wider spectral range of transmission. An accuracy of $\pm$ 0·0001 in refractive index from batch to batch is claimed. Some specimens of polystyrene have, however, been shown to scatter light internally.

Perhaps the main disadvantages are associated with the relative softness of the surface, the high temperature coefficients of expansion and change of refractive index, and the low softening temperature. Softening is said to begin between 60° C. to 120° C. depending on the specimen. In the earlier trials it was found difficult to make "plastic" lenses and prisms retain the figure initially given, but new processes have been devised by which it is claimed this trouble has been largely overcome.

The usual methods of manufacture of optical parts have hitherto been (a) moulding under heat and pressure in optically-worked stainless steel moulds; (b) grinding and polishing, using the normal glass-working technique; (c) casting the lens from monomer in optically-worked glass moulds. In the last case, polymerization is completed in the mould, and special means for overcoming the distorting effects of shrinkage have been devised. Further work on moulding processes is in active progress.

Advantages claimed include high impact strength and lightness, but perhaps the most important feature is the possible cheap production of aspheric surfaces in quantity; once the master surface has been prepared by whatever means, the development of successful moulding or casting techniques will allow cheap and quick reproduction. It is probable that the use of aspheric surfaces in eyepieces, etc., may become much more usual than has been hitherto deemed likely. An application already developed is in the manufacture of Schmidt plates (see Vol. II) for reflecting projectors up to 12 in. aperture. Considerable experience in the manufacture of various "ordinary" instruments using these materials has already been obtained. More information on crystals and plastics will be found in papers by Johnson[3] and Wearmouth.[3a]

Dispersion Formula. Inspection of the table of refractive indices for optical glasses shows that the partial dispersions rise or fall with the mean dispersion, and closer trials show that the relative partial dispersions of most glasses of the normal alkali-silica-lead series have a linear relation with the V values, i.e.

$$\frac{n_\lambda - n_d}{n_F - n_C} = A_\lambda + B_\lambda V$$

where A_λ and B_λ are functions of λ independent of the constitution of the glass; an alternative form of the equation is

$$n_\lambda - n_d = A_\lambda(n_F - n_C) + B_\lambda(n_d - 1) \qquad . \qquad . \qquad (805)$$

A plot of the data, and more accurately the use of least square methods, enables the best numerical values of A_λ and B_λ to be obtained for any given group of glasses. The values of B_λ are very small for the normal glasses, so that the partial dispersions will plot almost as straight lines against the mean dispersion. Thus the use of a formula such as

$$n_\lambda - n_d = A_\lambda(n_F - n_C) + D_\lambda,$$

is often valid for a group of glasses over a wide range of wave-length. Hence, once the values of A_λ and D_λ have been found for a number of glasses (or, better, the values of A_λ and B_λ in the previous equation), and n_F, n_C, and n_d have been measured for a new glass, the determination of the value of n_λ is possible. In practice, methods of this kind are used in work of "fifth-place" accuracy.

Writing (805) in the form

$$(n_\lambda - 1) - (n_d - 1) = A_\lambda\{(n_F - 1) - (n_C - 1)\} + B_\lambda (n_d - 1)$$

and applying the relation to a thin lens of total curvature **R**, we get

$$\boldsymbol{F}_\lambda - \boldsymbol{F}_d = A_\lambda(\boldsymbol{F}_F - \boldsymbol{F}_C) + B_\lambda \boldsymbol{F}_d,$$

and, again, if we apply this relation to a series of thin lenses in contact, all of glasses conforming to (805), we shall have

$$\Sigma(\boldsymbol{F}_\lambda - \boldsymbol{F}_d) = A_\lambda\Sigma(\boldsymbol{F}_F - \boldsymbol{F}_C) + B_\lambda\Sigma\boldsymbol{F}_d$$

so that if the system has "F — C" achromatism and $\boldsymbol{F}_F - \boldsymbol{F}_C$ in zero, the secondary spectrum depends upon B_λ, and cannot therefore differ in its relative amount when such glasses are used in combination. However, it is found that other glasses, including those containing much barium or boron, do not conform well to (805), so that modification of the secondary spectrum can be effected with their aid. With such glasses the simple interpolation methods have to be modified, and equations based on physical dispersion theories are often used. Naturally the constants in such equations differ from glass to glass, especially in the more abnormal cases.

Herzberger finds, however, that (if P_λ denotes the relative partial dispersion $(n_\lambda - n_F)/(n_C - n_F)$) the knowledge of two relative partial dispersions, the red partial $P_{A'}$, i.e. $(n_{A'} - n_F)/(n_C - n_F)$, and the violet partial, i.e. $P_h = (n_h - n_C)/(n_C - n_F)$, are sufficient to give the remaining partials with sufficient accuracy for optical calculations. This means that there are three universal functions, C_λ, D_λ, and E_λ, such that

$$P_\lambda = C_\lambda + D_\lambda P_{A'} + E_\lambda P_h$$

for *any* optical refracting medium with small limits of error. Conrady has made similar use of other pairs of partials.

Equation (706), modified so as to use the wave-length as the variable, takes the form (Ketteler),

$$n^2 = a^2 + \frac{M_1}{\lambda^2 - \lambda_1{}^2} - \frac{M^2}{\lambda_2{}^2 - \lambda^2} \qquad . \qquad . \qquad (806)$$

For example, the results of Rubens for quartz (ordinary ray) give

$$a^2 = 3 \cdot 4629, \; M_1 = 0 \cdot 010654,$$
$$M_2 = 111 \cdot 47, \; \lambda_1{}^2 = 0 \cdot 010627, \; \lambda_2{}^2 = 100 \cdot 77$$

The dispersion in the visible spectrum for many refracting substances is little affected by the second term, which takes account of the infra-red absorption band, and Sellmeir's formula,

$$n^2 = 1 + \frac{D\lambda^2}{\lambda^2 - \lambda_1{}^2} \qquad \cdot \qquad \cdot \qquad (807)$$

may be adequate for interpolation over short ranges of wave-length.

If λ is large in comparison with λ_1, equation (806), and small in comparison with λ_2, we may write an approximation to (805) by retaining only two terms in the expansion of each fraction; thus

$$n^2 = H\lambda^2 + A + B\lambda^{-2} + C\lambda^{-4} \qquad \cdot \qquad (808)$$

Herzberger[4] has claimed good success from a formula based on the supposition of *two* ultra-violet bands, i.e.

$$n = 1 + a + b\lambda^2 + \frac{c}{\lambda^2 - \lambda_1{}^2} + \frac{d}{\lambda^2 - \lambda_2{}^2} \qquad \cdot \qquad (809)$$

with λ_1 about $0 \cdot 20\mu$ and λ_2 about $0 \cdot 160\mu$, and has shown how to modify this into a form convenient for extrapolation in the infra-red.

An empirical formula proposed by Schmidt

$$n = n_o + A\lambda^{-1} + B\lambda^{-4}$$

has been modified by Conrady into a form which has proved very useful for ordinary purposes, i.e.

$$n = n_o + A\lambda^{-1} + B\lambda^{-3 \cdot 5} \qquad \cdot \qquad \cdot \qquad (810)$$

Smith and Anderson[5] show that this form is numerically consistent with the numerical form of (805), and is, therefore, to be preferred to the Cauchy equation,

$$n = A + B\lambda^{-2} + C\lambda^{-4}$$

which is inconsistent in that sense.

Such formulae are fairly safe for interpolation in "fifth-place" work over the range of the visible spectrum for ordinary glasses. The comparison of the relative accuracy of the various interpolation formulae is often rendered difficult by experimental uncertainties in the determination of the refractive indices, both for the set or sets of lines used to calculate the constants ("least square" methods are sometimes required) and the further lines used to test the results. Elaborate experimental precautions with good apparatus are necessary to reduce the experimental errors below 1 unit in the fifth-decimal place.

Production of Optical Glass. Good descriptions of many details in optical glass manufacture may be found in Wright's "Manufacture of Optical Glass and of Optical Systems."[6] A few notes must suffice here. The ingredients, especially the sand (chosen for its freedom from iron), have to be selected and mixed with care and thoroughness. They are fused in an uncovered crucible or pot, of clay chosen for its insolubility in the glass to be melted and for its freedom from iron. The open top allows of the stirring necessary to secure homogeneity. Stirring is commenced after the mass has been sufficiently long in the liquid state to get rid of most of the bubbles. The first comparatively quick cooling of the mass of glass results in fractures which split the material into a number of lumps of different sizes, which are re-heated, pressed into flat slabs, and subsequently examined for freedom from cloudiness, stones (fragments of undissolved material), large bubbles, crystallization, etc. The best parts, which often only comprise a quarter of the whole weight, are then re-heated and annealed. This process is carried out in order to avoid the unduly quick cooling and consequent solidification of the outer parts of a mass, while the inner portions are still hot. If this condition occurs, the inner parts will still tend, of course, to shrink on cooling, and thus set up a great tension in the material, since the outer parts, having already solidified, cannot shrink correspondingly. Radial stresses appear in the inner parts, and tangential compressional stresses in the outer parts, of a block. The process of annealing consists in cooling the material very slowly through certain ranges of temperature; by this means the development of strain is prevented through the fact that the glass has still a certain fluidity while solidifying, and sufficient flow can take place, if enough time is allowed, in order to obviate trouble. When the whole is sufficiently solid, it can be cooled more quickly without danger.

F. Twyman investigated the annealing question as a viscosity problem, and showed that the mobility of most glasses through the critical range from $400°$ C. to $800°$ C. doubles for each $8°$ rise in temperature. He studied the relief of stress in hot glass by examination in polarized light, and his results agreed with Maxwell's tentative suggestion that the rate of decrease of stress is proportional to the stress itself. Methods of testing for strain are dealt with below. Adams and Williamson in America corrected these ideas in detail, but confirmed the main trend of Twyman's physical results. The practical uses of this work were to determine for various glasses the particular range of temperature over which the cooling after melting should take place very slowly, and this knowledge of the annealing temperature enabled the whole cooling and annealing process for certain kinds of glass, which had sometimes occupied perhaps fourteen days, to be shortened to three and a half days.

The question of the annealing temperature of glass is important in the process of moulding "blanks" for lens manufacture, and also in the welding of optical parts. The determination of the critical range is now a well-recognized investigation, and apparatus can be obtained especially designed for the purpose. In Twyman's method

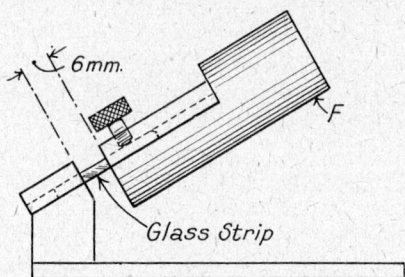

FIG. 150

for controlling the annealing of glassware, a strip of the glass 6·0 mm. wide, 2·0 mm. thick, and about 15 mm. long is clamped in a small jig (Fig. 150), and bears a weight F in such a way that a length of only 6 mm. is free to bend when heated. The jig is placed in an electric tube furnace and is kept under observation by a telescope as the temperature is raised. The rates of bending at two temperatures near the softening-point being observed, it is possible to obtain from a series of curves given by Messrs. Adam Hilger, Ltd., the makers of the apparatus, the temperature at which the deflection of the lever is 2·2° per hour.* Experience has shown that this is the best "annealing temperature" for domestic or chemical glassware. Very similar methods can be applied to optical glass.

The process of annealing consists in gently raising the glass to the annealing temperature and maintaining this for a sufficient period to allow the relief of strain (domestic glassware only requires about 15 minutes), and then allowing the temperature to fall, very slowly at first, and more rapidly afterwards.

Twyman gives the equation

$$\theta_o - \theta = \frac{\log_{10}\left(\dfrac{1}{1 - mbt}\right)}{m \log e} \qquad . \qquad . \qquad . \quad (811)$$

* Another criterion which may be useful in observations made of the relief of strain by examination in polarized light is that a strain causing a retardation of 0·1λ per cm. is reduced to 0·05λ per cm. in ten minutes.

(where $m = 0.0865$, b is a factor representing a chosen rate of cooling, $\theta =$ temperature, $\theta_o =$ the annealing temperature, $t =$ time for temperature to fall from θ_o to θ, and $e =$ base of Naperian logarithms) as a suitable one by which to ascertain the best time schedule for cooling.

Homogeneity of Glass. During the period before 1926, the *main* function of annealing was considered to be the avoidance of strain. It can be shown, however (see below), that the actual optical path differences in specimens showing recognizable strain are often not sufficient to cause appreciable deterioration of an image; on the other hand, interferometer tests of certain specimens of glass almost free from strain showed appreciable defects of homogeneity; i.e. variations of refractive index.

It is now known that glass maintained at a fixed temperature (above about 400° C. where the viscosity tends to fall) tends to acquire a certain molecular structure which is characteristic of the temperature. If such a specimen is rapidly and evenly cooled, the refractive index attained at ordinary temperatures is characteristic of the high (steady) temperatures at which the structure of the glass is acquired. The higher the "temperature of acquisition," the lower is the final refractive index; for example, on heating one specimen for a long period to 500° the final index after fast cooling in air was 1.5223; after heating to 550° the final index was 1.5192.

The rate at which the glass can acquire its characteristic structure has, however, been shown by Hampton[7] to be inversely proportional to the viscosity constant; consequently the effects during the cooling-down from the steady furnace temperature play an important part. For example, when a specimen of glass is cooled rapidly from a comparatively high temperature, say, 1000° C., the viscosity in the higher ranges of the temperature is so low that the molecular changes can follow the fall of temperature very rapidly. Hence, it is likely that the ultimate refractive index after cooling will be largely independent of the high steady temperature, provided that the latter *is* sufficiently high. But when the steady temperature lies in some range (like 500° C. to 550° C. in certain cases), the viscosity of the glass is higher; and if chilling takes place rapidly the index change cannot follow at such a rapid rate, but will have a final index rather higher than the actual equilibrium index for the steady temperature.

These results are of great importance in the theory of annealing. If a temperature difference exists in the glass during the annealing period when the temperature conditions are held steady for a long period, then, although mechanical stress may disappear, there will be a corresponding refractive-index difference. According to Hampton, "it is very difficult to get any sort of annealing kiln where the temperature differences are so small as to preclude variations of the order of 10° C. across a slab of optical glass." But research has now obtained conditions where the temperature of quite large slabs are even within 3° or 4° C. Good annealing implies, therefore, the maintenance of *even temperature*. Provided this is secured, the rate of cooling can be much higher than was previously thought possible.

Some variations of refractive index, perhaps affecting the third decimal place, must be expected between melts to the same batch formula. Particulars should be obtained from the manufacturers if reproducibility is important.

The annealed lumps may have been moulded into square blocks, prisms, etc., or may be still unshaped. They may be tested by immersion in a liquid of the same refractive index (carbon disulphide

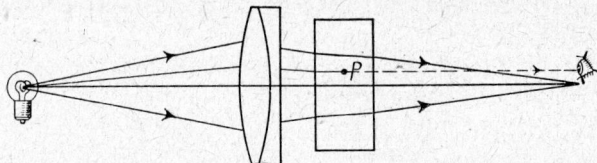

FIG. 151. TESTING FOR STRIAE, ETC.

and alcohol can be mixed in various proportions to obtain a wide range of refractive indices), or the pieces can be cut into slabs, if necessary, and opposite faces of the slabs can be optically ground and polished for inspection.

Striae. There may be local regions in the melt where the stirring has not yet perfectly mixed the material, but has produced threads or striae similar to those seen when syrup is being mixed in water. Heavy striae may involve differences in refractive index of one or two units in the third decimal place.

The usual method of testing for such defects, as well as bubbles and other small specks of undissolved material, is to place the plate in the path of a convergent beam of light, Fig. 151; AB and CD are the polished faces worked on the specimen. The source of light should not be too bright; a lamp flame serves excellently. The image may be 3 or 4 mm. in diameter. If, then, the pupil of the eye is placed in this image, the whole aperture of the lens appears filled with light of uniform brightness unless there are regions where, as suggested at P in the diagram, local variations of refractive index alter the path of some of the light and cause it to fall outside the pupil of the eye. The defect will then show up dark on the lighter ground. The sensitiveness of the test is enhanced by using a small and bright source, and moving the eye so that the image of the source falls just outside the pupil. The scattered light entering the eye from any striae then reveals them, bright on a dark background. A similar test may be applied to a rough or unpolished block if it is immersed in a liquid of the same refractive index contained in a tank with walls of optically-worked glass, but care is necessary to distinguish the effects of the surface in case the liquid is not correctly adjusted to the proper refractive index.

In one very simple test, a very small source of light (a 6-volt lamp, for example) illuminates a screen at a distance of a few feet; if the disc to be tested has polished faces, it can simply be held in the path of the light; striae become visible as shadows and streaks on the screen.

Effects of Strain. It appears probable that the most serious effects of strain lie in the slow movements in the material to which they give rise. Glass is not "solid" in the absolute sense, but must be regarded as a material of extremely high viscosity, even at ordinary temperature. The gradual movement may thus affect the figure of a lens or prism cut from the block, or may result in the fracture of the glass in the grinding or polishing operations; even after a lens is finished, it may suddenly crack from the effects of internal strain accentuated by some variation of temperature.

The usual method of inspecting a specimen for the presence of strain is to hold it in the path of the light in a simple polariscope (Fig. 125). In the simplest form of the test, the analyser is turned to produce a dark field, and the effects of strain are detected most readily when the direction of the stress in the specimen is at $45°$ to the plane of polarization.

The effects of increasing amounts of strain are a transmission of light in the formerly dark field, first grey, then yellow, red, blue, and so on, as was described in the chapter on polarization. Owing to the variation of the double refraction with wave-length, the retardation first reaches $\lambda/2$ in the blue end of the spectrum; light is then being restored as a greyish-blue. As the retardation of the blue increases to a whole wave-length, the remaining light becomes straw-coloured, yellow, red, and so on, as the extinction travels through the spectrum. The table on page 210 shows the *relative* retardation, in microns, for sodium light. The colour produced when white light is employed as the illuminant is also given in the next column.

A piece of glass which shows no "lighting-up" in the dark field of the ordinary polariscope is perfectly suitable for the majority of optical purposes, and even those which show a faint greyness near the borders are usually tolerated. Anything like bright colour, yellow, or red, would be indicative of very bad annealing, and would be rejected.

A method of increasing the sensitiveness of the test should be mentioned. It is to place in front of the analyser a thin plate of doubly refracting material of such thickness that the retardation is nearly $1 \cdot 0\lambda$ for sodium light. This produces a violet coloration in the field, and an inspection of the table (p. 210) will show that a slight change of retardation produces a considerable alteration in the hue of the field. Thus, slight strain in a glass specimen may show up as an indigo or red.

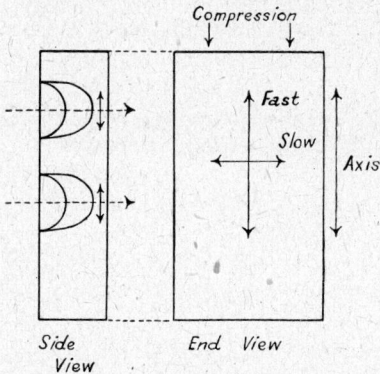

FIG. 152

Quantitative Aspects of Stress Measurement. Brewster found in 1813 that a glass plate under compression acts as a negative uniaxial crystal, the optic axis being the direction of application of the load; also that the difference between the effective refractive indices for light traversing the plate in a direction perpendicular to the load (that is, for the components of this light vibrating parallel and perpendicular to the stress respectively) is proportional to the compression. The difference is a measure of the bi-refringence.

It was shown above that in a negative uniaxial crystal the ray velocity ellipsoid is outside the sphere, and that the single optic axis is the diameter in which the sphere touches the ellipsoid. Hence, considering a ray passing perpendicularly through a plate cut with faces parallel to the optic axis, the vibrations which lie in the plane containing the ray and the axis will take place parallel to the axis; they will constitute the extraordinary ray, and in the case of the negative crystal will travel faster than those vibrating perpendicular to them. Hence, the fast direction in a stressed block of glass is the direction of compression, Fig. 152; and, conversely, for a block under tension, the direction of tension will be the slow direction. The diagram is intended to help the memory, the long arrow suggesting the "fast" vibration direction.

Adams and Williamson showed experimentally that the bi-refringence resulting from a load of 1 kilogram per sq. cm. to a block of crown glass is about $2 \cdot 6 \times 10^{-7}$, i.e. the relative retardation of the yellow ray components ($\lambda = 589 \times 10^{-7}$ cm.) would be $2 \cdot 6 \times 10^{-7} \times t$ cm., where t is the thickness in cm. Hence, a load of about 113 kg. per sq. cm. on the ends of a plate 1 cm. thick would produce a retardation of $\lambda/2$. Their corresponding value for barium flint is $3 \cdot 1 \times 10^{-7}$; for light flint, $3 \cdot 2 \times 10^{-7}$; but for extra dense flint only $1 \cdot 22 \times 10^{-7}$.

It is estimated from experience that the amount of bi-refringence tolerable in optical glass should not exceed 20 $m\mu$ or 20×10^{-7} cm. per cm., and should be reduced to one quarter of this amount if possible. For ordinary domestic glassware, Schulz states (*Das Glass*, Munich, 1923) that a tolerable limit is 50×10^{-7} per cm., when the glass suffers about $\frac{1}{20}$th of the breaking stress.

If the test on a stressed block is carried out with the sensitive-tint plate, suppose the plate and block are so orientated as to raise the order of the polarization colour to a maximum amount, taking, as example, a case when this colour is recognized (by comparison with the colours exhibited in a "wedge") as the greenish blue, the retardation is $0 \cdot 728\mu$. Subtracting the retardation ($0 \cdot 575\mu$) of the plate, we have $0 \cdot 153\mu$, or 153×10^{-7} cm. for the block. If the latter were 10 cm. thick, the bi-refringence would be estimated at $15 \cdot 3 \times 10^{-7}$, a medium amount.

The department of Glass Technology of the University of Shef-field supplies glass discs calibrated in terms of the bi-refringence which they exhibit, and are thus convenient for comparison pur-poses. There are naturally many complex factors (liability to temperature shock, etc.) which have to be considered in discussing the tolerable limits of stress for glassware.

If a plate or prism has varying amounts of strain in differing parts, this will tend to produce a variation of relative optical path between disturbances passing through unstrained parts; but it will be appreciated that even if the bi-refringence considerably exceeds the figures suggested above for optical glass, there is no reason to fear loss of definition from this cause alone.

If it is desired to *measure* the amount of the double refraction due to strain, the Babinet compensator is employed.

Transmission of Glass. Let $(1 - \beta)$ be the transmission factor of the surface of a glass block with plane parallel faces, and of thick-ness t. Imagining parallel light incident normally on the block, the intensity I_o of the radiation before entering the first surface will be diminished, through reflection at each surface. The amount of this first component transmitted by the block will be

$$(1 - \beta)^2 I_o e^{-\alpha t}$$

where α is the absorption coefficient and e is the base of natural logarithms. Some of the light reflected back at the second surface is again sent forward by the first surface. Interference effects can be neglected in this treatment if the film is thick; since they tend to suppress some wave-lengths but enhance others, there is a compensation as regards the total photometric effect. Additional amounts sent forward in this way by internal reflections are

$$(1 - \beta)^2\beta^2 I_o e^{-3\alpha t}, \quad (1 - \beta)^2\beta^4 I_o^{-5\alpha t},$$

the total amount I being

$$I = (1 - \beta)^2 I_o e^{-\alpha t}(1 + \beta^2 e^{-2\alpha t} + \beta^4 e^{-4\alpha t} + \text{etc.})$$
$$= (1 - \beta)^2 I_o e^{-\alpha t}(1 - \beta^2 e^{-2\alpha t})^{-1}$$

For the case of a thin piece of glass with negligible internal absorption, we put $\beta = (n - 1)^2/(n + 1)^2$, as on p. 184, then the formula becomes

$$I = \{2n/(n^2 + 1)\}I_o.$$

If the absorption is small but appreciable, a working formula is

$$I \approx I_o\{2n/(n^2 + 1)\}e^{-\alpha t}.$$

This applies, however, only if the internally reflected components add to the brightness of the resultant beam. This will generally not be so in transmission by a lens system where the internally reflected light may be widely spread. In such a case, the apparent luminosity B of the image transmitted by a lens with surfaces of reflection coefficient β, and material of absorption coefficient α, will be closely represented by

$$B = B_o(1 - \beta)^2 e^{-\alpha}$$

provided the light goes through the lens so nearly normally that β and t can be considered single valued.

Bunsen and Roscoe[8] introduced the term "extinction coefficient" for an absorption coefficient referred to the base 10; thus

$$I = I_o 10^{-xt}$$

where x is the extinction coefficient; but some confusion has arisen in the literature owing to the varying use of this term.

Slight coloration in glass always indicates appreciable absorption in some region of the visible spectrum. Its most usual cause is iron from the sand, or from the walls of the pot, but other impurities, such as cobalt, copper, chromium, nickel, manganese, or vanadium, may introduce coloration. "Ferrous" iron produces a green coloration which is more marked than the yellowish coloration produced when the iron becomes oxidized to the ferric condition. Success in optical glass production largely depends on the successful removal of such impurities.

Transparency. The absorption coefficient was taken above to be
the fractional diminution of intensity per unit thickness. If we take
inch units, the following table shows the absorption coefficients of
some typical Chance glasses—

Glass Type	BSC 510644	HC 519604	MBC 572577	DBC 610573	LF 578407	DF 623360	DEDF 748278	SDF 749455
Wave-length (Microns)								
0·6500	·0183	·0300	·032	·0307	·0230	·0180	·0178	·036
0·5790	·0101	·0169	·020	·0185	·0151	·0117	·0171	·033
0·5461	·0089	·0135	·018	·0152	·0124	·0104	·0152	·033
0·4916	·0165	·0188	·025	·0242	·0195	·0145	·0440	·068
0·4358	·0220	·0367	·055	·0516	·0380	·0406	·109	·164
0·4048	·0146	·0248	·088	·0780	·0490	·0630	·491	·280
0·3650	·0582	·0782	·592	·655	·260	·511	—	·75

Some glasses have a composition which confers increased transparency in the ultra-violet, for example *Vita-glass* (Pilkington Bros.),

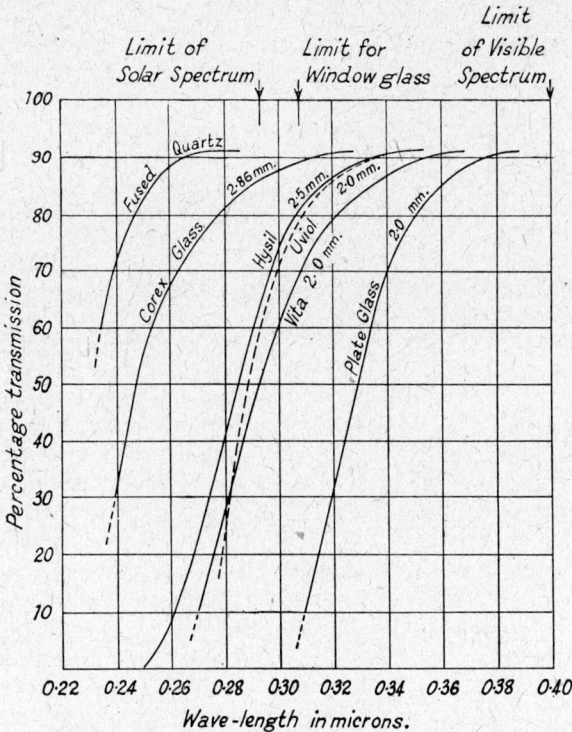

Fig. 153. Ultra-violet Transmission of Plates of Certain Glasses

Corex (Corning Glass Works), *Hysil* (Chance Bros.), *Uviol* (Schott and Genossen), have been advertised in this respect. Some of these are apt slightly to decrease ultra-violet transmission after exposure to light (solarization); thus, for example, a glass similar to the "vita-glass" type may reduce its transmission at 0.302μ from 62 per cent to about 45 per cent after prolonged exposure. Corex is also subject to this, but to a less degree. Transmission curves for some of the above glasses are shown in Fig. 153. Vita-glass at 2·0 mm. thickness transmits 79 per cent at 0.32μ, 59 per cent at 0.30μ, and 24 per cent at 0.28μ.

Coloured Glasses. Light Filters. Glass may be coloured by the use of various metallic compounds, some of which seem to impart their colour directly as solutions in the glass. Others produce the coloration by the "excretion" of colloidal particles in the material. Various metallic oxides, cobalt, nickel, iron, copper, chromium, manganese, and uranium belong to the first group of these direct-colouring materials, while cuprous oxide, gold, and selenium are examples of the second group.

The following table shows some of the materials used in particular cases—

Colour	*Material*
Red	Cuprous oxide, selenium.
Purple	Gold (metallic).
Rose	Selenium and its compounds.
Violet or amethyst	Manganese oxide, nickel oxide.
Yellow	Cadmium sulphide, uranium oxide, ferric oxide, nickel oxide, carbon, metallic silver.
Green	Cupric oxide, chromium oxide, ferrous oxide.
Blue	Cobalt oxide, copper oxide.
Neutral	Various mixtures.

Coloured glasses can be obtained commercially from various firms, and their production, which was at one time somewhat uncertain, has become capable of more precise control. Particulars have been published by Chance Bros. and other firms for various-coloured glasses, which include glasses designed to transmit special limited regions of the spectrum, as for railway signalling, three-colour printing, photography, filters for use with panchromatic plates, and the like.

An important use of coloured glass is for eye-protective spectacles. These are required by furnace workers, welders, and others to protect the eyes from the intense light and heat radiations (infra-red) which are liable to produce cataract. Extensive researches on the production of suitable glasses were carried out by Crookes,[9] who found that green glass containing ferrous iron absorbs the infra-red very strongly. Protex (see Fig. 154) is a glass of this type made by Chance. A good absorption of the infra-red is shown by glasses containing cupric oxide, and cobalt with ferric iron, according to measurements by the present writer,[10] who also suggested the use of gold-coated glass for such protective spectacles. Such are now obtainable commercially.

Persons who have to deal with light sources rich in ultra-violet radiation, such as are now used extensively for clinical purposes,

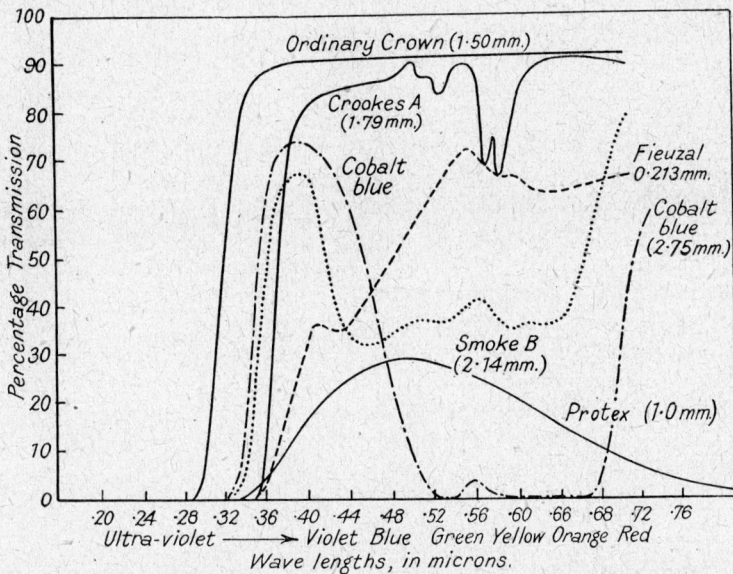

FIG. 154. TRANSMISSION OF VARIOUS GLASSES FOR EYE-PROTECTION

require light-filters which will effectively stop all those radiations of wave-length shorter than about 0.38μ, showing increasing "abiotic" action with decreasing wave-length, which may damage delicate tissues and, in particular, cause marked inflammation of the moist surfaces of the eyeball and eyelids (conjunctivitis). The work of Crookes, who experimented with glass containing cerium, lead, neodymium, and praseodymium, etc., in addition to the substances mentioned above, showed that cerium conferred marked powers of absorption in the ultra-violet, while not greatly affecting the transmission of the visible wave-lengths. Neodymium glass has marked absorption bands in the neighbourhood of the sodium (D) lines. It is thus useful for protective spectacles for glass-blowers and others. Titanium is said to confer absorption of the ultra-violet.[11] Various glasses of secret composition are sold commercially under the name of Crookes' glasses. In many cases, of course, the intensity of the visible radiation has to be reduced for the sake of comfort.

In very bright sunlight, in the tropics, or by the sea, and especially on the mountain snows, the relative intensity of the ultra-violet in sunlight may increase considerably, though ozone absorption is held to account for the absence of the more harmful radiations of wave-lengths below 0.295μ. In such conditions, spectacles which eliminate the ultra-violet, and preferably somewhat reduce the intensity of the visible light, are found very useful.

Useful information on the relative transmission of coloured glasses and light filters has been given[12] by Gibson, Tyndall, and McNicholas, whose investigations have covered the visible and ultra-violet regions of the spectrum. Some typical results of interest are given in Fig. 154.

Use of " Non-reflecting " Films. In 1892 H. Dennis Taylor[13] found that the loss of light by reflection at a glass surface is reduced if the surface is tarnished. The formal discussion of the summation of amplitude contributions from the surfaces of a thin film was given above (p. 190); it was shown that if the reflection coefficients at the surfaces are equal, the reflection can be completely annulled (for a single wave-length) by the choice of a proper thickness. If a thin plate of refractive index n_2 separates media of indices n_1 and n_3, the intensity reflection coefficients at the two faces are for normal incidence

$$\left(\frac{n_2 - n_1}{n_2 + n_1}\right)^2 \quad \text{and} \quad \left(\frac{n_3 - n_2}{n_3 + n_2}\right)^2$$

They are equal if $\qquad n_2 = \sqrt{(n_1 n_3)}$

By taking numerical examples, it is found that if n_2 has a value between n_1 and n_3, the sum of the two reflection coefficients is less than that for a single surface separating the outer media (n_1 and n_3). Thus, even a film so thick that the phase relations of reflected white light need not be considered in a photometric discussion, would lessen the loss by reflection; if, however, the thickness t is made so small that $t = \lambda/4n_2$, the disturbances reflected at the successive surfaces will have an optical path difference of half a wave-length (a phase change of π occurs at *both* surfaces). Thus, if λ corresponds to the brightest part of the spectrum, we have the most favourable condition for the diminution of the reflected intensity; if, however, the thickness is made $\lambda/2n_2$, the amplitude contributions will add together and the whole advantage of the film will be lost.

In practice, the surface films usually consist of either magnesium fluoride, cryolite (a double fluoride of sodium and aluminium), or calcium fluoride; they can be deposited by the process of vacuum distillation.[14] The refractive indices are usually higher than the square root of the index of the glass.

	n	n^2
Calcium fluoride . . .	1·434	2·056
Cryolite . . .	1·36	1·84
Magnesium fluoride . .	1·378–1·390	1·90–1·93
Cadmium arachidate (treated)	1·54–1·30	2·37–1·69

Perfect annulment cannot be attained unless the square root condition is fulfilled. Films of cadmium arachidate or barium stearate can be given a skeleton structure with sub-microscopical cavities (Blodgett[15]), but they are not so stable as those of the other substances, which can stand gentle cleaning with soft rag or wash-leather. Improved results can be obtained by multiple evaporated films; but it appears that the fluoride films sometimes have a skeleton structure; if so, it would explain why sometimes the results are better than theory would indicate. Various other techniques, etching, etc.,[16] have been described, whereby films of silica, sometimes with skeleton structure, can be produced; but the vacuum distillation process seems to be more generally applicable.

If a film annuls reflection for one wave-length (say, 0·589μ) in the spectrum, other colours exhibit more or less reflection; thus, in an ideal case there might be about 3 per cent at the violet end and 1 per cent at the red end of the spectrum, and the residual light would appear purple-blue. If the zero of reflection shifts towards the green, the residual purple becomes more red; if towards the red, the purple tends to blue. Thus control of thickness during distillation is effected by watching the colour of the reflected light, using a white source. For visual instruments the minimum should be at about 0·555μ, and the reflection shows a dark plum colour. For photographic lenses the requirement varies; thus, if the lens will be used with ordinary photographic materials and without a yellow filter the minimum reflection should be in the blue-violet, and the residual reflection will be yellow-brown.

The use of these films enhances the efficiency of most optical instruments; they offer a useful means of controlling "ghost" reflections. It is to be expected that their use on optical surfaces will become general. The technique of preparation demands considerable care, however, if mechanically hard films are to be produced; the distillation process requires a "hard vacuum" and careful control of conditions generally. Some workers advocate a technique of baking after removal from the vacuum. (See British Patent 538274.)

Multiple films may be employed. The British Thompson-Houston Co. proposes (B.P. 537591) to coat a surface of ordinary glass with dense glass of high index in a layer 5μ or more in thickness, and the surface of this layer is etched to give a "$\lambda/4$" coating of silica. In some procedures protected by the British Scientific Instrument Research Association, the multiple layers may be given a foundation of a layer, a few molecules thick, of chromium.

Optical Work—Lens Blanks. Optical glass arrives from the glass works in the form of small slabs, or, sometimes, moulded blanks, for which the glass has been pressed when plastic into the rough shapes of the lenses. The slabs were reduced in the method usually employed until recent times, by a "slitting machine," to square pieces of a required diameter and thickness. This machine employs a rotating iron disc, the cutting edge of the disc being charged with diamond dust. The square pieces were then reduced to a fairly circular form by the use of "shanks," a tool slightly resembling a pair of nut-crackers. The blanks were then cemented together, and the resulting "roll" was made truly cylindrical by grinding, thus producing a number of circular discs. In some modern works, however, the circular pieces are cut directly from the slabs by means of tubular cutters.

Slabs up to $\frac{3}{4}$ in. thickness are sometimes cut up by first making a fairly deep cut with a glazier's diamond, and then pressing along the line of the cut with an iron rod heated almost to redness.

Blanks for spectacles are often made by first rolling the melt into plates; these are inspected for bubbles and other defects, which are avoided when the plate is cut up (with a diamond) into pieces of the right weight. The pieces are then heated, and moulded in suitable dies approximately to the curves required; the moulded blanks are then annealed at a temperature which allows relief of internal strain while the "figure" is retained. The blanks or moulded lenses were in the earlier days given the necessary true external curvatures and approximately correct thickness by grinding with a coarse abrasive on an iron grinding tool, but in recent times the use of diamond-charged laps has become common. Fig. 155 is intended to suggest the principle involved. The headstock has a horizontal spindle on which the lens is mounted; it can also be moved (slowly) about a vertical axis (H). The cylindrical lap (copper or soft iron charged with diamond particles) rotates at a high speed (the linear velocity of the surface is about 1,600 ft. per min.) about a vertical axis (L). The distance between H and the surface S of the lap in contact with the glass determines the radius to be given to the surface; if the headstock is moved radially outwards with respect to the vertical axis H, the thickness of the lens can be reduced. A lubricant (soap emulsion type) is essential.

Many variants on this general principle are encountered in machines in present use, and it is possible also to grind prisms by means similar to those of the milling machine, but using high-speed diamond laps or carborundum or corundum wheels with the

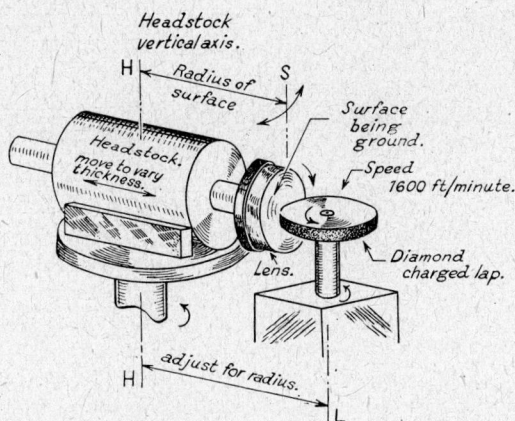

FIG. 155

movement of the lap or wheel on the work perpendicular to the direction of feed. In this way, prisms can be produced with angles correct to ± 3 min. if the direction of cutting is carefully controlled (preferably by optical means rather than a rough scale and vernier).

Grinding and Polishing. The process of optical grinding and polishing of spherical surfaces depends mainly on the fact that a pair of spherical or plane surfaces are the only ones which will fit each other in all relative positions. The grinding tools are of iron and are made to screw to the spindle of the grinding machine. The spherical surface is first prepared on a lathe, as shown in Fig. 151. The grinding "tool" shown, shaded, in section, is rotating about a horizontal axis, while a cutter C is mounted on a "slide rest," which enables it to rotate about the vertical axis. The distance CD in the figure determines the radius of the resulting surface.

An optical factory keeps a wide range of these tools, always in

pairs, convex and concave. The figures of the surfaces are perfected by grinding them together.

Small glass surfaces of very short radius, and very large surfaces,
are ground singly; but for small lenses of medium curvature, a
number of lenses, from three upwards, may be ground while mounted

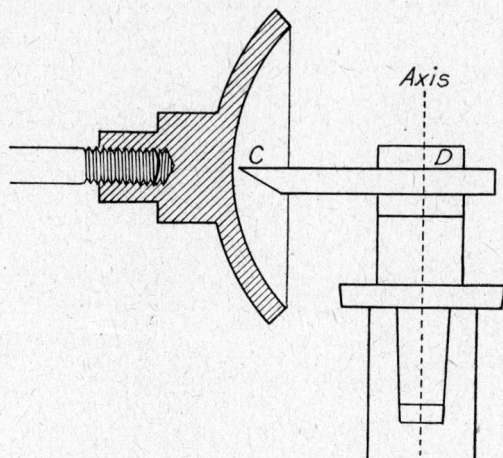

FIG. 156

on the same "block." In the preparation of the block, the separate
lenses are first given a backing or "mallet" of pitch, which is given
while the glass is hot enough to ensure adherence, and to enable
the mallet to be given a roughly hemispherical form. After coating,
the lenses are now placed face downwards (Fig. 157) on the

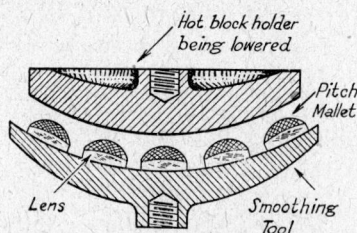

FIG. 157

smoothing tool in their appropriate positions (the radii of
the lens faces and the tool will
have been equalized in the
roughing process), care being
taken to ensure that no dirt or
pitch prevents good contact.
The block-holder is then heated
(sufficiently to make pitch
adherent and plastic) and
placed centrally on the lenses. As it settles by its own weight,
it will thin and spread the mallets, but there should be a remaining cushion of pitch between the lens and the block-holder. After
cooling, the block of lenses may be lifted out and screwed on to
the spindle of the smoothing machine.

Different methods of blocking are often adopted, especially for prisms, which are usually blocked together in plaster, or Wood's fusible metal.

The abrasives used in grinding are usually emery or carborundum. These powders are graded by screening for the coarse varieties and by elutriation in water for the finer ones, so that a series of grades having different-sized particles is available.

Physical Processes in the Grinding and Polishing of Glass and Metals. When glass is fractured, the freshly-formed surfaces are usually "shiny," although not regular in form; this effect might be termed "fracture polish." Fracture naturally occurs along the surfaces of maximum tension in the material.

Now when a flat glass surface is submitted to pressure at a point, the maximum tension occurs in an approximately conical surface in the material, the axis of the cone being normal to the flat, and the semi-apical angle being about 45°. If the pressure is great enough, this results in the well-known conchoidal fracture characteristic of glass or flint; but other fractures may be found, for example, a fracture at the base of the cone running parallel to the surface, and fractures in planes containing the conical axis. Thus, if numerous small conchoidal fractures occur at closely adjacent points the "cracks" meet below the surface. Material may thus be detached and removed. This is probably characteristic of the process in sand-blasting.

When an abrasive material is used between the surface of a metal tool and glass, the hard irregular grains partly roll, and partly embed themselves in the tool. When the point of a grain presses strongly into the smooth glass surface, characteristic conchoidal fracturing would no doubt occur at first, but once the surface has become irregular by the process suggested above, subsequent action of the grains is bound to be most severe on the sloping sides of the cavities in the surface. Under these conditions the characteristic cone of fracture is distorted and the axis deviated towards the surface. The detachment of the surface material now leaves rounded hollows separated by ridges not unlike those seen on prehistoric flint implements formed by the process of "knapping," but on a very much smaller scale; moreover, the glass surface will contain depressions of all sizes corresponding to the variously-sized grains. The action of a grain fixed in the tool or of a diamond splinter in a grinding wheel ploughs a groove formed by continuous fracturing of this kind. The surfaces of the hollows seen under the microscope show a "fracture polish," modified by rippling and striations here and there, between the ridges separating the hollows.

The operation of smoothing removes glass from the higher parts of the surface till the average level is reduced to near the bottom of the deepest holes or "pits" left by the coarser abrasive (Fig. 158). This may be done in several stages. The extreme importance of the careful grading of the abrasive can be realized; it must contain no particles much larger than the average size. In fine-grinding astronomical mirrors, for example, the worker will follow-up the application of fresh abrasive to the tool by a preliminary rub with a smaller piece of glass (of the right curvature) called a "bruiser." This catches, and breaks down, any exceptionally large grains accidentally present. The final nature of the surface befor polishing is thus a surface with very fine corrugations and probably a complex system of tiny cracks below it. But also a flowing process more akin to polishing is produced by the finer grains.

The grinding of metals with abrasive powders is probably a ploughing or groove-cutting action; there is no conchoidal fracturing.

The operation of polishing of glass is to some degree a continuation of the grinding process, as it has been shown that glass continues to be removed from the surface. In polishing, however, the grains of the material employed are much finer, and they partly embed themselves in the relatively soft material of the polisher (cloth, paper, or pitch, etc.) so that the conchoidal fracturing (if it takes place at all) is much reduced. Instead, there is probably an action in which the grain only projects far enough into the surface to plough a shallow smooth-sided groove (sleek) without splintering. It is thought that a considerable degree

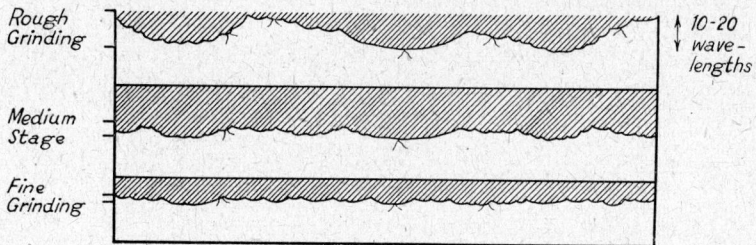

FIG. 158

of "flowing" of the material may also take place so that minute depressions may be filled in. This view (advanced by Sir George Beilby) has received support by electron diffraction experiments (Finch and Quarrell[17]). In such work evidence has emerged that if a metal showing crystalline structure is polished, the surface layer has a vitreous or non-crystalline structure differing markedly from the inner substance. The depth of this "Beilby layer" is supposed to be about 30A. Support to this view is lent by the experiments of Bowden and Ridler who investigated the temperatures caused in sliding point contacts (metal on metal) and found that there may be a local rise of temperature of as much as 1000° C. Local melting and flowing in the immediate vicinity of the polishing grains is thus understandable. Glass is itself a vitreous material, and there may be no comparable change of nature in the polished surface layer, but Lord Rayleigh has shown that the particular polishing process used may modify the refractive index of the surface, as compared with that of the inner material. It is well known that etching of a polished surface by a suitable reagent will reveal sleeks which have been hidden by the polishing. It thus appears that the "flowed" material is in a different condition from the rest. Moreover, when a polished surface is examined under very critical conditions (Foucault test) it will reveal a structure in which the curved strokes of the polisher are distinguishable, though these irregularities are small in comparison with the wave-length of light.

Sufficient has been said to illustrate the complex physical character of these processes. Many features, such as the function of the water or other lubricant in the work are only partially understood, and there are still problems which await fuller investigation. J. W. French[18] believes that the water plays an essential part in the filling-in of the sleeks in polishing.

Theory of Grinding and Polishing Processes ; " Fixed Post " Operation. The grinding process involves, in general, the attrition suffered by two surfaces in relative movement, and occasioned by the ploughing or disruptive action of grains of abrasive pressed between them. The wear of these opposing surfaces may be unequal if they are of differing materials, but the instantaneous rate of wear at a point of one surface will be roughly proportional to their relative velocity, supposing other things equal. The simplest considerations are encountered in the relative attrition of two flat circular discs moving thus one upon the other. If the lower one is larger than the upper (Fig. 159) and the upper moves in straight strokes without acceleration or overlap, the relative velocity will be equal at all contacting points, and if the abrasive cuts uniformly there will at first be equal wear at all parts of the upper surface. But as regards the lower tool there would be no wear at all outside the lines LL and HH, and the attrition must be greatest in the area (shaded in the figure) always covered by the upper one. Outside this area the wear will be proportional to the total time covered.

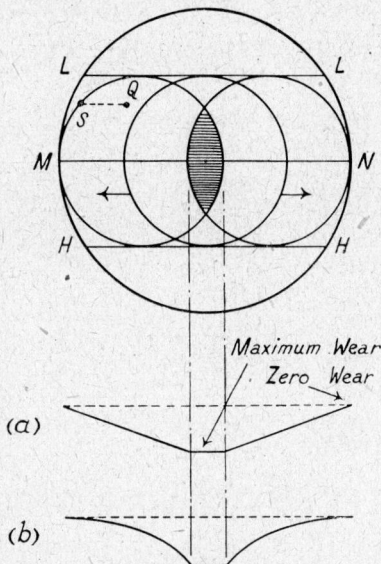

FIG. 159

The relative wear at various points can be estimated ; for example the time covered at a point Q is proportional to the distance QS to the edge of the disc in its extreme position, taken in a direction parallel to the stroke. The *relative* wear along the line MN is represented by the depression of the full line (a) below the dotted line.

If the direction of the stroke is changed progressively (as in the use of the fixed post for working astronomical mirrors, etc., in which the lower disc may be mounted on a fixed support while the manual operator moves round the post, pushing the top disc backwards and forwards) the wear of the lower disc (b) acquires a circular symmetry around its centre. If the lower tool is larger than the upper, and there is no overlap, a concavity would tend to develop on the lower disc, which would then tend to modify the figure of the upper one.

When the discs are of equal size (as in truing up a pair of iron tools) the stroke *must* result in some overlap; by this term is meant that the edge of one tool projects beyond the other. Parts of the marginal regions of both tools will be left exposed during parts of the stroke. Thus the mere "velocity and time" factors would first tend to produce a concavity in each disc, though, of course, this would soon result in a diminished general pressure in the central regions, and hence set up a correcting tendency. However, if the overlap of the upper disc is considerable its weight in the extreme position will tend to be transferred to the marginal regions of the lower one. The greatest pressure, therefore, is between the inner parts of the upper, and the outer parts of the lower disc, which results in a tendency to make the upper disc concave, while the lower one becomes convex. Thus, starting from a flat, an astronomical mirror can be ground concave by working it over a fixed disc of glass of about

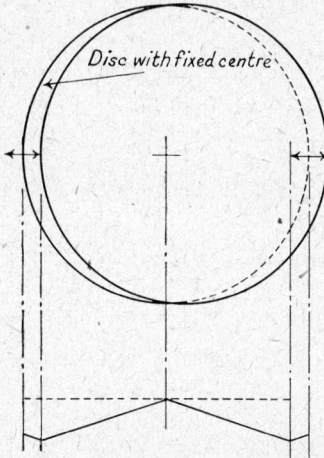
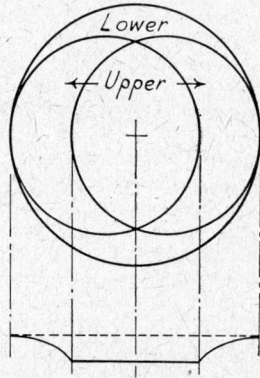

Fig. 160   Fig. 161

the same diameter with an extreme overlap of about half the diameter. The use of wet abrasive is "understood," in all the above remarks.

If the overlap is small the tendency to depart from the plane surface is much reduced; good plane surfaces can be obtained by mutual short-stroke rubbing of three equal discs taken two at a time, according to a systematic plan so that each is used as much in the upper position as in the lower.

Kinematics of Lapping by Machinery. If the lower disc is continually turned on a vertical spindle while the upper is moved across it without rotation, the relative velocity of movement at any contacting point of the upper disc will be found by compounding the velocities of the two plates; but the velocity of a point of the lower one is proportional to its radial distance from the spindle. Hence, if the diameters of the two plates are equal and the stroke is short, the rate of wear is much greater towards the periphery of each (at least while the pressure is still uniformly distributed), Fig. 160. There is diminished action, of course, in the overlapping parts.

If, however, the upper disc is the smaller and is pivoted by a pin which allows it to move and rotate without overlap, it will acquire an angular velocity equal to that of the lower disc. The relative movement is then equal at all points of the upper disc, and its wear will be uniform while the pressure and the abrasive action are equally distributed. However, as regards the lower disc the wear can only be uniform over those areas which are continually covered, and in the outer zones there is a diminished action (Fig. 161).

Consider, again, the case of tools of equal size. Let the upper one be pivoted as before, so that it can rotate freely, then in an extreme overlap position (Fig. 162a), the upper one will have an equal angular velocity but opposite to that of the lower. If they are moved over each other in contact so that the centres approach, the angular velocity of the upper diminishes, vanishes, and reverses till it equals that of the lower (ω) when the centres coincide; thus the effect of any overlap is a "braking" of the angular speed of the upper disc. Suppose that for a small overlap the angular velocity of the upper is ($\omega - \alpha$), Fig. 162b. Suppose, also ω is anti-clockwise. Let the distance between the centres $= E$.

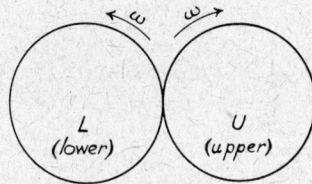

(a) Wear on MN in fixed stroke direction

(b) " " (direction of stroke varies)

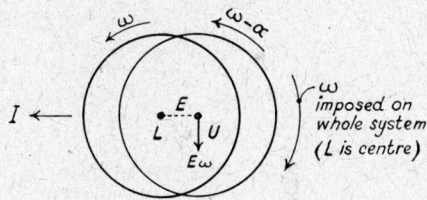

(a)

(b)

Fig. 162

In order to study the relative movement of the upper disc with respect to the lower suppose that the rotation of the lower is annulled by imposing *on the whole system* a rotation of angular velocity "$-\omega$" around L the centre of the lower disc. The linear velocity of the centre U of the upper disc is now $E\omega$, and the resultant angular velocity of this disc is α in a clockwise direction. This implies that it is (at this instant in effect) rotating around an "instantaneous centre of rotation" (I) at a distance $E\omega/\alpha$ to the left of U in the direction UL in the diagram. The centre itself always lies on this line UL; it partakes of the "imposed" angular velocity, $-\omega$, but if the imposed velocity is considered annulled, the instantaneous centre of rotation is stationary. It is important to realize that the movement with regard to the instantaneous centre I (i.e. the relative movement) determines the wear of the disc, and the wear of an element will therefore be closely proportional to its distance from I. It will be noticed that if the angular velocities are equal, $\alpha = 0$, and the instantaneous centre is at infinity.

The case when $\alpha = \omega$ is that of the stationary upper disc; the point I coincides with L. When the discs rotate equally and oppositely $\alpha = 2\omega$, and the point I is midway between the centres.

Thus, in Fig. 163 the distance IU is l, and r is the radius of the ring containing the point P defined by the angle θ. Then the average distance d of the elements of the ring from I is given by

$$d = \frac{1}{2\pi} \int_0^{2\pi} (l^2 + r^2 + 2lr \cos \theta)^{\frac{1}{2}} d\theta$$

It can be shown (Williamson's *Integral Calculus*, 1906 Edn., p. 233) that this integral is the total circumference of an ellipse with major and minor semi-axis equal to $(l + r)$ and $(l - r)$ respectively. Thus the average distance d is found by dividing the length of the perimeter by 2π. It differs little from $\sqrt{(l^2 + r^2)}$ owing to the variation of sign of the

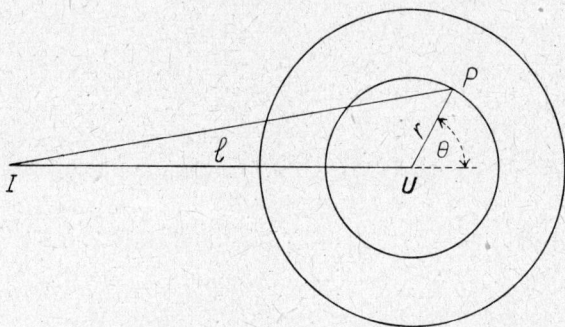

I   *instantaneous centre of rotation.*
U   *centre of upper tool.*

FIG. 163

$\cos \theta$ term. Hence, the ratio K of the wear on a ring of radius r, to the wear at the centre is

$$K \simeq (l^2 + r^2)^{\frac{1}{2}}/l = \sqrt{(1 + r^2/l^2)}$$

It will be seen that this indicates a hyperbolic curve of wear increasing outwards from the centre U.

If, however, the ring is only partly covered by the other tool the wear (distributed evenly round the ring owing to the relative rotation of the upper disc) will be proportional to the length actually covered. Thus the wear, increasing at first with r, in the hyperbolic curve, will be relieved in the region of overlap.

There is the further complication that in any of the usual surfacing machines (Fig. 164), the eccentricity of the discs is constantly changing through the action of the crank and radial arm. Hence the relative wear during the operation can only be calculated if this "relief" is taken into account in addition to the corresponding variation of the instantaneous centre of rotation.

It is possible to carry out a theoretical investigation of the position of the instantaneous centre by assuming that the action of the abrasive continually transfers angular momentum from the lower (or driving) disc to the upper one (driven). The rate of transfer can be assumed proportional to the relative angular velocity of the contacting elements of area with respect to the centre of the driven disc, and the integration carried out over the area of contact. The driven disc will take such an angular velocity that the total rate of change of angular momentum is zero.

Alternatively the question may be tackled by considering that the driving disc is stationary and that movement of the driven disc around the instantaneous centre will set up frictional forces for which the total angular momentum with respect to the centre U of the latter must be zero. Both methods involve troublesome numerical integrations.

The value of any such calculation is prejudiced, moreover, by the effects of overlap in causing the uneven distribution of weight and pressure between the discs in any actual practical case. The wear

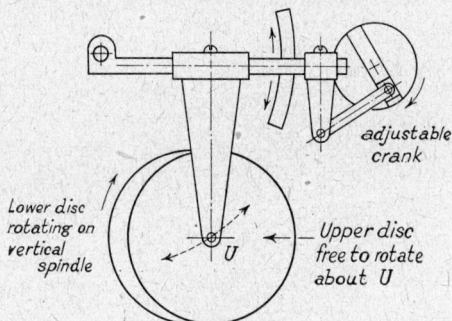

Fig. 164

actually experienced is also greatly dependent on the rate of action of the abrasive, but the cutting action is reduced between any parts of the surface which do not receive abrasive which is periodically exposed to the air. A little consideration will show that if two equal discs overlap in the machine so that the maximum eccentricity is half the radius, then all parts of the discs can receive abrasive exposed to the air. Fresh abrasive can of course be supplied more easily to exposed parts unless the discs are pierced with holes for this purpose.

For these reasons Dévé has made a semi-experimental study of this matter, and has embodied the results in a scheme for the rough calculation of the wear between discs under certain assumed conditions. His book (*Optical Workshop Principles*[19]) should be consulted for a detailed discussion. The above treatment will, however, indicate the main factors which enter into grinding operations for flat or nearly flat surfaces.

Similar factors are encountered in polishing, but with modifications owing to the relatively great accommodation between the polishers and the surface (much greater in cloth or felt polishers than with pitch). There is now the very important factor that control of the figure can be effected not only by the variation of the stroke, but by removing parts of the polisher. The whole question is outside the scope of this book, but valuable discussions will be found in the books by Dévé and Twyman.[20]

The Grinding of Spherical Surfaces. The mutual interaction of spherical surfaces involves more complex considerations. Suppose, for example, that a concave tool moves over a convex one which is made to rotate about an axis of symmetry, OA (Fig. 165a). The concave tool is held centrally by a pin P, which leaves it free to rotate around the axis OB, where O is the centre of the spherical surface of contact; it is driven by the frictional forces at a speed which depends on the angle θ between OA and OB. If these axes coincide the angular velocity ω of the concave will clearly be equal to the "convex" angular velocity ω_0; if now OB is taken round to OB' so that θ is 90° (supposing the surface of the convex tool extended if necessary), then ω_0 will have no component around OB', and the concave tool will cease to rotate. It may be assumed that the concave takes up the angular velocity of the convex according to its component around the axis OB; thus,

$$\omega = \omega_0 \cos \theta.$$

Supposing both surfaces extended, it can now be shown that the instantaneous velocity of each will be equal and parallel at the point C,

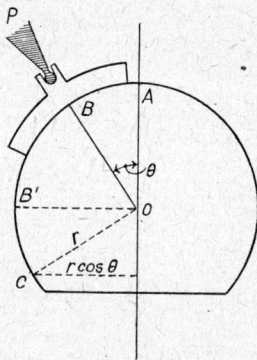 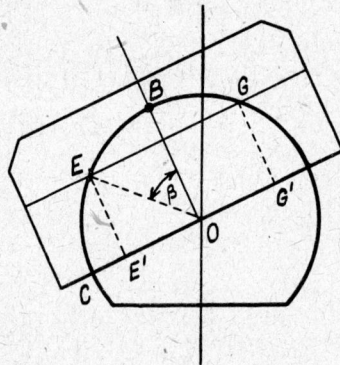

FIG. 165a FIG. 165b

where OC is perpendicular to OB and lies in the same plane as OB and OA. If r be the radius of the spheres the linear velocity of the concave tool at C (perpendicular to the diagram) will be equal to $r\omega$, i.e. to $r\omega_0 \cos \theta$. The linear velocity of the point C on the convex tool will be equal to ω_0 multiplied by the perpendicular distance of C from the line OA; the product is clearly $\omega_0 \times r \cos \theta$. Since there is thus no relative movement at C, the axis OC is the instantaneous axis of rotation of the concave on the convex tool. Therefore the wear of the concave surface occurring during a very short interval of time will be proportional to the distance of the surface element concerned from the line OC. Referring to Fig. 165b, the wear at E and G will be proportional to the distances EE' and GG', i.e. to $r \cos \beta$ where β is the semi-angular aperture of the zone EG of the concave tool. But consider also the diameter of this zone perpendicular to EG; the distance of its extremities from O will be equal to OB. Consequently the mean wear of the zone EFG will be proportional to $\frac{1}{2}(OB + EE')$, i.e. to $\frac{1}{2}(1 + \cos \beta)$. Considering now the fact that the concave tool rotates around the axis OB, it is clear that the mean wear must be distributed evenly around the zone. Apart, therefore, from other considerations, the wear of the concave is greatest at the centre, and falls off only slowly with increase of β.

There is, however, the important consideration that in the case of one hard spherical tool resting upon another, of equal radius, under gravity, the pressure between the two surfaces would be unevenly distributed, being proportional to the cosine of the angle β if surfaces were of perfect form and the concave surface were symmetrically disposed with respect to the vertical. If, however, the surfaces were separated by a fluid, the hydrostatic pressure would tend to become uniform between them. An intermediate case is represented by a pitch polisher which can flow to some extent, and can thus relieve pressure inequality; though the hydrostatic analogy is less applicable if the polisher is channelled by grooves. In the case of polishers the pressure may be more nearly proportional to $\sqrt{\cos \beta}$.

According to Dévé, the result of the foregoing factors of relative movements and relative pressures is to make the relative wear at $\beta = 30°$ vary from 0·81 with hard surfaces to 0·93 with very plastic surfaces. At $\beta = 20°$ the relative figures are 0·91 and 0·97. All these are relative to a wear of unity for $\beta = 0°$. It is important to notice that this is practically independent of the angle θ, i.e. of the eccentricity of the pin P which holds the driven tool, provided the latter is free to rotate. However, oscillatory movements of P will be required from a machine in the interests of even wear of the convex tool.

Now if the concave tool receives an independent rotatory movement, the instantaneous axis of rotation will no longer remain perpendicular to OB, but will take some other inclination so that the region of greatest wear occurs at some zone other than the centre; for an extreme example if the concave were prevented from rotation altogether, there would be an eccentric distribution of the wear, which would be proportional to the distance of the element from the vertical axis OA (neglecting pressure inequality). It is therefore possible, by controlling the rotation, to obtain symmetrical wear which may be made equal in two or more zones of the concave tool, the pressure effect being balanced against the effect of relative movement. The practical details are further discussed by Dévé.

The general question of the control of figure in polishing is a large one, and other special publications[21] [22] should be consulted.

It is not difficult to estimate the fineness to which outstanding irregularities must be reduced before the surface has the characteristic appearance (or *non-appearance*) of perfect polish. In previous work we have seen that vibratory disturbances must arrive in a focus with a difference of path not exceeding $\lambda/4$ if the effect on the image is not to be perceptible.

The thick parabola in Fig. 166 shows an imaginary perfect parabolic reflecting surface, and WW_o an incident plane wave-front, the ray directions being parallel to the axis; hence, the paths WAF and W_oA_oF are identical. If a bump of thickness d is pushed out from the surface at A, the disturbance now meets the reflector in the point A', which acts as a secondary centre of disturbances. The relative path difference is found (in a similar manner to the argument for reflection at a thin film) to be $2d \cos i$, where i is the angle of incidence. The greater the angle of incidence, the greater the allowable value of d; hence, a surface which is only partly polished will reflect red light better than blue. This has been used as a method of estimating the relative state of fineness of a surface.

In the case of a transmitting surface, the path difference arising through a similar elevation d may be expressed as $\dfrac{d(n - \cos \overline{i' - i})}{\cos i}$

where i and i' are the angles of incidence in glass and air respectively, and n is the refractive index of the glass.

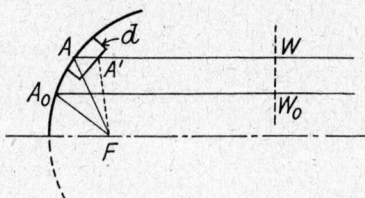

FIG. 166. EFFECT OF SURFACE ELEVATION

Hence, we see that for a reflecting surface with normal incidence, the condition is

$$2d < \lambda/4 \text{ or } d < \lambda/8$$

For a transmitting surface, normal transmission,

$$d(n - 1) < \lambda/4 \text{ or } d < \lambda/2 \text{ approx., where } n = 1 \cdot 5.$$

The requirements of perfection of the surface are evidently not so strict for transmission as for reflection, but in either case the outstanding irregularities must be small in comparison with the wavelength of light.

In a good fine-ground surface the grain of the structure is about five to six wave-lengths deep. With badly-graded carborundum, pits and cracks up to fifteen wave-lengths may be encountered. The "Sira" abrasive developed by the British Scientific Instrument Research Association is especially useful in this respect; the grain is very uniform in size, hence no very deep pits are produced and, owing to the absence of deeper pits, the time of polishing can be very much shortened.

Polishing is performed by rubbing the fine-ground surface on a polisher of pitch carrying wet rouge or putty powder, etc., as a polishing medium which is, in reality, a *very* fine grained abrasive. Cerium oxide, though more costly than rouge, will polish faster, and is white in colour.

The pitch polisher is made by covering the surface of a tool having very nearly the required radius with melted pitch (suitably tempered in hardness by mixture with other ingredients, such as resin or turpentine), which is moulded, as it cools, into a curve of the true required radius by pressure against the appropriate iron tool.

A number of V-shaped grooves may be cut into the surface of the

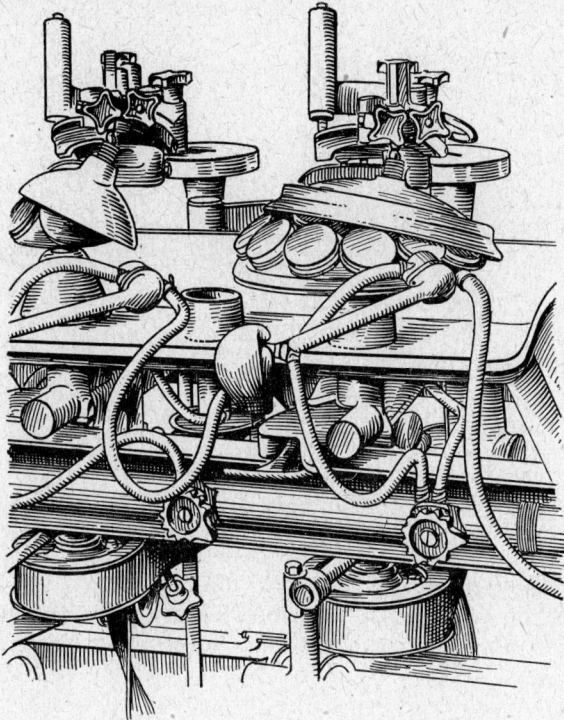

FIG. 167. A MODERN BENCH OF POLISHING SPINDLES

polisher, partly for the collection of debris, and also to relieve the wear on certain parts of the surface, as may be necessary.

During the polishing process the surfaces of the polisher and the glass are periodically supplied with rouge and water; it is the practice to let the surfaces get *almost* dry before putting on a fresh supply. In machines (Fig. 167) made by Messrs. Taylor, Taylor & Hobson, Ltd., of Leicester, the extra torque on the spindle, which occurs when the work gets dry, automatically works a squirt, thus supplying the necessary moisture.

Fig. 168 is to illustrate the principle of the type of machine employed for polishing large surfaces—astronomical mirrors and objectives. The block, or surface, is rotated steadily on a vertical axis, while the tool is given cross movements by one or two cranks while free to rotate independently. The combination of the cross movements can be arranged in almost any way by varying the eccentricities and relative speeds of the cranks, thus producing circular, elliptical, "figure of eight," and other movements as required.

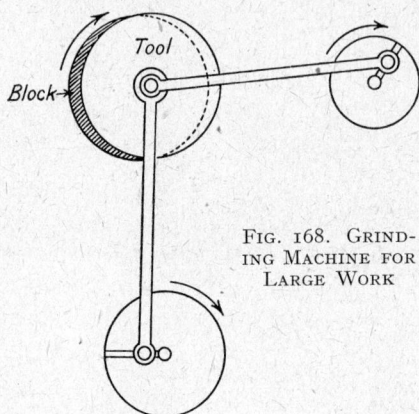

FIG. 168. GRINDING MACHINE FOR LARGE WORK

Control of Figure. As soon as a reasonable degree of polish appears, the form of the surface can be tested by means of a "test plate," a method introduced by Fraunhofer. This is a piece of glass, one side of which has been worked to the radius required and is truly spherical, but opposite in curvature to the surface to be tested. A set of convex lenses on the block would be tested with a concave test plate. Both surfaces being wiped clean, the test plate is slid into contact so closely that the interference colours can be observed in the thin film between them. Precautions have to be taken regarding the temperature of the blocked lenses. If the latter prove to be (say) too convex, circular coloured rings may be observed. Sometimes the direction of greater thickness in the film can be inferred from the progression of the colours (see Quincke's Table, p. 210), but if this fails, another simple test is to move the head so that the light is reflected at a greater angle of incidence and watch the movements of the rings. The retardation in the film is given by $2d \cos i$, where i is the angle of incidence in the air film. If i increases, the retardation decreases; to compensate for this, the fringes will move towards a thicker part of the film. Thus, if the blocked lenses are too convex and make contact in the centre of the test plate, the rings will move outwards when the above test is made.

When large surfaces are polished, say, 12 in. in diameter and over, for large telescope object-glasses, telescope mirrors, and the like, the testing of the figure is not so conveniently done with a test plate; with concave surfaces of long radius, the test is usually made by the Foucault knife-edge method, illustrated in Fig. 169.

A small source of light S (a pinhole in metal foil illuminated by a lamp-flame is adequate) is imaged by the concave mirror M at S'. An eye placed close behind this image receives light from all points on the mirror, which thus appears evenly illuminated. If a knife-edge is brought across the exact focus, the light from all points is cut off uniformly; if introduced at A the shadow appears to move

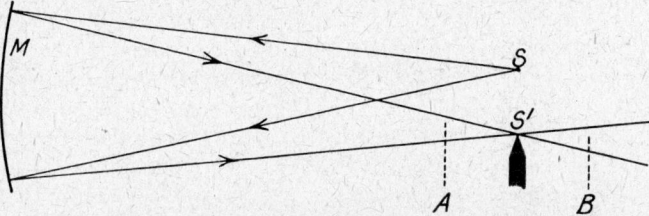

FIG. 169. THE FOUCAULT KNIFE-EDGE TEST

upwards; if at B the shadow moves downwards. It is thus easy to fix the exact focus of a spherical mirror with considerable precision or even to determine the possible differences of the foci of successive annular zones with the aid of cardboard diaphragms. If the mirror is parabolic, the whole gives a characteristic shadow figure, Fig. 170, and the distance between the foci of central and marginal portions is y^2/r, where y is the radius of the circular aperture and r the radius of the curved surface. The whole method of the test will be found well described in Ellison's *Amateur's Telescope*. The ease of making this test makes the optician able to produce concave surfaces of great accuracy with more certainty than the corresponding convex ones.

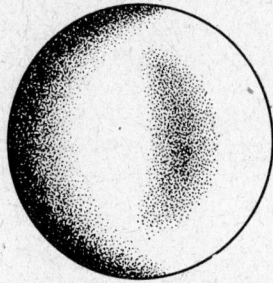

FIG. 170. CHARACTERISTIC SHADOW FIGURE GIVEN BY PARABOLOIDAL SURFACE IN THE KNIFE-EDGE TEST

Having by some means or other tested the curvature of the surfaces undergoing the polishing process and thus knowing the tendency of the "figure" in formation, it is possible by various means to control the final result, the required balance being maintained between the wear of centre and edge by the adjustment of the stroke, etc.

Especially when dealing with small surfaces, more pitch can be chipped from near the central or marginal portions of the polisher when it is desired to lessen the wear towards the centre or edge respectively, or to correct some zonal irregularity.

It is by the aid of methods of this kind, carefully controlled, that a concave mirror can be gradually made to take a parabolic curvature. Elliptic or hyperbolic figures of small eccentricity can be produced if required, but, except for special purposes, spherical curves are of the greatest importance for small surfaces.

Cylindrical and Toric Surfaces. The general freedom of movement in grinding and polishing cylindrical surfaces is naturally much more restricted than for spherical surfaces, but the corresponding standard of accuracy need not usually be attained for the modest requirements of spectacle lenses. Motion in grinding or polishing is restricted to a rotary movement of the cylinder (represented by the blocked-up lenses) about the cylindrical axis, combined with a movement of the tool, to and fro, parallel to this axis. The rotation may be only backwards and forwards through a definite angle, or may be continuous, depending on the design of the machine and the methods adopted. A good idea of the action may be obtained if the palm and fingers of the right hand rub the wrist of the left hand parallel with the direction of the forearm, while the left hand twists backwards and forwards, as in turning a screw.

The toric surface is one in which the curvature is different in the principal sections, just as in a pneumatic tyre. The radius in one section of a tyre is the radius of the wheel; in the other direction it is the radius of the circular section of the tube. This is, of course, a case in which the difference is extremely accentuated, and in most forms of lenses the radii are more nearly equal. Here the relative movement of block and tool is much more restricted. The block of lenses (often a complete ring) represents the tyre, while the tool could be represented by a "cast" of a portion of the outer surface of the tyre.

In practice, the movement of the tool is limited to comparatively small arcs of rotation about an axis which would be represented (on the tyre analogy) by a short length of the central axis of the tube; this is combined with the circular movement of the block about the axis of symmetry.

Figuring. Various methods have been employed in producing non-spherical surfaces of rotation, from quite early times. Machines for constructing elliptical, parabolic, or hyperbolic surfaces were devised by Fraunhofer before 1814, and an account was recently re-issued. In this case, the grinding and polishing tools hang as pendulums, their motion being controlled by a ring bearing on a non-spherical pivot. A number of patents and papers, notably one by Gullstrand,[23] have described kinematic linkage mechanisms mostly for generating second degree surfaces of revolution. A short account of recent methods will be given in Vol. II.

The most serious defects in many well-designed lens systems, like telescope object glasses (and, in fact, in many microscope objectives), are not defects of optical aberration as usually understood, i.e. those calculable from the radii of curvature, refractive indices, and separations of the components. They are the defects arising from the irregularities of construction, lack of homogeneity of the components, lack of true centring, and the like. They often account for the lack of adequate concentration of the light in the image, and are revealed at once by the interferometer or the "star test." Either of these methods, but especially the first in this case, may indicate to the experienced optician the possible necessity of *local* figuring (often done by local rubbing with a chamois leather pad charged with rouge), which is the final stage in the making of many of the finest and most perfect lenses. Prisms also are subjected to treatment of this kind.

Centring of Lenses. When the two surfaces of a lens are polished it is usually necessary to give it an edge which is concentric with the optical axis. Unless this is done, the axis would evidently be tilted when placed in a circular mount, and it would be impossible to get the lens coaxial with other lenses of the instrument. A piece of tubing is spun in a lathe and the edge is turned down, rounded and smooth, so that it runs perfectly true. The diameter of the tube is somewhat smaller than the lens. The tube being warmed, the lens can be mounted on it with sealing-wax, or a cement with a basis of pitch, and adjusted by pressure with a wooden peg while rotating, so that the glass surfaces run true also. This is indicated by the steadiness of the reflected images. The edge of the glass may then be ground down true by wet-grinding with carborundum, the "grinding tool" being a piece of sheet brass, usually bent into an angle plate, so that contact is made in two places. The abrasive in water should continually drop between the stationary brass and the edge, while the latter is rotating at a high speed. In this way the diameter of the lens is reduced to the exact value required.

REFERENCES

1. *Silikat Zeitschrift,* p. 237 (1913).
2. Brit. Patent, 462,304 and 534,680.
3. Johnson: *Proc. Phys. Soc.,* 55, 257 (1943); see also Wearmouth, *ibid.* p. 301.
4. Herzberger: *Jour. Opt. Soc. America,* 32, 70 (1942).
5. Smith, T., and Anderson, J. S.; *Dictionary of Applied Physics,* IV, p. 318.

6. Washington, Ordnance Department Document No. 2037.
7. Hampton: *Proc. Phys. Soc.*, 54, 391 (1942).
8. Bunsen & Roscoe: *Pogg. Ann.*, 101, 235 (1857).
9. Crookes: *Phil. Trans. Roy. Soc. A.*, 214, 1 (1914).
10. Martin: *Trans. Opt. Soc.*, 18, 31 (1917).
11. Taylor: U.S. Patents, 1,292,197 and 1,292,148.
12. Bureau of Standards Technologic Papers, 118 and 148.
13. H. Dennis Taylor, *The Adjustment and Testing of Telescope Objectives*; Cooke, Troughton & Simms, Ltd.
14. Brit. Patents, 538,272, 538,273, 538,274, 538,301.
15. Blodgett: *Phys. Rev.*, 55, 391 (1939).
16. Ferguson & Wright: *Trans. Ill. Eng. Soc. Amer.*, 2, 220 (1916).
17. Finch and Quarrell: *Nature*, 28th March, 1936.
18. French: *Dictionary of Applied Physics*, IV, p. 326.
19. Dévé: *Optical Workshop Principles* (Trans.), Adam Hilger, Ltd.
20. Twyman: *Prism and Lens Making*, Adam Hilger, Ltd.
21. *Amateur Telescope Making*, Scientific American Publishing Co.
22. Strong: *Physical Laboratory Practice,"* Blackie & Son, Ltd.
23. Gullstrand, *Kungl. Svenska Velensk. Handl.*, 60, Feb. 1919.

CHAPTER IX

SPECTACLES

THE extremely large amplitude of accommodation in youthful eyes is not maintained with advancing years. At 10 years a child can often focus on an object about 7 cm. distance from the eye, but at 40 years no object closer than about 20 cm. can usually be clearly seen by a normal eye, which can, however, sharply focus very distant objects. The nearest point for distinct vision is termed the "near point" of accommodation; the point which the eye sees clearly with the accommodation entirely relaxed is the "far point of accommodation."

We shall adopt the usual "left to right" direction of light with the eye "looking" from right to left, so that the distance of the near point for a young normal eye will be negative, and the distance of the far point will be "$-\infty$." At the age of 55, or over, the eye may lose so much refractive power that, when unaccommodated, the incident light must be slightly convergent to arrive in a sharp focus on the retina. The far point is then behind the eye; its distance has the positive sign.

The following table (after Donders) shows the position of the near point and the far point for average normal vision at different ages, the distances being measured in centimetres. If the reciprocals

TABLE

Age in Years	Distance of Near Points in cm. (b)	Distance of Far Point in cm. (k)	Amplitude of Accommodation in diopters $A = \left(\dfrac{1}{k} - \dfrac{1}{b}\right)$
10	$-$ 7·1	∞	14
15	$-$ 8·3	∞	12
20	$-$ 10·0	∞	10
25	$-$ 11·8	∞	8·5
30	$-$ 14·3	∞	7·0
35	$-$ 18·2	∞	5·5
40	$-$ 22·2	∞	4·5
45	$-$ 28·6	∞	3·5
50	$-$ 40·0	∞	2·5
55	$-$ 66·6	400	1·75
60	$-$ 200	200	1·0
65	$+$ 400	133	0·5
70	100	80	0·25
75	57·1	57·1	0·0
80	40	40	0·0

of these distances expressed in metres be computed, and their difference taken, the result gives the difference in power, expressed in diopters, of the optical system of the eye when accommodated for the near and far points respectively.

The following symbols will be used—

$$
\begin{array}{llll}
\text{Position of the macula} & . & . & . & . & \text{M}' \\
\text{Far point (punctum remotum)} & & . & . & \text{M}_\text{R} \\
\text{Near point (punctum proximum)} & . & . & \text{M}_\text{P} \\
\end{array}
$$

Distance from 1st principal point of eye to far point $= k$
,,   ,,   ,,   near ,, $= b$

The reciprocal of the distance from the 1st principal point to the far point is termed the "principal point refraction" or "ocular refraction," and is denoted by

$$K = 1/k$$

If k is expressed in metres, K will be expressed in diopters. It is to be noted that M' will be a conjugate point to M_R in the unaccommodated eye, and to M_P in the fully accommodated eye. The

Amplitude of Accommodation, A, is the difference $\left(\dfrac{1}{k} - \dfrac{1}{b}\right)$

Normal vision with the far point at ∞ is termed the condition of *Emmetropia*. The condition of vision characteristic of age is signified by the term *Presbyopia*. Donders applied this term particularly to cases of vision in which the near point withdraws beyond – 22 cm. approximately, which usually occurs at about 40 years of age.

The condition in which the far point lies behind the eye is known as *Hypermetropia*; then the condition generally developing after age 50 in a normal eye is "acquired hypermetropia."

In the following section the unaccommodated condition of the eye will be assumed. There are various common defects of the eye, the results of which can be alleviated with the aid of spectacles.

*Hypermetropia,** in which the far point lies behind the eye, may result from too short an axial length of the eye-ball, or in some cases from a flattening of the cornea, or an abnormal refractive index in one of the media. The eye can only bring to a focus on the retina such rays as are already slightly convergent (i.e. to the far point) when they reach the cornea. Parallel incident rays fail to reach a focus as shown by the broken lines in Fig. 171A.

Myopia, in which the far point lies in front of the eye, but at a finite distance, may result from an unduly great anatomical length of the eye-ball, or from too great curvature of the cornea, etc. Thus, parallel rays entering the cornea are brought to a focus before

---

* Sometimes shortened to "Hyperopia."

reaching the retina, but rays which are still divergent (i.e. from the far point) are focused at the macula. See Fig. 171*b*.

Astigmatism arises very frequently from a difference of curvature of the cornea in its various meridians, i.e. sections by planes containing the optical axis. It may also arise from similar defects in the

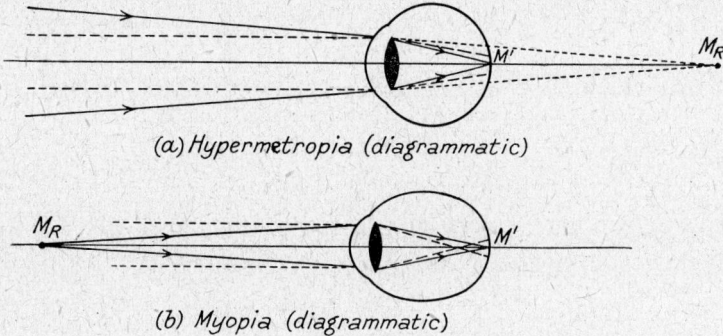

(a) *Hypermetropia (diagrammatic)*

(b) *Myopia (diagrammatic)*

FIG. 171

lens. Thus, the refraction of the eye is different in various sectional planes or meridians, and the position of the far point will vary with the meridian. If the astigmatism is regular, there will be two perpendicular meridians in which the maximum and minimum values of the refraction are found. The axial astigmatism must not be

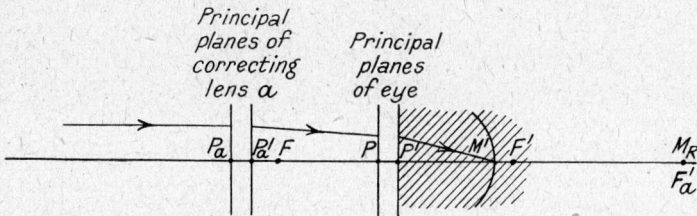

FIG. 172. TO ILLUSTRATE THE CORRECTION OF A HYPERMETROPIC EYE

The shading is to indicate that the points M' and F', the macula and second principal focus of the eye respectively, are referred to the medium of the image space, i.e. the vitreous humour. The curve passing through M' indicates the retinal surface.

confused with the astigmatism of oblique pencils, which latter only affects images formed away from the optical axis.

Spectacles for Distance Vision. In cases of hypermetropia and myopia, when adequate accommodation is present, *the function of the spectacle lens is to project an image of an infinitely distant (axial) object into the far point, which must therefore coincide with the second principal focus of the spectacle lens.* Thus, in Fig. 172, the points

P and P' are the principal points of a hypermetropic eye, of which M' and F' (imagined both to lie in the same image space medium), are the macula on the retina, and the second principal focus of the eye respectively. The principal points and second principal focus of the lens, P_a, P_a', and F' are shown. Incident parallel light falling on lens a is converged towards the second principal focus F'; if this coincides with the far point of the eye M_R, the optical

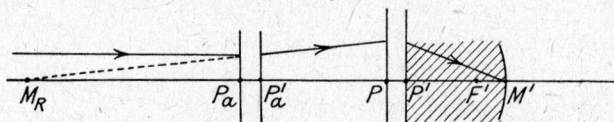

FIG. 173. CORRECTION OF A MYOPIC EYE

system of the eye will bring the light to a focus at M', since M' and M_R are conjugate points.

Writing $PM_R = k$, $K = \dfrac{1}{k}$, and if $P_a'P = d$, the focal length of lens a is given by

$$f_a' = d + k$$

This may be written

$$f_a' = k\left(1 + \frac{d}{k}\right) = \frac{1 + dK}{K}$$

and in accordance with the usual notation, in which F_a is the power of the correcting lens,

$$F_a = \frac{K}{1 + dK} \cdot \qquad \cdot \qquad \cdot \qquad \cdot \qquad (901)$$

The correcting lens necessary in hypermetropia is clearly of the converging type with a positive power.

The correction of a myopic eye is illustrated by Fig. 173. M_R is now to the left of the eye, at a distance which is numerically negative, and the lens required is therefore one of a diverging type, of negative power, with its second principal focus at M_R. The form of the equations remains the same as those given above.

It is *again* to be noted that lengths in such an equation must be expressed in metres if the powers are given in diopters.

Examples of the Practical Use of such Equations. 1. An eye with a principal point refraction of + 4·25D is to be corrected by a lens which is to be placed so that its second principal point is at a distance of 14 mm. in front of the first principal point of the eye. Find the power of the lens required.

$$F = \frac{4 \cdot 25}{1 + (0 \cdot 014)\,(4 \cdot 25)} = 4 \cdot 01 D$$

2. It is found that an unaccommodated myopic eye is enabled to view distant objects distinctly with a lens of $-8D$ when the distance between the adjacent principal points of lens and eye is 11 mm. Find the principal point refraction of the eye and the position of the far point.

In this case an alternative equation would be more useful. Since

$$f' = d + k$$

$$k = f' - d = f'\left(1 - \frac{d}{f'}\right) = f'(1 - dF)$$

and

$$K = \frac{F}{1 - dF}$$

In our numerical case

$$K = \frac{-8}{1 - (\cdot 011)(-8)} = \frac{-8}{1 \cdot 088} = -7 \cdot 35D$$

and

$$k = \frac{1}{-7 \cdot 35} \text{ metres} = -13 \cdot 6 \text{ cm.}$$

Lenses which produce a true distance correction for the same eye when properly positioned are said to possess the same "effectivity." They have the same effective power at the eye.

Vertex Refractions. The practical aspect of the problem is somewhat simplified if distances are measured from the vertices of the refracting surfaces. Fig. 174 represents the correction of hypermetropia. A_1, A_2, and A_3 are the consecutive surfaces of the lens a and of the eye. M_R coincides with F_a' as before. Then

$$A_2F_a' = A_2A_3 + A_3F_a'$$

or

$$f_v' = d_v + k_v$$

where d_v is the distance between adjacent vertices of lens and eye, and k_v is the distance from the vertex of the eye to the far point. This equation becomes (as above), employing the suffix v to denote the reciprocals of the vertex distances,

$$K_v = \frac{F_v}{1 - d_vF_v}$$

where

$$K_v = \frac{1}{k_v} \text{ and } F_v = \frac{1}{f_v'}$$

Hence, if the back vertex focal length (f_v') or vertex power F_v of a correcting lens is accurately known, the distance k_v of the far point from the vertex of the cornea can be found directly; this is the "vertex refraction," or "refraction referred to the cornea."

There are two important steps in the determination of the required spectacles for an ametropic eye.

1. Examination to find the power of a lens which corrects vision when held at a measured distance from the eye.

2. Calculation of the lens required to correct vision when held at a prescribed distance from the eye, which distance may not be identical with that of the lens used in the test in (1).

The test in (1) may be carried out by trials in which a special spectacle frame is used to hold any required lens (or combination of two or three lenses) from a "trial case." Such a case usually contains positive and negative "powers" of 0·25, 0·5, 0·75 diopters, and so on up to 3 or 5, then 3·5, 4·0, 4·5, 5·0, 6·0, and then every integral value up to 20, besides positive and negative lenses for correcting astigmatism, as well as various prisms, etc., the use of which will be referred to below. The "powers" should be the

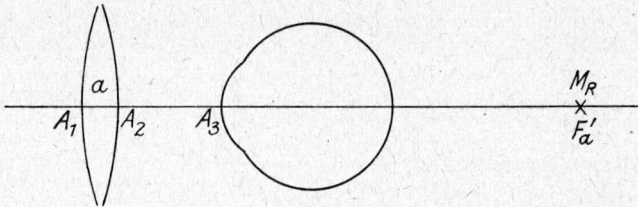

FIG. 174

"vertex refractions" of the lenses;* the true powers referred to the principal points are thus slightly weaker than the nominal powers in the case of the positive lenses.

Full details of the various methods of sight testing are outside the scope of this book, although some information on visual acuity and test-charts will be found in Chapter V. Details may be found in Souter's *The Refractive and Motor Mechanism of the Eye*,[1] Laurance's *Visual Optics*,[2] or Emsley's *Visual Optics*.[3]

When the lens or combination of lenses giving the best visual correction has been found with the aid of the trial case and trial frame, it is necessary to mount the new lenses in the actual spectacles for the patient's use, so that they have the same effective power at the eye. It is usually sufficient for low powers to position the lens in the trial frame so that it just clears the eye-lashes; then so to design and make the spectacle frame that the actually used spectacle lens falls in the same position. For very high-power lenses,

---

* See below, section on "Neutralization." In the negative lenses the powers may actually represent the value $1/f'$ in the Gaussian sense, i.e. the "equivalent power," but the positive lenses are made to neutralize the negative ones of equal numerical powers.

however, the distance between the adjacent vertices of the lens and the eye is *measured*, preferably with the aid of a small instrument* shown in Fig. 175. It consists of a scale mounted in front of a lens with a small stop in its principal focus. The only rays which can reach the observer's eye constitute narrow pencils which travel parallel to the axis of the lens before passing through it. Hence, the scale may be used to measure the size of a near object parallel to it, even though not actually in contact, without fear of errors arising through parallax.

The procedure is direct in the case where the lens has a convex surface turned towards the cornea (Fig. 175),

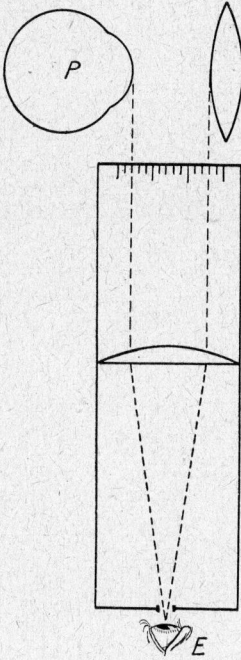

FIG. 176

but in the case shown where the correcting lens is concave (Fig. 176), the distance d_1 would be measured by the instrument, and d_2 would be measured by a small depth gauge.

By the methods outlined above, it will be clear that we can determine the back vertex focal length or power of a lens which, when placed in a definite coaxial position with regard to an eye of known "vertex refraction," will produce a true distance correction.

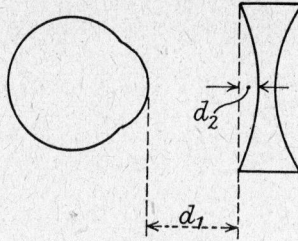

FIG. 175
P. Patient's eye.
E. Observer's eye.

Optical Properties of Spectacle Lenses. Spectacle lenses are commonly given a diameter of about 4 cm., at any rate in the horizontal diameter; their various peripheral shapes aim at allowing an adequate angular field of view unobstructed by the rim. The thickness necessary at the rim will be approximately 1 millimetre if the

* Called a "keratometer" by some books. This name is, however, usually applied to a more elaborate instrument for measuring the curvature of the cornea.

lenses are to be of positive power, and the centre thickness will have to be sufficient to allow of this.

In the negative lenses the thickness at the centre will be least, and this must be sufficient to produce the necessary mechanical strength, say, 0·7 mm. Figs. 177 and 178 shows how the principal

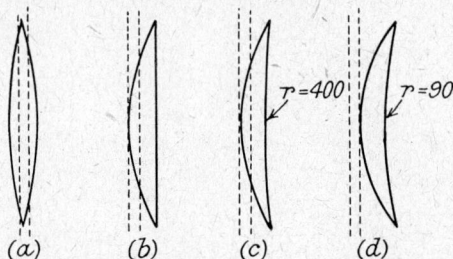

FIG. 177

Positive lenses : {(a) Double convex.   (c) "Periscopic" form (standard).
{(b) Plano-convex.   (d) "Meniscus" form (standard).

planes tend to move as the lens is "bent," so that its power remains constant though the curvatures of the surfaces vary.

The double-convex and plano-convex forms of lens are manufactured for all powers, but there are advantages in giving a more or less meniscus figure to the lens. The "periscopic" form has a second surface of 400 mm. radius, while the "meniscus" form

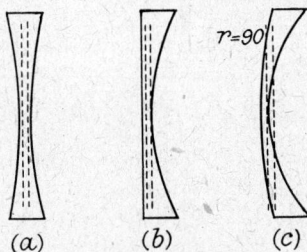

FIG. 178

Negative lenses : {(a) Double concave.   (c) "Meniscus" form (standard).
{(b) Plano-concave.

usually has the second radius of 90 mm. These surfaces are those which are turned to the eye in the ordinary use of the lens. In the case of the negative lenses, the surface of greater curvature is again turned to the eye; the periscopic and meniscus types have radii of 400 mm. and 90 mm. respectively on their front faces.

In a spectacle lens of + 10D, bi-convex type, with a thickness of (say) 5 mm., the principal points will be found to be about 1·65 mm.

within each surface; thus the Gaussian or equivalent focal length of such a lens will exceed the "back vertex focal length" by about 1·65 mm. In a lens of the same power, of the meniscus type, the difference may increase to 5 mm. when f_v' is measured from the second surface of greater curvature.

In the case of diverging lenses, however, these differences are

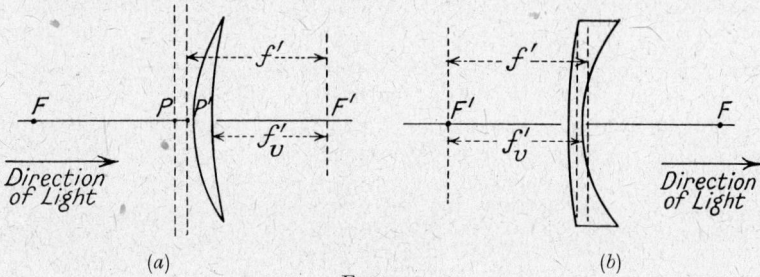

FIG. 179

very much smaller. An equi-concave lens of thickness 0·7 mm. has the principal planes 0·2 mm. within the vertices; the numerical excess of the back vertex focal length* over the real focal length vanishes for the plano-concave form; if the lens is bent into the meniscus form, the differences change sign and only increase to 0·3 mm. for a lens of − 10D. The differences may therefore be neglected for most purposes in spectacle work. Fig. 179 illustrates the manner in which such differences arise in positive and negative meniscus lenses.

The Lateral Test. Let the lens L, Fig. 180, project a virtual image B′ of an axial object point B. The apparent *direction* of the

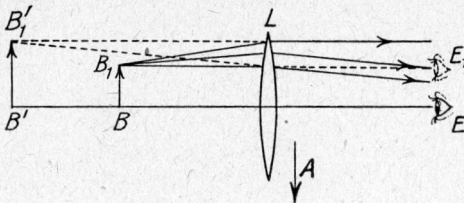

FIG. 180

object is obviously not modified by the introduction of the lens, provided the observing eye is situated on the axis of the lens also. Now, let the lens be moved a short distance in the direction of the arrow A. The optical effect is realized by imagining the lens to keep still while B moves upwards to B_1 and the eye moves upwards

* The vertex focal length measured from the concave surface.

an equal distance to E_1. The virtual image as seen by the eye has evidently moved in a sense *opposite* to that of the lens.

If the lens were negative or divergent, the image moves in the *same* direction as the lens. The test forms a useful means of distinguishing between weak positive and negative lenses.

We must, however, beware of applying the test in any case where a strong positive lens might form a real image between the lens and the eye. The test is only valid when the image is virtual, or is formed behind the observing eye. As the test is of more use with very weak lenses or combinations, these conditions are usually fulfilled.

Test for Neutralization. In Fig. 181, let B_1 suggest an object at some convenient distance viewed by an eye E, at first without the interposition of any lenses. Let two lenses, *a* and *b*, now be placed

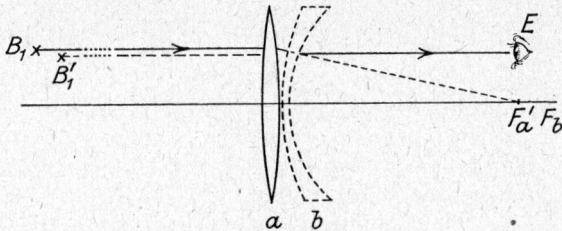

FIG. 181

in position between object and eye; they are to be such that their vertex powers are equal in the sense that F_a' coincides with F_b, the lenses being held coaxially. Tracing a ray from B_1 parallel to the axis, it will be refracted towards the point F_a' after leaving lens *a,* but will evidently be rendered parallel to the axis again after traversing *b*. It is, however, displaced downwards. If the object B_1 is at a finite distance from the lens, its image (which will not generally lie far from the object) is shifted a little towards the axis, since the final direction of the ray must intersect the image.

Suppose the lenses reversed so that the negative lens is nearest the object. It will then be seen that the emergent ray is parallel to the axis, but displaced upwards; the shift of the image would therefore be reversed.

In making the test for neutralization, the two lenses are therefore held together in such a way that they have a common axis. With trial case lenses the mounts or rims are of the same diameter, and the two lenses can be held between a thumb and forefinger at about 24 in. from the eye when looking towards some suitable object, such as a vertical window-bar. It is then possible to see the bar above and below the rims, and also its image formed by the system, as the lenses are moved slowly from side to side. When the image is seen through the right-hand side of the lenses, it will be displaced to the right if the combination is positive, and vice versa.

According to the argument above, we may conclude that the lenses have coincident focal points if the combination appears to be weakly negative with the positive lens held the nearer to the object at a finite distance, but weakly positive with the negative lens the nearer. Such a refinement of the test is, however, hardly of much significance in practice.

Considerable care is necessary in determining the vertex powers of lenses by the neutralization method. Suppose, for example, it is desired to find the vertex power of a meniscus lens, Fig. 182a. The intercept required to be measured is A_2F_a'. The trial case

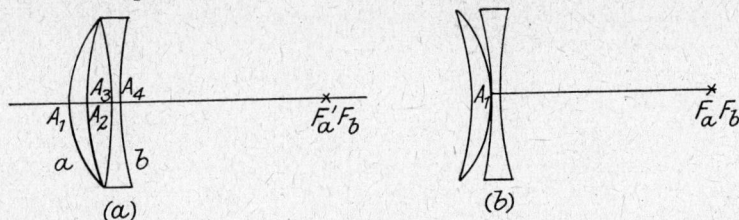

FIG. 182

lenses enable us to select one for which A_3F_b is known, and the intercept between the vertices, A_2A_3 must be measured with the help of a depth gauge.

If, as sometimes happens, the meniscus lens is reversed so that the lenses come into contact at their vertices (Fig. 182b), the vertex focal length of the meniscus lens so measured will not be the one which is usually required in the selection of spectacles. It is, however, possible to obtain specially small lenses for the neutralization test, so that the intercept A_2A_3 in the above arrangement becomes very small.

Since the positive and negative lenses of a trial case have, or should have, the same series of vertex refractions, equal powers should neutralize when held in contact. The necessary powers of the surfaces of a lens to give a definite vertex refraction can be calculated from the elementary formulae.

Curvature for a given Vertex Refraction. Consider an equi-convex lens to be given a vertex refraction of $+20D$ with thickness 9 mm. (say). The general formula for refraction of a paraxial beam is

$$\frac{n'}{l'} - \frac{n}{l} = \frac{n' - n}{r} = F_1,$$ where F_1 is the power of the surface.

Taking the case of a lens having refractive index n in air, and assuming parallel incident light, $F_1 = n/l_1'$, whence $l_1' = n/F$. Since the diopter units are being employed the thickness of the lens, 9 mm., becomes 0·009 (in metres) and $l_2 = l_1' - 0·009 = (n/F_1) - 0·009$.

Refraction at the second surface gives

$$\frac{1}{l_2'} - \frac{n}{l_2} = F_2$$

but $\frac{1}{l_2'}$ is to be 20, and $F_2 = F_1$, so that $20 - n/l_2 = F_1$

or, substituting from above,

$$20 - \frac{n}{\left(\dfrac{n}{F_1} - 0·009\right)} = F_1$$

This simplifies to a quadratic equation in F_1

$$0·009F_1^2 - F_1(2n + 0·18) + 20n = 0$$

giving two roots, the lower of which is 9·73 when n is taken as 1·5. (The higher root does not concern the problem in hand.)

Hence $F_1 = \dfrac{0·5}{r_1} = 9·73$, and $R_1 = 19·46$.

Such calculations are readily carried through with the formulæ of Chapter II. Thus for a thick lens (refractive index $= n$ and thickness d) in air

$$F_1 = \frac{n-1}{r_1} \qquad F_2 = \frac{1-n}{r_2} \qquad \bar{d} = \frac{d}{n}$$

$$F = F_1 + F_2 - F_1 F_2 \bar{d} = (n-1)\left\{\frac{r_2 - r_1 + (n-1)\bar{d}}{r_1 r_2}\right\} \qquad . \quad (902)$$

(All distances in metres.)

Also to calculate the vertex powers

$$\frac{1}{FA_1} = \frac{F}{1 - F_2\bar{d}} = \frac{Fr_2}{r_2 + (n-1)\bar{d}}$$

Thus *front vertex power* $= (n-1)\left\{\dfrac{r_2 - r_1 + (n-1)\bar{d}}{r_1 r_2 + (n-1)r_1\bar{d}}\right\} \qquad . \quad (903)$

(All distances in metres.)

Similarly $\dfrac{1}{A_2F'} = \dfrac{F}{1 - F_1\bar{d}} = \dfrac{Fr_1}{r_1 - (n-1)\bar{d}}$

And *back vertex power* $= (n-1)\left\{\dfrac{r_2 - r_1 + (n-1)\bar{d}}{r_1 r_2 - (n-1)r_2\bar{d}}\right\} \qquad . \quad (904)$

(All distances in metres.)

These formulæ lend themselves to the calculation of the radii of lenses, such as trial case lenses, which must be given a definite vertex power.

Size of the Image Obtained by the Use of Spectacles. The size of
the image of a very distant object subtending a small angle ω is
$f\omega$, where f is the *object-space* focal length of the image-forming
system.

Let a lens system of focal length f_a be placed coaxially with
another system of focal length f_b, the distance between the adjacent
principal focal points being g, then equation (207) gave

$$\frac{1}{f} = \frac{g}{f_a f_b}$$

If the separation of the adjacent principal points is d, then

$$d = f_a' + g - f_b$$

whence $$g = d - f_a' + f_b = d + f_a + f_b$$

if the system "a" is in air, and

$$\frac{1}{f} = \frac{1}{f_a} + \frac{1}{f_b} + \frac{d}{f_a f_b}$$

Compare this with equation (219).

This equation can be applied directly to ascertain the change in
anterior focal length of the system forming the retinal image consequent on the use of a spectacle lens. The distance of the anterior
focal point of the normal eye from the surface of the cornea is
15·31 mm., according to Gullstrand. Hence, the posterior principal
point of the spectacle lens, which usually falls in practice at about
12 mm. from the cornea, will not be far from the anterior focus.
Assuming for a moment that these points might be actually coincident, we evidently have $d = -f_b$, whence

$$\frac{1}{f} = \frac{1}{f_a} + \frac{1}{f_b} - \frac{f_b}{f_a f_b} = \frac{1}{f_b}$$

The power of the entire system is the same as that of the unaided
eye, but the necessary position of the sharp image has now been
attained; i.e. on the retina. In this case, therefore, the size of the
sharp image in the corrected eye will have the same size as that in
the normal eye of the same focal length. (Remember that myopia
and hypermetropia often arise from an abnormal length of the
eye-ball and not from a difference in the refracting power of the
optical system.)

The user of spectacles is conscious, however, of the magnifying
or minifying power of his glasses. The retina of the uncorrected
hypermetropic eye intercepts the rays proceeding towards any
image point in the principal focal plane of the refracting system

before they reach their focus. It will be understood from Fig. 183 how the centre of the diffuse patch lies closer to the axial point than the sharp image point. The dotted line H is to represent the position of the retina in hypermetropia; M represents the case of myopia, in which the centres of the diffuse image patches are at a greater distance than in the normal eye.

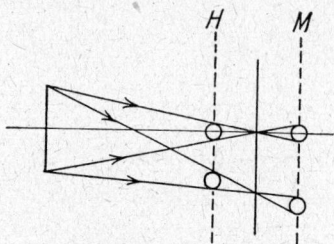

FIG. 183. RELATIVE IMAGE SIZES IN HYPERMETROPIA, EMMETROPIA, AND MYOPIA

A thorough discussion of this subject necessitates the investigation of the path of a principal ray. This will be given in Vol. II, Chapter I.

Spectacle Lenses for Vision of Near Objects. Although such defects as myopia and hypermetropia exists in youthful eyes, it is usually the case that the amplitude of accommodation is practically as great as in normal eyes. Hence, a young person usually requires only one pair of spectacles, which gives clear vision of distant objects when the eyes are at rest. Near objects are then viewed by exerting the accommodation.

As age increases, however, the power of accommodation is lost, and it is no longer possible to see near objects when wearing the distance glasses.

Consider a myopic eye with a principal point refraction of (say) — 2D, and an amplitude of accommodation of 1D. The far point lies at a distance of 50 cm. in front of the principal point of the eye, and the near point at a distance of $1/(-2-1)$ metres = — 33·3 cm.

The distance correction to be given by a lens with its second principal point at 12 mm. from the first principal point of the eye would be from the equation

$$F_a = \frac{K}{1 + dK} = \frac{-2}{1 + (\cdot 012 \times -2)} = -2 \cdot 05D$$

If the full amplitude of accommodation is now exerted, any image projected into the plane of the near point is distinctly seen. The near point lies at a distance of 33·3 — 1·20 = 32·1 cm. in front of the second principal point of the spectacle lens.

To find where an object must be situated in order to project an image into the near point we have

$$\frac{1}{l'} - \frac{1}{l} = F_a$$

or

$$\frac{1}{-0 \cdot 321} - \frac{1}{l} = -2 \cdot 05$$

whence $l = -(1/1 \cdot 07)$ metres = — 93·5 cm. from the 1st principal point of the spectacle lens. Hence, the nearest object which could be seen when wearing the spectacles would be nearly 1 metre distant.

Suppose, now, it is desired to obtain spectacles for reading type situated at a minimum distance of 25 cm. from the first principal point of the eye. Let the separations of the adjacent principal points of lens and eye be 12 mm. as before and let the distance between the principal points of the lens be δ, say. Then the distance of the object from the 1st principal point of the lens will be

$$l = - (25 - 1\cdot2 - \delta) = - (23\cdot8 - \delta) \text{ cm.}$$

With a diverging lens the error created by neglecting δ will be small. Hence, if the image is to be projected into the near point, $l' = - 32\cdot1$ cm.

Expressing these distances in metres the equation becomes

$$\frac{1}{(- 0\cdot321)} - \frac{1}{(- 0\cdot238)} = F$$

whence
$$F = 1\cdot08$$

The lens required is now one of weak positive power.

With a hypermetropic eye the distance correction is positive and the "near" correction is naturally obtained by increasing the positive power. The ordinary "reading distance" is taken as 40 cm., but may vary for individual needs.

Use of Lenses in Series.
When using a trial case it may be desired to find a suitable correction for near objects by using, say, the equi-convex trial lens. It must be pointed out that the condition for equal performance with lenses of other shapes may not be the same. It is not sufficient to substitute a lens with the same vertex power, but a lens must be used such that the distance from the vertex to the image of the (near) object is the same as with the trial lens; i.e. the "vergencies" to the images of the near objects must be the same.

The near object may be real, or may be represented by placing a weak negative lens in front of the spectacle glass to form a virtual image at a finite distance, if using a very distant object.

Let l be the distance of the near object and let D_v be the vertex power of the lens, then with very thin lenses we have with sufficient accuracy

$$\frac{1}{l'} - \frac{1}{l} = D_v$$

or, in terms of "vergences," $L' - L = D_v$, from which $L' = L + D_v$, or, if the near object was obtained by using the virtual image of a distant object projected by an auxiliary weak lens of power D_a,

$$L' = D_a + D_v$$

This is, however, not quite sufficiently accurate in the case where a strong spectacle lens is concerned.

Take the case of the equi-convex lens of vertex power $+$ 20D, as used with a near object at a distance of 1 metre. The approximate equation for the vergence is

$$L' = -1 + 20 = 19$$

We must, however, follow the refraction surface by surface. From p. 298 above, each surface has a power of 9·73 when the refractive index is 1·5; the thickness is 9 mm.

The general equation

$$\frac{n'}{l'} - \frac{n}{l} = F_1$$

gives for the first refraction

$$\frac{n'}{l_1'} - \left(\frac{1}{-1}\right) = 9·73$$

whence $l_1' = 0·172$ metres (for $n = 1·5$).

Since the thickness $t = 0·009$ metres

$$l_2 = 0·163 \quad ,,$$

For the 2nd refraction

$$\frac{1}{l_2'} - \frac{1·5}{0·163} = 9·73$$

whence

$$\frac{1}{l_2'} = 18·94 = 20 - 1 - 0·06.$$

The true value for the vergence L' or $1/l'$ therefore differs from the simple sum of the powers $D_a + D_v$ by a correcting term $- 0·06$.

The same calculation relates to the case where an auxiliary lens is employed, but it is assumed in the above case that the auxiliary lens is in close contact with the main spectacle lens. If this is not the case, the distance between the vertices is an additional factor. Henker[4] gives a useful table showing the effects of various positive powers in conjunction with spectacle lenses. As will be seen below, this table is especially useful in connection with the determination of astigmatism. Students should calculate some typical cases, assuming the usually correct refractive index for spectacle glass (say) 1·523, A systematic scheme of calculation, such as that given on page 52, should be devised and five-figure "logs" should be used.

The effective vertex refraction of a close combination of two diverging lenses may usually be taken as the simple sum of the powers owing to the small thicknesses in the lenses. Any finite distance should be considered in relation to the case in hand.

The Axial Astigmatism of the Eye and its Correction. About the years 1825–26, G. B. Airy[5] investigated the axial astigmatism of the eye and the mode of correcting it with lenses having cylindrical surfaces, suitably disposed. It has already been stated that an astigmatic eye usually possesses differences of curvature in the various meridians of the cornea.

We imagine the optic axis of the eye and a series of planes passing through this axis; their intersections with the outer surface of the cornea mark the "meridians."

In order to understand the manner in which the variation of power in the different meridians may be corrected with the help of such lenses as used by Airy, it is necessary first to study some of the properties of cylindrical and "toric" surfaces.

A general theorem due to *Euler* shows that at any point of a curved surface free from discontinuities there may be distinguished two perpendicular sections of maximum and minimum curvature. Then these are the "principal sections" of the surface. Let their directions define the y and z directions. As suggested in Fig. 184, let the surface be tangent to the yz plane at the origin, so that the centres of curvature lie in the axis of x. The centres of curvature c_y and c_z for the principal sections have a maximal separation, while the centre for any intermediate section lies between

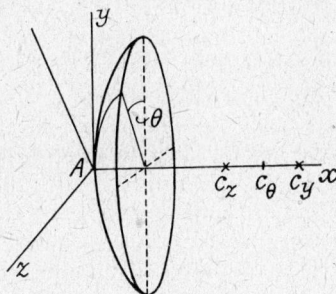

FIG. 184

them. Let the intermediate meridional section making an angle θ with the xy plane have a "curvature" $R_\theta = 1/r_\theta$, where r_θ is the radius of curvature, then according to Euler's theorem

$$\boldsymbol{R}_\theta = \boldsymbol{R}_y \cos^2 \theta + \boldsymbol{R}_z \sin^2 \theta \qquad . \qquad . \qquad (905)$$

In a section perpendicular to this first one,

$$\boldsymbol{R}_{\theta + 90°} = \boldsymbol{R}_y \sin^2 \theta + \boldsymbol{R}_z \cos^2 \theta$$

Therefore, adding the two equations, we obtain

$$\boldsymbol{R}_\theta + \boldsymbol{R}_{\theta + 90°} = \boldsymbol{R}_y + \boldsymbol{R}_z$$

Hence, the sum of the curvatures of any two perpendicular sections has a constant value.

The refracting power of such a surface is proportional to the change of refractive index and to the curvature. Since the power of the surface is

$$\boldsymbol{F} = (n' - n)\, \boldsymbol{R}$$

then
$$\boldsymbol{F}_\theta = \boldsymbol{F}_y \cos^2 \theta + \boldsymbol{F}_z \sin^2 \theta \qquad . \qquad . \qquad . \qquad (906)$$

Such an equation would apply to a thin lens having one surface with variable curvature in different meridians and one plane surface. Suppose such a lens held against an eye with a cornea of variable curvature in the different meridians, and let the lens be turned so that the principal sections of the lens and cornea coincide. Let $F_{b\theta}$ be the power of the cornea in the intermediate section

$$F_{b\theta} = F_{by} \cos^2 \theta + F_{bz} \sin^2 \theta$$

So that the total powers of lens and cornea are

$$F_\theta + F_{b\theta} = (F_y + F_{by}) \cos^2 \theta + (F_z + F_{bz}) \sin^2 \theta.$$

Provided that

$$F_y + F_{by} = F_z + F_{bz},$$

we shall have $(F_\theta + F_{b\theta})$ constant, and the power of the combination in all meridians will be the same. An astigmatic refracting surface can therefore be corrected in *all* meridians by another suitably chosen and disposed surface, provided the principal sections are made to coincide and that the effective powers of the combination are the same in these two sections.

With regard to the above theory, it should be noted that Euler's theorem applies generally only to infinitesimally small areas of curved surfaces over which the curvatures may be regarded as reasonably constant in any meridian within the limits of the area. The refracting surfaces of the eye have areas of a definite size, and thus the theorem, while offering a general guide, is often not accurately obeyed in practice; case of *irregular astigmatism* may thus be encountered in practice in which the meridians of maximum and minimum power (when found by tests using the whole diameter of the pupil) are not apparently perpendicular. In such cases the defect of vision cannot be completely corrected by the use of cylindrical or toric surfaces, or by crossed cylinders.

Forms of Lenses for Correcting Astigmatism. The simplest possible form of surface for correcting astigmatism is that of the cylinder, which is generated by the revolution of one straight line about another one parallel to it, i.e. the *axis* of the cylinder. This is suggested in Fig. 185, where AA' is the cylinder axis. If we take a slice of the cylinder by cutting it in a plane parallel to the axis, we have the form of a lens with one cylindrical and one plane face. This will be a "positive cylinder." If we place a piece of moulding clay on a plane surface and press the cylinder into it (holding the cylindrical axis parallel to the plane), we shall produce the form of a lens with one surface plane, and one concave and cylindrical. Such a lens in glass would constitute a "negative cylinder." Such lenses are held before the eye in such a position that the optical axis of the eye is normally perpendicular to the cylindrical axis.

It is often the case that astigmatism exists in the eye concurrently with other deficiencies, such as myopia, hypermetropia, or the usual conditions of presbyopic vision. In such cases it is often necessary to provide a spherical correction for an eye as well as that for astigmatism, and, moreover, to accomplish this by one lens, which may accordingly be given one spherical and one cylindrical surface. Such a lens is technically called a "sphero-cyl."

In the majority of cases the cylindrical correction is not large, and the cylindrical surface may be more or less flat. It will be shown, however, that spectacle lenses are most free from the astigmatism of oblique pencils when they are given forms which are usually of the meniscus type, the centres of curvature of both surfaces lying on the eye side of the lens. When such lenses must correct astigmatism, the use of "toric" or "toroidal" surfaces is called for, which possess a finite curvature in both principal sections.

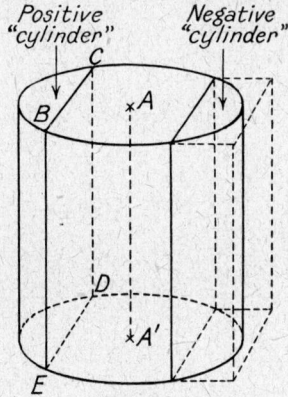

FIG. 185

In Fig. 186a the curve BB'B″ lies in a plane containing the axis AA′ and has its centre at C_1. When revolved around C_2 on that axis, it generates a barrel-shaped toric surface in which the radii of the principal sections are B′C_1 and B′C_2. A segment of such a surface

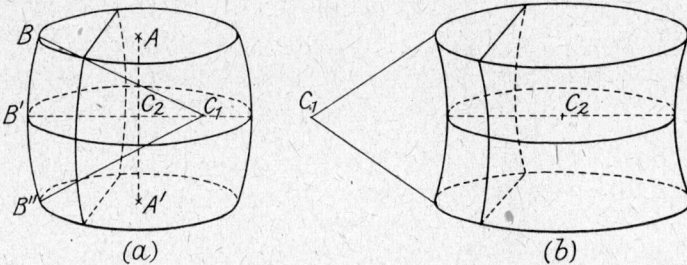

(a)   (b)

FIG. 186

might represent the form given to one face of a toric lens, the other face being simply spherical.

The various forms of possible toric surfaces can be studied by the revolution of different curves about the cylinder-axis. Fig. 186b shows the generation of a saddle-shaped surface, which is convex in one section and concave in another.

Effects Near the Focus of an Astigmatic Lens. An instructive model may be made to illustrate geometrically the crossing of the ray paths near the focus of an astigmatic beam. Threads are stretched between corresponding points on (1) a circular ring and (2) an elliptical ring, the correspondence being such that the points lie on radii making equal angles with the major and minor axes of the ellipse and the corresponding diameters of the circle, as suggested in Fig. 187, the threads crossing between the circle and the ellipse.*

It will be found that there are two perpendicular lines through which all the rays pass. The sections in intermediate and external planes have the forms suggested in the figure. Each focal line is perpendicular to the principal ray of the bundle, and is parallel to

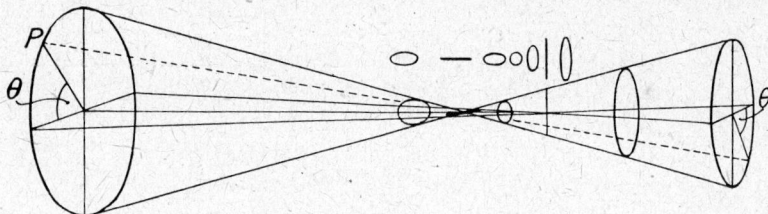

FIG. 187

the major or minor axes of the ellipses, which represent the sections of the bundle in various positions.

These effects are characteristic of the simplest form of "astigmatism," and were first investigated by Sturm. In practice, the actual section of the bundle beyond or within the focus may not be truly elliptical, and the effects in the actual distribution of light near the focus are not thoroughly investigated by the mere discussion of the ray paths, since they depend on the diffraction of the non-spherical wave-front passing through the (usually circular) aperture of the lens. However, the focal lines are to be actually observed, though they are not strictly *lines* in the ordinary sense, having at least the finite breadth of the usual diffraction disc.

Prevalent Type of Astigmatism in the Human Eye. It is most frequently the case that the curvature in the vertical meridian of the cornea is greater than the horizontal when any difference is found. This is the case of astigmatism "with the rule." The opposite case, where the horizontal curve is the greater, is "astigmatism against the rule."

Visual Characteristics of Astigmatism. Since astigmatism is usually due to a difference of curvature in the meridians of one of

* It is convenient in practice to stretch the threads between two plates punched with the necessary holes in the loci of circle and ellipse; the holes may correspond to $\theta = 0°$, $30°$, $60°$, $120°$, etc.

the refracting surfaces of the eye, we shall, if the astigmatism is regular, find a maximum difference of power of the refracting system in two mutually perpendicular meridians.

If, then, the principal point refractions of the eye in these meridians be K_m and K_a, the necessary powers of the correcting lens in the same meridians are (in accordance with equation (901))

$$F_m = \frac{K_m}{1 + dK_m} \qquad\qquad F_a = \frac{K_a}{1 + dK_a}$$

The difference between these two principal point refractions of the eye in the principal sections is the TOTAL ASTIGMATISM of the eye.

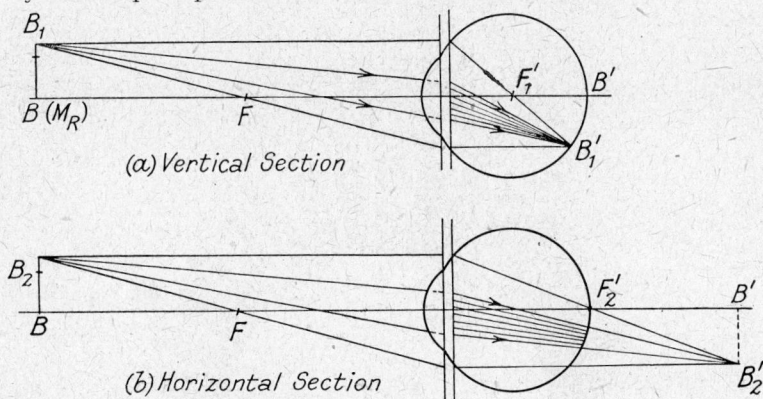

FIG. 188

Consider now an eye which is near-sighted in the vertical principal section, and normal sighted in the horizontal principal section. This case is represented by Fig. 188 (a) and Fig. 188 (b), showing in a diagrammatic way a vertical section and a horizontal section of such an eye, together with image-forming rays.

The eye is near-sighted in the vertical section, and the principal focus F_1' therefore lies in front of the retina. The principal planes enable us to find the image $B'B_1'$ which corresponds to the object BB_1 situated at the far point M_R. This image lies on the retina, where it is sharply focused as far as the rays situated in the plane of the diagram are concerned.

In the horizontal section, however, the eye is normal-sighted and the principal focus F_2' lies at the retina. The far point is at infinity, and the object at B would therefore be imaged behind the retina. The rays consequently fail to reach the focus and these rays (from points such as B or B_2), which lie in the plane of the diagram, meet the retina in a line.

Note that, although the principal planes are useful to enable us to find the position of the focus, the rays actually passing into the pupil are the only ones which can have effect. Their limitation is suggested in the diagram in an obvious manner.

Object   *Image*

Fig. 189

Consider the rays from B_1 (Fig. 188 (a)). Those which lie in the vertical plane meet the retina in one point. Those which

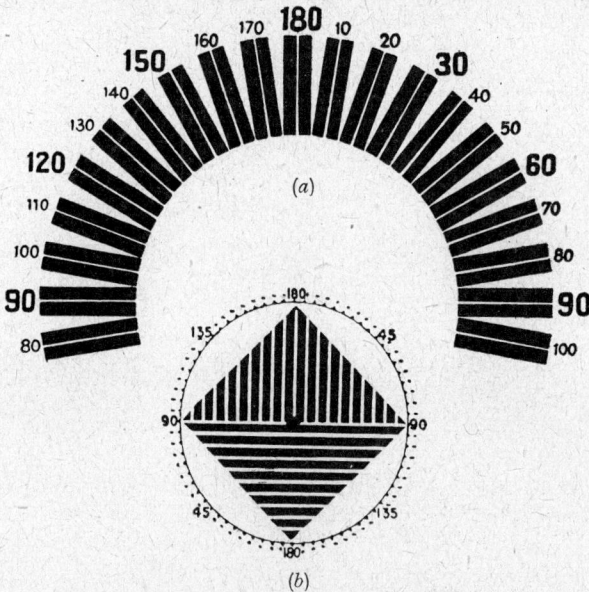

Fig. 190. Objects for Testing Astigmatism
Laurance.

lie in a plane perpendicular to the vertical section meet the retina in a horizontal focal line through which all the rays pass. Every point in a short horizontal line passing through B_1 is therefore imaged in a horizontal focal line, and the overlapping of such lines imaging successive points forms a continuous line image apparently sharp, although a vertical line such as BB_1 has a diffuse image. The relations between object and image in such a case are suggested in Fig. 189.

It is characteristic of astigmatism that lines in different directions are not seen equally clearly. Fig. 190 shows types of test objects for astigmatism. If the effect is slight, it is detected merely in an apparent difference between the blackness of the various radial lines, those in some one direction appearing darker than those in the direction perpendicular thereto. The "diamond" can be rotated until the radial lines are seen most distinctly; this determines one of the directions of the principal sections. The axis of the correcting cylinder will be perpendicular to the most distinct lines. The actual test objects have to be well printed in considerably larger size.

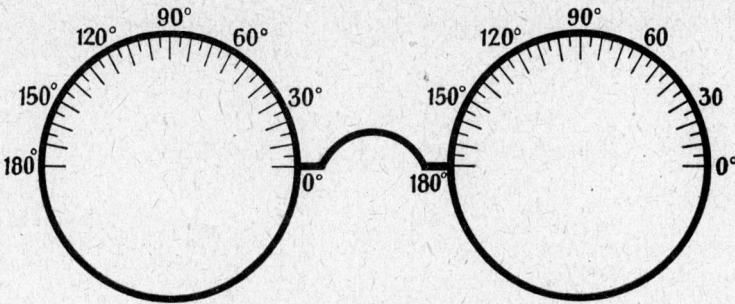

FIG. 191. CONVENTION FOR AXIS DIRECTION
Front of frame as seen by a person facing the wearer.

Direction of the Axis. Fig. 191 illustrates the front of the spectacle frame with the convention adopted in England and America, and almost universally elsewhere,* for the reckoning of the direction of the cylinder axis. The test of astigmatism is made with the aid of the cylindrical lenses in the trial case, the cylinder being usually placed in front of any necessary spherical correction lens. The axis direction is marked on the cylindrical lens, and its position can be read off on the trial frame when the power and direction have been adjusted so as to obtain the best correction.

Suppose that a spherical power Q is required, combined with a cylinder of power P placed with its axis at ϕ degrees, the whole correction is usually conventionally written

$$Q \text{ sph.} \supset P \text{ cyl. Ax. } \phi$$

* Owing to past difficulties with different conventions, many ophthalmologists still think it wise to include a *diagram* of the axis direction in writing a prescription.

As, for example,

$$+ 5D \text{ sph.} \smile - 0 \cdot 75D \text{ cyl. Ax. } 120°$$

Alternatives are to write

$$\frac{Q \text{ sph.}}{P \text{ cyl. Ax. } \phi}, \text{ or } Q \text{ sph.}/P \text{ cyl. Ax. } \phi$$

Transposition. Consider the case of an eye which is near-sighted in both principal sections, but to different amounts. Suppose that it requires a correction of $- 5D$ in the vertical section to bring images of distant horizontal lines to a sharp focus, and a power of $- 3D$ in the horizontal section to bring images of vertical lines to a sharp focus. (Assume that this distance correction is all that is required.)

The necessary lens can theoretically be made up in several different ways—

1. 1st face. Cylinder $- 5D$ axis horizontal.
   2nd ,,   Cylinder $- 3D$,, vertical.

The corrections are given separately in each face.

2. 1st face. Spherical $- 5D$.
   2nd ,,   Cylinder $+ 2D$ axis vertical.

The cylinder has no power in a vertical direction, the resultant powers thus being $- 5D$ vertical, $- 3D$ horizontal.

3. 1st face. Spherical $- 3D$.
   2nd ,,   Cylinder $- 2D$, axis horizontal.

The cylinder has no power in the horizontal direction.

4. 1st face. Toric. Powers $\begin{cases} (P - 5), \text{ vertical section.} \\ (P - 3), \text{ horizontal section.} \end{cases}$
   2nd ,,   Spherical Power $- P$.

The powers of P on the first face and $- P$ on the second neutralize.

5. 1st face. Spherical $+ P$
   2nd ,,   Toric $- (P + 5)$, vertical section.
                        $- (P + 3)$, horizontal section.

All these forms could be reversed in front of the eye, rotating the lens through 180° about either of the principal directions (horizontal or vertical), while still retaining the prescribed correction. Not all of these arrangements are, however, equally advantageous.

Cylindrical surfaces cost more than spherical; toric are more expensive than either. As mentioned above, the conditions for maximum freedom from oblique astigmatism usually call for a bent form, which, if axial astigmatism is to be corrected, must have one of its surfaces toric. Hence the choice of the lens actually used as a spectacle glass depends upon several considerations. The most inexpensive form in ordinary cases is the "sphero-cyl" when astigmatic correction is needed. The meniscus forms which give better oblique vision will be selected when their cost is not an obstacle.

General Case of Transposition. In general, when the axis of the correcting cylinder lies in any direction ϕ, the following transpositions are possible, excluding toric lenses—

		Power Parallel to the Direction ϕ	Power Perpendicular to the Direction ϕ
Sphero-cyl. Q sph.	⊃ P cyl. Ax. ϕ .	Q	P + Q
„ (P + Q) sph.	⊂ − P cyl. Ax. $(\phi \pm 90°)$	Q	P + Q
Cross cyl. (P + Q) cyl. Ax. ϕ ⊃ Q cyl. Ax. $(\phi \pm 90°)$		Q	P + Q

In any combination it is easy to check the result by considering the power parallel to one cylindrical axis and the power perpendicular thereto. In addition to the above there are, of course, all the possibilities of meniscus lenses with toric surfaces.

EXAMPLES OF TRANSPOSITION

$$a \begin{cases} - \text{ 1·25 sph.} & ⊃ + \text{1·75 cyl. Ax. 160°} \\ + \text{ 0·5 sph.} & ⊃ - \text{1·75 cyl. Ax. 70°} \\ - \text{ 1·25 cyl. Ax. 70°} & ⊃ + \text{0·5 cyl. Ax. 160°} \end{cases}$$

$$b \begin{cases} + \text{ 3·50 cyl. Ax. 120°} & ⊃ - \text{0·75 cyl. Ax. 30°} \\ + \text{ 3·50 sph.} & ⊃ - \text{4·25 cyl. Ax. 30°} \\ - \text{ 0·75 sph.} & ⊃ + \text{4·25 cyl. Ax. 120°} \end{cases}$$

"Bending a Lens." The total power of a thin lens is often expressed as the sum of the powers of the two surfaces.

$$F = F_1 + F_2 = (n - 1)(R_1 - R_2) = (n - 1) R_1 + (1 - n) R_2$$

The optician speaks of "bending a lens" when he changes (on paper) the curvatures of the two surfaces by an equal numerical amount, k, say,

$$F = (F_1 + \delta) + (F_2 - \delta) = (n - 1)(R_1 + k) + (1 - n)(R_2 + k)$$

This operation thus adds to the power of one surface the same amount that it removes from the other.

In this way we may look upon the meniscus lenses as simply the result of "bending" the simple forms such as the sphero-cyls.

The "base curve of a toric surface" is *usually* the one having the lower power. If, for example, a specification

$$+ \text{ 1 sph. } ⊃ \text{ 1·5 cyl.}$$

is required in toric form with a + 6D base, it would be obtained by using a front surface having powers in the two principal sections of $+ 6D$ and $+ 7\cdot5D$ respectively. Since the total power of the lens is to be $+ 1D$ and $+ 2\cdot5D$ in the principal sections, the second surface of this meniscus is given a power of $- 5D$.

Obliquely-crossed Cylinders. When two cylindrical lenses are used in series, as is sometimes the case in sight testing, their combined effect is in general that of a sphere with one cylinder.

Let OA and OB, Fig. 192, be the principal sections of maximum power of cylindrical lenses a and b; these sections are perpendicular

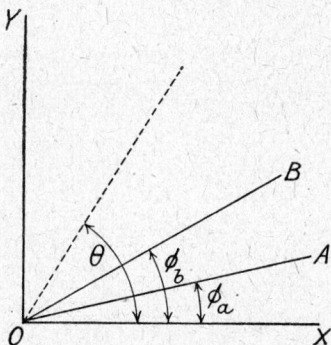

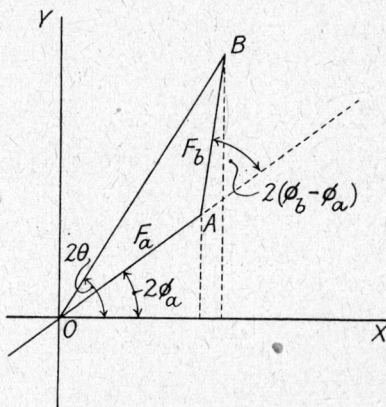

FIG. 192   FIG. 193

to the axes of the cylinders; they make angles ϕ_a and ϕ_b with the axis of X. The lenses have no power in the direction parallel to the cylinder axis.

The power in some other direction θ is calculable from equation (906). Let F_a and F_b be the powers of the cylinders, then the effective power D_θ in direction θ is

$$D_\theta = F_a \cos^2 (\theta - \phi_a) + F_b \cos^2 (\theta - \phi_b)$$

which may be written more concisely

$$D_\theta = F_a \cos^2 \alpha_a + F_b \cos^2 \alpha_b$$

where $\qquad \alpha_a = \theta - \phi_a$ and $\alpha_b = \theta - \phi_b$.

The power in a direction perpendicular to that given by θ will be

$$D_{\theta + 90} = F_a \sin^2 \alpha_a + F_b \sin^2 \alpha_b$$

Now, assuming that the powers of the equivalent sphere and cylinder are Q and P respectively, the maximum power of the equivalent lens will be P + Q and the minimum will be Q.

If the power in the direction θ is the maximum,

$$\mathbf{D}_\theta = P + Q = \mathbf{F}_a \cos^2 \alpha_a + \mathbf{F}_b \cos^2 \alpha_b$$

and
$$\mathbf{D}_{\theta + 90} = Q = \mathbf{F}_a \sin^2 \alpha_a + \mathbf{F}_b \sin^2 \alpha_b$$

by adding $P + 2Q = \mathbf{F}_a + \mathbf{F}_b$

and by subtracting

$$P = \mathbf{F}_a(\cos^2 \alpha_a - \sin^2 \alpha_a) + \mathbf{F}_b(\cos^2 \alpha_b - \sin^2 \alpha_b)$$
$$= \mathbf{F}_a \cos 2\alpha_a + \mathbf{F}_b \cos 2\alpha_b$$

The maximum power must also conform to the condition that the differential coefficient of the power with respect to the variable θ must be zero.

Hence
$$\frac{d(\mathbf{D}_\theta)}{d\theta} = -\mathbf{F}_a(2 \cos \alpha_a) \sin \alpha_a - \mathbf{F}_b(2 \cos \alpha_b) \sin \alpha_b = 0$$

whence
$$0 = \mathbf{F}_a \sin 2 \alpha_a + \mathbf{F}_b \sin 2\alpha_b$$

From above
$$P = \mathbf{F}_a \cos 2\alpha_a + \mathbf{F}_b \cos 2\alpha_b$$

Squaring and adding these last equations,

$$P^2 = \mathbf{F}_a{}^2 + \mathbf{F}_b{}^2 + 2\mathbf{F}_a\mathbf{F}_b \cos 2(\alpha_a - \alpha_b)$$
$$= \mathbf{F}_a{}^2 + \mathbf{F}_b{}^2 + 2\mathbf{F}_a\mathbf{F}_b \cos 2(\phi_b - \phi_a)$$
$$P = \pm \{\mathbf{F}_a{}^2 + \mathbf{F}_b{}^2 + 2\mathbf{F}_a\mathbf{F}_b \cos 2(\phi_b - \phi_a)\}^{\frac{1}{2}} \quad (907)$$

Of course, $(\phi_b - \phi_a)$ is the angle between the principal sections of maximum power. In order to obtain Q, we can substitute the positive value of P found above in the equation

$$Q = \frac{\mathbf{F}_a + \mathbf{F}_b - P}{2}$$

From the equation above,

$$\mathbf{F}_a \sin 2\alpha_a + \mathbf{F}_b \sin 2\alpha_b = 0$$

$$\mathbf{F}_a(\sin 2\theta \cos 2\phi_a - \cos 2\theta \sin 2\phi_a)$$
$$+ \mathbf{F}_b(\sin 2\theta \cos 2\phi_b - \cos 2\theta \sin 2\phi_b) = 0$$

whence
$$\tan 2\theta = \frac{\mathbf{F}_a \sin 2\phi_a + \mathbf{F}_b \sin 2\phi_b}{\mathbf{F}_a \cos 2\phi_a + \mathbf{F}_b \cos 2\phi_b} \quad . \quad . \quad (908)$$

This enables us to find the direction of maximum power.

The negative solution for P corresponds to the case where we have instead of

$$Q \text{ sph.} \supset P \text{ cy. Ax. } \phi$$

the alternative $(P + Q)$ sph. $\supset - P$ cyl. Ax. $(\phi + 90°)$

which can be obtained from the first by simply transposing. The cylinder in the second case is of the opposite sign but equal power.

Graphical Method. A simple graphical method of obtaining these relations is shown in Fig. 193. $OA = F_a$ is set off on some convenient scale at an angle $2\phi_a$, and $AB = F_b$ at an angle $2\phi_b$, with the direction of OX.

Since $OB^2 = F_a^2 + F_b^2 + 2F_aF_b \cos 2(\phi_b - \phi_a)$, from the triangle BOA, OB must represent P by its length.

Further, since $\tan \widehat{BOX} = \dfrac{F_a \sin 2\phi_a + F_b \sin 2\phi_b}{F_a \cos 2\phi_a + F_b \cos 2\phi_b}$ we see that $\widehat{BOX} = 2\theta$.

Thus we can at once find θ the direction of maximum power.

Since the axis directions are always at right angles to the direction of maximum power, the calculation and construction may be performed by treating OA as the reference direction. Then from Fig. 193,

$$\tan 2(\theta - \phi_a) = \frac{F_b \sin 2(\phi_b - \phi_a)}{F_a + F_b \cos 2(\phi_b - \phi_a)} \qquad . \qquad . \qquad (909)$$

$$\text{and } P = \frac{F_a + F_b \cos 2(\phi_b - \phi_a)}{\cos 2(\theta - \phi_a)} \qquad . \qquad . \qquad (910)$$

H. H. Emsley has devised a useful calculator or protractor by means of which the combination of obliquely-crossed cylinders can be obtained without the necessity of drawing, although its fundamental principles rest upon the above construction. It may be obtained from the Elliott Optical Co.

It will be noticed that with two cylindrical lenses of equal power we can produce by relative rotation the effect of sphero-cylindrical lenses with cylindrical components of any magnitude from zero up to double the power of either.

In case the visual test for astigmatism is made with a fairly strong cylinder and a strong positive lens in the trial frame, some care must be exercised in finding the effective powers in the principal meridians, as discussed above in the section on "Lenses in Series." Corrections for those effects and also for the distance (if any) between the vertices of the lenses may be required. Tables may be consulted for such corrections, which are, however, mainly negligible with weak positive lenses and most negative lenses.

The Image Field and Its Curvature. It was shown in the case of a single spherical refracting surface that an object surface concentric with the refracting surface would possess a correspondingly concentric image surface. If the curvature of the object surface is modified, the image surface has a new curvature, of which the radius is calculable; in such a way the curvature of the final image surface can be calculated surface by surface through a system, as in equations (433) and (436).

Coddington and Petzval independently investigated this theory. The curvature of the field corresponding to a plane object is the "Petzval curvature," and the curved image surface itself, calculated in this way, is called the "Petzval surface." In the presence of aberration, no sharp image may be found in such a surface, but when, for example, the oblique astigmatism is removed from a thin lens used in conjunction with a suitable stop, the best image is duly found in or very close to the Petzval surface.

Oblique Astigmatism in Spectacles. In the chapter on aberrations it was also shown that the rays derived from the extremities of two

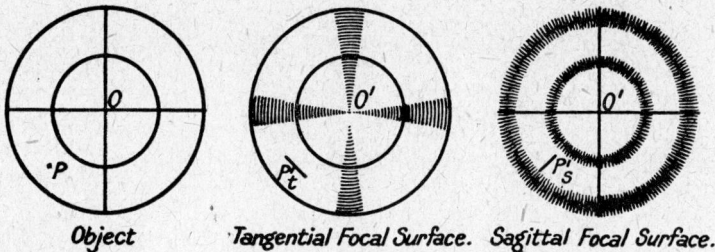

Object   Tangential Focal Surface.   Sagittal Focal Surface.

FIG. 194. EFFECTS OF ASTIGMATISM

perpendicular diameters Y and Z in the circular exit pupil of a system subject to astigmatism of oblique pencils, and passing towards an image point away from the axis of the system in the Y direction, intersect each other so that the intersection of the Y pair is at three times the distance away from the Petzval surface of the intersection of the Z pair. This condition results, as was illustrated in Fig. 78, in the formation of two focal lines, T and S, the first, T (the "tangential" focal line), being perpendicular to the radial line (in the focal surface) from the optic axis to the image, the other, S (the "sagittal" focal line), being itself radial. In cases where the coma and spherical aberration are negligible, the sagittal focal line may be thought of as perpendicular to the principal ray. See the note on p. 135. We thus have a condition of the *oblique* rays very similar to that suggested in Fig. 187, showing astigmatism of the type caused by refraction by a cylinder.

As was pointed out in the previous discussion, each object point is imaged as a line in two focal surfaces, the line being tangential in the tangential focal surface, radial in the sagittal surface. Thus, in Fig. 194, the point P is imaged in such lines at P'_t and P'_s. The diagram of the object is to be imagined as placed with the point

O on the optical axis. The two "images" are to suggest the results found in the tangential and sagittal image surfaces respectively. Each point in a line or circle is imaged as described, so that we have a series of short overlapping lines in the apparently sharp circles or in the radial lines in the image surfaces. Thus, in the tangential focal surface we have clear circles and diffuse radial lines; in the sagittal surface the radial lines are clear. If the object contains

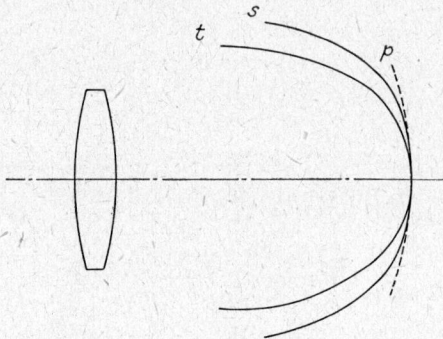

FIG. 195

lines which are neither radial nor tangential, they will not be sharply imaged in any surface.

The Petzval surface of a simple thin lens has a radius of curvature

$$r = -nf'$$

where n is the refractive index and f' is the focal length. When the stop which limits the aperture is close against the lens, or when the boundary of the lens itself limits the rays, the astigmatism of oblique pencils cannot be eliminated, and the tangential and sagittal focal surfaces can be distinguished (Fig. 195). They depart greatly from the spherical form as the angles of the rays with the axis increase. (See also Fig. 79.)

Consider the case of a spectacle lens mounted in front of a moving eye, as suggested by Fig. 196. As the eye rotates, the pupil, of course, moves with it, and the rays focussed on the fovea in various positions of the eye are those transmitted by different parts of the spectacle lens. The rays are evidently limited in the same way as would be the case if a diaphragm of suitable diameter were placed at the centre of rotation of the eye-ball.

The point of rotation may be taken as 13 to 15 mm. behind the vertex of the cornea in the average eye. The vertex of the spectacle lens is usually placed 12 or 13 mm. from the cornea, in order to allow adequate room for the eyelashes. Hence the "effective stop" may be taken as 25 to 28 mm. behind the vertex of the lens.

It can be shown that when a lens is used in conjunction with such a stop at a finite distance, it is possible within certain limits of lens power to remove the astigmatism of oblique pencils by "bending" the lens to the appropriate form. This calls for meniscus forms with the concavity towards the stop.

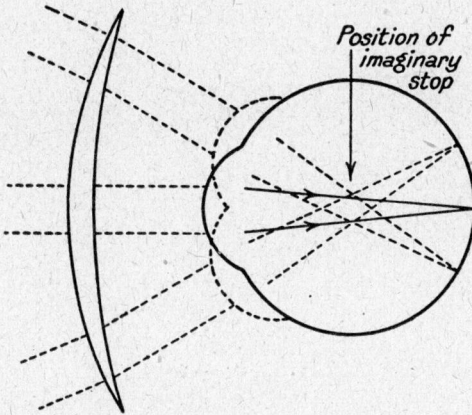

Position of imaginary stop

FIG. 196

Action of Lenses Free from Astigmatism. The large aperture of spectacle lenses (35–40 mm., perhaps) in proportion to the diameter of the pupil itself, which scarcely ever rises as high as 8 mm., and is usually only 3 to 4 mm., is only required to give a sufficiently large angular field of vision as the eyes rotate.

It is possible to calculate the spherical aberration and coma produced by a lens under such conditions; these aberrations prove negligible, at least with ordinary spectacle lenses. The astigmatism of oblique pencils of, say, a 5D lens (equi-convex) is, however, considerable, and the variation of accommodation required to focus tangential and radial images at an angle of 25° with the axis of the spectacle lens is rather more than 1 diopter.

Should the oblique astigmatism be removed by the selection of a suitable figure for the lens, the sharp images of distant objects are then formed in the Petzval surface. The lens will, of course, have the required vertex power, and its principal focus in the centre of the Petzval surface will coincide with the far point of the eye.

As the eye rotates, the locus of the far point is the far point sphere, with its centre in the point of rotation of the eye, i.e. the position of the effective imaginary stop. This is illustrated by Fig. 197. Consider a + 10D lens (back vertex refraction). The distance of the principal focus from the vertex of an eye 12 mm. behind the lens will be 8·8 cm. The vertex refraction of the corrected eye is thus 11·36D.

The distance of the far point from the centre of rotation will be about 7·3 cm., and this gives the numerical value of the radius of the far point sphere. The radius of the Petzval surface is, however, $- nf' = - 1·5 \times 10 = - 15$ cm. sufficiently nearby; both surfaces have

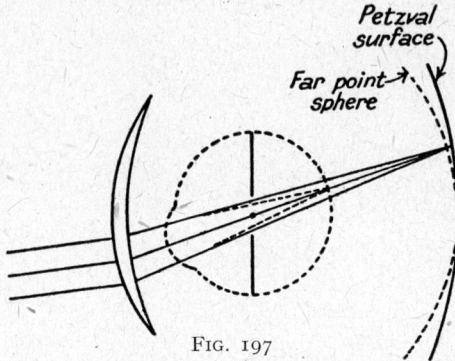

FIG. 197

their centres to the left in the diagram. Since the Petzval surface is flatter than the far point sphere, the distance of the focus from the vertex of the eye when the latter is inclined at 20° to the axis of the spectacle lens is found to be approximately 9·08 cm.—calling for a vertex refraction of 11·01D—a difference of about one-third of a diopter, which would have to be allowed for by changing the accommodation of the eye.

The corresponding case of the negative lens used with the myopic eye will easily be worked out. In such a case both far point sphere and Petzval surfaces will have their centres to the right of the surfaces as in the case illustrated in Fig. 198. It will be noticed that the centre of

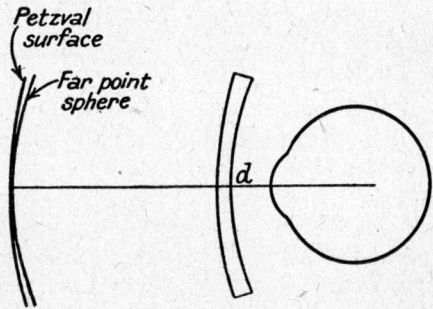

FIG. 198

the Petzval surface must (from the equation for the radius) be situated about half the focal length to the right of the spectacle lens, while the centre of the far point sphere is not far from 2·5 cm. to the right of the lens. Hence the difference in the curvatures of the surfaces, which is generally less than with positive lenses, would vanish for a lens (not likely to be used as a spectacle lens) of − 5 cm. focal length, of − 20 diopters.

Removal of Astigmatism from a Lens with the Aid of a Narrow Axial Stop. In Fig. 199, AP is a refracting surface. A narrow axial stop is situated at R′. Let the ray LP be the principal ray directed towards the centre of the entrance pupil R, which pupil may be regarded as the image of R′, formed by the refraction of imaginary light passing from right to left through the surface. Let AR = l, and AR′ = l'. Let the "object point" be astigmatic,* O_t and O_s

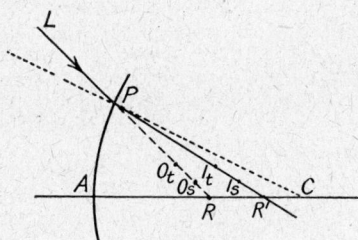

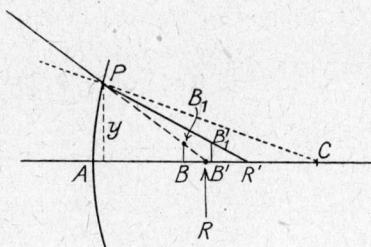

FIG. 199   FIG. 200

being the tangential and sagittal foci respectively; then I_t and I_s are the corresponding image points; the separations O_tO_s and I_tI_s are both so small that their squares are negligible.

Now
$$\frac{n' \cos^2 i'}{t'} - \frac{n \cos^2 i}{t} = \frac{n' \cos i' - n \cos i}{r} = \frac{n'}{s'} - \frac{n}{s}$$

or
$$\frac{n' \cos^2 i'}{PI_t} - \frac{n \cos^2 i}{PO_t} = \frac{n'}{PI_s} - \frac{n}{PO_s}$$

The principal ray must only be allowed a small angle of obliquity. (The diagram exaggerates this obliquity only for the sake of clearness of the lines and points.) Then the following approximation may then be introduced—

$$\cos^2 i = 1 - i^2$$
$$\cos^2 i' = 1 - i'^2$$

Then
$$\frac{n'}{PI_t} - \frac{n'i'^2}{PI_t} - \frac{n}{PO_t} + \frac{ni^2}{PO_t} = \frac{n'}{(PI_t + I_tI_s)} - \frac{n}{(PO_t + O_tO_s)}$$

If we write $1/(PI_t + I_tI_s) = (1 + I_tI_s/PI_t)^{-1}/PI_t$ and expand the bracket term by the binomial theorem, neglecting terms in I_tI_s

* The "object" may be an astigmatic image formed by another part of the optical system.

higher than the first power, it will be seen that the right-hand side of the foregoing equation can be written

$$= \frac{n'}{PI_t} - \frac{n' . I_t I_s}{PI_t{}^2} - \frac{n}{PO_t} + \frac{n . O_t O_s}{PO_t{}^2}$$

Thus

$$\frac{n' . I_t I_s}{PI_t{}^2} - \frac{n . O_t O_s}{PO_t{}^2} = \frac{n'i'^2}{PI_t} - \frac{ni^2}{PO_t}$$

or

$$\frac{n' . I_t I_s}{t'^2} - \frac{n . O_t O_s}{t^2} = \frac{n'i'^2}{t'} - \frac{ni^2}{t}$$

If y denotes the distance of P from the axis, we may write

$$i = y\left(\frac{1}{l} - \frac{1}{r}\right), \text{ and } i' = y\left(\frac{1}{l'} - \frac{1}{r}\right)$$

sufficiently nearly, and also for small angles of obliquity the law of refraction gives as a first approximation $n'i' = ni$.

Then
$$\frac{n' . I_t I_s}{t'^2} - \frac{n . O_t O_s}{t^2} = n'^2 i'^2 \left(\frac{1}{n't'} - \frac{1}{nt}\right)$$

$$= n'^2 y^2 \left(\frac{1}{l'} - \frac{1}{r}\right)^2 \left(\frac{1}{n't'} - \frac{1}{nt}\right) \quad . \quad (912)$$

In order to simplify the expression, we may introduce

$$Q_t = n\left(\frac{1}{r} - \frac{1}{t}\right) = n'\left(\frac{1}{r} - \frac{1}{t'}\right)$$

$$Q_l = n\left(\frac{1}{r} - \frac{1}{l}\right) = n'\left(\frac{1}{r} - \frac{1}{l'}\right)$$

Now, Fig. 200 represents the same case of refraction as Fig. 199, except that the separation of the astigmatic foci* is now not shown, and the conjugate positions are B_1 and B_1' respectively. The points B and B' are conjugate positions on the axis, so that $BB_1 = h$ and $B'B_1' = h'$ are a small "object" and "image" respectively, both perpendicular to the axis.

We have $y/l = h/BR = h/(l - t)$ (very nearly); remember that the investigation is limited to small values of y, so that $(l - t)/l = h/y$; and

$$Q_l - Q_t = n\left(\frac{1}{t} - \frac{1}{l}\right) = n\left(\frac{l - t}{lt}\right) = \frac{nh}{yt}$$

Hence,
$$y = \frac{nh}{t(Q_l - Q_t)} . \qquad . \qquad . \qquad . \qquad . \quad (913)$$

* The separation suggested in Fig. 199 was greatly exaggerated for the sake of clearness in the diagram.

Also the relation

$$nh\alpha = n'h'\alpha' \qquad \text{(Equation (109))}$$

can be put into the form (by imagining a ray PB refracted through PB′)

$$nhy/\text{AB} = n'h'y/\text{AB}'$$

which, under the limitations of angle and incidence height adopted in the present investigation, can be written sufficiently nearly

$$nh/t = n'h'/t' \qquad . \qquad . \qquad . \qquad . \qquad (914)$$

Equation (912) thus becomes, using (913) and (914),

$$\frac{I_t I_s}{n'h'^2} - \frac{O_t O_s}{nh^2} = \frac{Q_i^2}{(Q_i - Q_t)^2}\left(\frac{1}{n't'} - \frac{1}{nt}\right)$$

If this equation be applied to a series of refracting surfaces, and the resulting equations are added, there will be a cancellation of terms on the left-hand side of the equation, finally leaving

$$\text{(final)} \ \frac{I_t I_s}{n'h'^2} - \text{(initial)} \ \frac{O_t O_s}{nh^2} = \Sigma \ \frac{Q_i^2}{(Q_i - Q_t)^2}\left(\frac{1}{n't'} - \frac{1}{nt}\right) . \qquad (915)$$

The condition for the absence of astigmatism for an instrument must therefore be that the sum on the right-hand side of the equation is zero. This is known as the Zinken-Sommer condition.

Application to the Case of a Thin Lens. As in Chapter I, the formula for the focal length of a thin lens

$$1/f' = (n_a - 1)\left(\frac{1}{r_1} - \frac{1}{r_2}\right)$$

may be written

$$\mathbf{F} = (n_a - 1)(\mathbf{R_1} - \mathbf{R_2}) = (n_a - 1)\ \mathbf{R}$$

where $\mathbf{R} = \mathbf{R_1} - \mathbf{R_2}$ is the difference of the curvatures of the two faces. In order to evaluate the Q values, it is convenient to assume t, the object distance, as infinite. The distance of the pupil or stop from the lens will be l', and the distance of the corresponding entrance pupil will be l. Both are finite (in practice, l' will be about 28 mm., in the case of a spectacle lens).

Since, if $\mathbf{F}$ is the power of the complete thin lens,

$$- \mathbf{L_1} = \mathbf{F} - \mathbf{L_2}'$$

where $\mathbf{L_1}$ and $\mathbf{L_2}'$ are the vergencies to the entrance and final exit pupil positions respectively.

Hence, we have for the first surface, since $n = 1$,

$$Q_i = \mathbf{R_1} + \mathbf{F} - \mathbf{L_2}'$$

If $n = 1$ and $t = \infty$, $\qquad Q_t = \mathbf{R_1}$,

whence $\qquad\qquad Q_i - Q_t = \mathbf{F} - \mathbf{L_2}'$.

Since $t = \infty$, the refraction at the first surface gives

$$\frac{n_a}{t'} = F_1$$

where F_1 is the power of the first surface.

Hence A_1, the contribution of the first surface to the sum in equation (915), is

$$A_1 = \frac{(R_1 + F - L_2')^2}{(F - L_2')^2} \cdot \frac{F_1}{n_a{}^2}$$

2nd Surface. The refraction at this surface is represented by

$$L_2' - n_a L_2 = (1 - n_a) R_2 = F_2$$

whence $\quad Q_i = n'\left(\dfrac{1}{\gamma} - \dfrac{1}{l'}\right)$ in the general expression,

$$= R_2 - L_2' = R_1 - R - L_2'$$

and $\quad Q_t = n'\left(\dfrac{1}{\gamma} - \dfrac{1}{t'}\right)$ in the general expression,

$$= R_2 - \frac{1}{f'}$$

since the final image will be situated in the focal plane, as the object point is at infinity. Thus,

$$Q_t = R_2 - F = R_1 - R - F$$

To evaluate the bracket: $\left(\dfrac{1}{n't'} - \dfrac{1}{nt}\right)$, for the second surface, note that $t' = f'$ sufficiently nearly for our calculation. The standard equation gives

$$\frac{1}{t'} - \frac{n_a}{t} = F_2$$

or

$$F - \frac{n_a}{t} = F_2$$

whence

$$\frac{n_a}{t} = F_1$$

Hence the bracket is evaluated as

$$F - \frac{F_1}{n_a{}^2}$$

and the contribution of the second surface, A_2, is given by

$$A_2 = \frac{(R_1 - R - L_2')^2 \, (n_a{}^2 F - F_1)}{(F - L_2')^2 \, n_a{}^2}$$

The total sum on the right of equation (915), evaluated for this case, therefore becomes (omitting the suffix to L'),

$$A = \frac{(R_1 + F - L')^2 F_1 + (R_1 - R - L')^2 (n_a{}^2 F - F_1)}{(F - L')^2 n_a{}^2}$$

The condition for the elimination of astigmatism of oblique pencils is obtained by equating the above expression to zero.

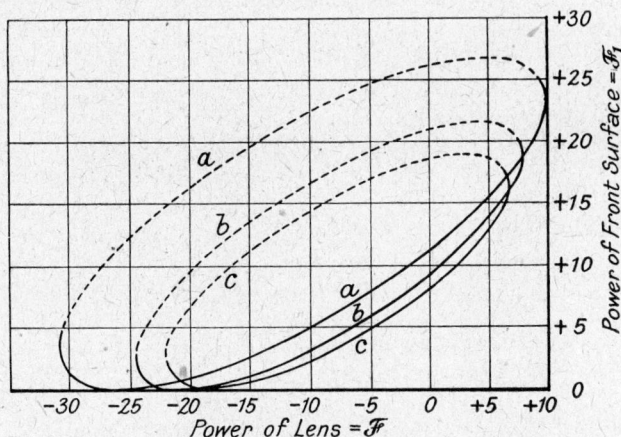

FIG. 201. FORMS OF LENS USED FOR REMOVAL OF OBLIQUE ASTIGMATISM WHEN USED WITH A ROLLING EYE
Distance of centre of rotation: (a) 20 mm.; (b) 25 mm.; (c) 28 mm.

It may be simplified by writing

$$R_1 = \frac{F_1}{(n_a - 1)}$$

$$R = \frac{F}{(n_a - 1)}$$

and the final condition reduces, after some algebraical transformations, to

$$nF^2 - (n + 2)FF_1 + (n + 2)F_1{}^2 - 2(n^2 - 1)L'F_1 \\ + n(n - 1)^2 L'^2 + 2n(n - 1)L'F = 0$$

in which n is written for n_a, the refractive index of the lens.

If L' and n are taken as constant, this is an equation of the second degree in F and F_1. It plots as an ellipse.

Fig. 201 shows the ellipses a, b, and c resulting from the assumption of different values for the distance of the effective pupil, viz. 20, 25, and 28 mm. Note that the value of $L' = 1/l'$ as it appears in the equation must be expressed in the same units as the other "powers," viz. in diopters. The refractive index assumed is 1·52.

It will be seen that the powers F of the lenses are plotted horizontally, the powers of the front surfaces vertically. With a value of $l' = 25$ mm. it is possible to select forms giving freedom from astigmatism for all powers *between* about $- 24·75D$ and $+ 7·5D$. With $l' = 20$ mm., the range is greater.

In order to illustrate the significance of the figure, it will be noticed that when $l' = 28$ mm. a lens of $- 10D$ can be corrected by using a front surface of either $+ 2·5D$ or $+ 14·5D$ approximately (requiring radii of about 21 and 3·6 cm.). The powers of the back surfaces would therefore be (approximately) $- 12·5D$ and $- 24·5$ D (radii about 4·2 and 2·1 cm.). Both are thus meniscus lenses; the one with shallower curves being obviously the more practical type, and cheaper to make. The profiles of the two lenses are illustrated in Fig. 202.

It will be seen that the range of negative or diverging lenses possible to correct thus is adequate to cover all ordinary requirements. When $l' = 28$ mm., the positive lenses of higher powers than about 7·5D cannot be corrected by "bending." Recourse must thus be had to the use of non-spherical surfaces, and lenses of this kind for use by patients who have had the lens of the eye removed for "cataract" were suggested by Gullstrand and actually computed in 1908 by M. von Rohr. Such lenses, under the name "Katral lenses" were produced by the firm of Zeiss, an optical performance of some difficulty. (See p. 284, Chapter VIII.) For a discussion of method of designing lenses with aspheric surfaces, reference may be made to a paper by Burch,[6] and a symposium[7] held by the Physical Society. Further discussions on aspheric surfaces will be found in Vol. II, Chapter VIII.

(a)   (b)

FIG. 202

(a) Ostwalt type.
(b) Wollaston type.

It is of interest to note that the use of meniscus lenses was suggested on more or less empirical principles by Wollaston, and also on theoretical grounds by Ostwalt. The two forms of meniscus lens possible in correcting oblique astigmatism have been named after Ostwalt and Wollaston, as shown in Fig. 202.

The thin lens theory outlined above is a useful guide, but in the actual designing of "best-form" lenses, trigonometrical trials are advisable. It is not difficult to calculate the tangential and sagittal foci, for a ray passing through the centre of a given stop, by the aid of formulae (115) and (116).

Prisms. Ophthalmic prisms are employed in the correction of strabismus or "squint." Their "power" is reckoned in terms of the apparent lateral displacement (in centimetres) produced in the image of an object at a distance of 1 metre. Thus, in Fig. 203, the

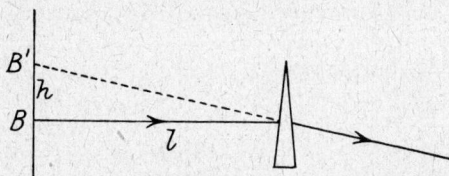

FIG. 203

displacement of the image from B to B', a distance of h cm., indicates a power of h/l "prism diopters," where l is the distance of the object in metres. The notation usually employed is exemplified by $6\triangle$, signifying a prism of six "prism diopters."

Let a prism of power $\triangle$ be placed in front of an eye at a distance

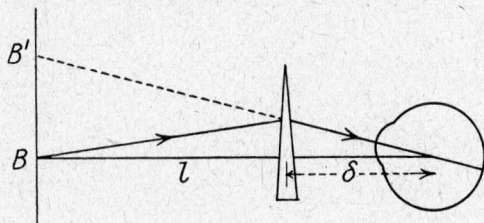

FIG. 204

δ from the point of rotation. The eye rotates so as to receive the image, on the fovea, Fig. 204.

The displacement h is given by

$$h = \triangle l$$

where l is the distance in metres. The deviation of the eye is the same as would be produced by a prism of power

$$\frac{h}{l+\delta} = \frac{\triangle l}{l+\delta}$$

placed in the position of the centre of the eye. The effective power of a prism is therefore somewhat less for nearer than for distant objects.

Decentration of Lenses. Prismatic effects are produced by mounting a lens in front of an eye so that the optical centre of

the lens is displaced from the normal intersection point of the
visual axis.

In Fig. 205, consider the action of a lens, focal length f', decentred
through a distance y. The axis of the lens is GAF'. A ray parallel
to the axis incident at a height y is deviated towards the principal
focus F', i.e. through an angle equivalent to the deviation produced

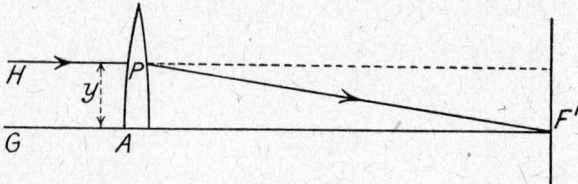

FIG. 205

by a prism of power y/f' prism diopters, if y is measured in centimetres and f' in metres.

Prismatic power $= y\mathbf{F} =$ (decentration in centimetres) times
(power of lens).

The effect is modified when the lens is held before a rotating eye.
In Fig. 206, let C be the centre of rotation of the eye, and let HC

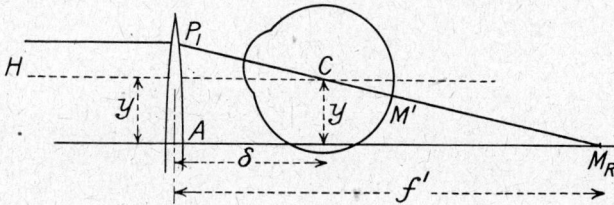

FIG. 206

be the original direction of the visual axis, along which the distant
object is seen with the aid of a centred lens of requisite power.

Let the lens be decentred by a distance of y (cm.), keeping the
axis parallel to the original direction. The eye has then to be
rotated so that its far point M_R coincides with the new position
of the principal focus, the object being seen apparently in the
direction CP_1.

The actual deviation of the eye is therefore expressed as

$$\frac{AP_1}{f'} = \frac{y}{f' - \delta} = \frac{y\mathbf{F}}{1 - \delta\mathbf{F}}$$

Decentration for Required Prismatic Effect. In optical prescrip-
tions it is usual, when a correction for strabismus is to be given,

to specify the prismatic power required for an eye in the horizontal and vertical directions, the direction of the base being also indicated. Thus a prescription might read—

"Right eye 4·5D Sph with 1△ base out and 2△ base up."

When a spherical surfaced lens is in use, the prismatic effects are easily obtained by the necessary decentrations calculated from the formula above. Thus

$$\text{Decentration} = \frac{\text{Prism power}}{\text{Power of lens}}$$

In the case given, the decentration necessary will be 1/4·5 = 0·22 cm. outwards, plus 2/4·5 = 0·44 cm. upwards.

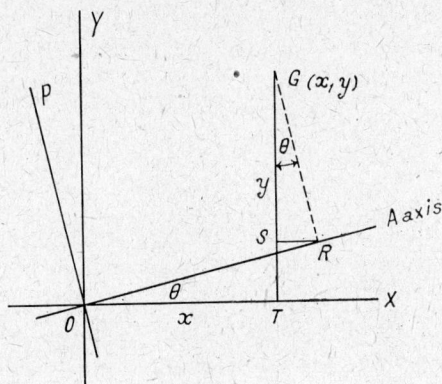

FIG. 207

When cylindrical or toric surfaces are prescribed for an eye, it is possible to obtain a prismatic effect by decentration of the lens along one of the principal sections. If the axial direction of the effective cylinder should be oblique, it is not possible to obtain a simple horizontal or vertical effect alone by decentring the lens in the corresponding directions.

It is possible, however, to calculate the horizontal and vertical components of the necessary decentration to give a required prismatic effect.

Let F_s = power of spherical component of the lens.

F_c = power of cylindrical component of the lens.

θ = axis direction of the cylinder.

Let the centre of the lens be situated at the centre of co-ordinates, then the components of the prismatic deviation at any point x, y, such as G, Fig. 207, may be determined.

The prismatic effect of the spherical component in the direction GO is $F_s \times$ GO, and this may be resolved into

Vertical component $= F_s y$ (base down)

and   Horizontal component $= F_s x$ (base left)

The prismatic effect due to the cylinder is understood if we draw the principal directions OA (the axis) and OP. Draw also GR perpendicular to OA, and RS, the perpendicular to GT, as shown in the diagram.

The prismatic effect at G due to the cylinder is $F_c \times$ GR in the direction GR, and this may be resolved into

Vertical component $= F_c \times$ GS (base down).

Horizontal component $= F_c \times$ SR (base to right).

It is not difficult to see that

$$GR = (y - x \tan \theta) \cos \theta = (y \cos \theta - x \sin \theta)$$
and $$GS = (y \cos \theta - x \sin \theta) \cos \theta$$
and $$SR = (y \cos \theta - x \sin \theta) \sin \theta$$

Adding the total Vertical and Horizontal components, denoting the vertical (base down) by V, and the horizontal base left by H, we thus obtain

$$V = F_s y + F_c \cos \theta \, (y \cos \theta - x \sin \theta), \text{ base down.}$$
$$H = F_s x - F_c \sin \theta \, (y \cos \theta - x \sin \theta), \text{ base left.}$$

These equations give, by straightforward algebra,

$$x = \frac{HF_s \times HF_c \cos^2 \theta + VF_c \sin \theta \cos \theta}{F_s (F_s + F_c)}$$

$$y = \frac{VF_s + VF_c \sin^2 \theta + HF_c \sin \theta \cos \theta}{F_s (F_s + F_c)}$$

If, therefore, the required vertical and horizontal components V and H for the prismatic effect are given in prism diopters, the lens has to be decentred, so that the line of vision cuts it in the point G with co-ordinates x and y given by the above equations.

Spectacles of Special Types. Owing to limitations of space it has not been possible to include discussions of spectacles of special types, such as the bi-focal lenses, telescope spectacles, and the like.

Reference may be made to Emsley and Swaine's *Ophthalmic Lenses*[8] for a technical account of both ordinary and special spectacle lenses.

References

1. Souter: *The Refractive and Motor Mechanism of the Eye* (Keystone Publishing Co., Philadelphia, 1910).
2. Laurance: *Visual Optics* (The School of Optics, Ltd.).
3. Emsley: *Visual Optics* (Hatton Press, Ltd.).
4. Henker: *Introduction to the Theory of Spectacles*, p. 253.
5. G. B. Airy: *Camb. Phil. Trans.*, 2, 267 (1827).
6. Burch: *Proc. Phys. Soc.*, 55, 433 (1943).
7. T. Y. Baker and Others: *Proc. Phys. Soc.*, 55, 481 (1943).
8. Emsley and Swaine: *Ophthalmic Lenses* (Hatton Press, Ltd.).

APPENDIX I

Note on Sign Conventions. In the computing classes at the Imperial College, the formulae developed in Chapter I are used for ray-tracing with either direction of the light, i.e. from left to right or right to left. The "dash" added to a length then means a quantity measured to the right of a point or surface, the absence of a dash indicates a quantity measured to the left. Thus, the paraxial equation for refraction at a curved surface

$$\frac{n'}{l'} - \frac{n}{l} = \frac{n' - n}{r} = F$$

gives an identity which must remain unaffected by the reversal of the direction of a ray because the path of a ray is unaltered by such reversal.

The standard computing equations retain the same forms, whether we proceed from "plain" to "dash" quantities, or vice versa. Thus, the equations

$$i' = \frac{l' - .r}{r} u'$$

$$i = \frac{i' \cdot n'}{n}$$

$$u = u' + i' - i$$

$$l - r = \frac{r \cdot i}{u}$$

$$l = (l - r) + r$$

are in the same form as those of p. 16. Very similar use can be made of the various other formulae, and this is the general method advised in Prof. Conrady's *Applied Optics and Optical Design*.

For the purposes of the general Gaussian theory, however, it may be required to deal with cases of reflection, in which the direction of light is actually physically reversed in proceeding from object to image. In order to be able to deal with such cases, we shall here assume that a "dash" signifies a quantity in the image space, while its absence denotes a quantity in the object space. Consider, then, the equation

$$\frac{n'}{l'} - \frac{n}{l} = \frac{n' - n}{r} = F$$

Let the quantities on the left of the curved surface be n_1, l_1, while on the right they are n_2, l_2. Then "left to right" the general equation becomes

$$\frac{n_2}{l_2} - \frac{n_1}{l_1} = \frac{n_2 - n_1}{r} = F$$

but "right to left" it becomes

$$\frac{n_1}{l_1} - \frac{n_2}{l_2} = \frac{n_1 - n_2}{r} = -F$$

The necessity of altering the sign of the power of a surface or system would not be acceptable to ophthalmic opticians, who always assign the same positive sign to the "converging" type of spectacle lens. In order to remove this difficulty, note that the signs of angles made by rays with the axis are independent of the direction of the light. Thus, if a ray intersects the axis at a distance l from a surface, and intersects the latter in the height y, the tangent of the angle made between the ray and the axis will be given, to the usual approximation, as

$$\tan \alpha = y/l$$

Also, if a ray crosses the axis in a point X, and meets a plane perpendicular to the axis at a height h, the axial distance from X to this plane being k, the angle ω between the ray and the axis will be given by

$$\tan \omega = -h/k$$

The condition of reflection of a ray at the axial point of a reflecting surface would, therefore, evidently be expressed by $u' = -u$. (See Fig. 208.)

The ordinary law of refraction at an axial point of a surface,

$$n' \sin u' = n \sin u$$

takes this form if we put $n' = -n$, whence $u' = -u$. This device now enables us to deal with the general formula

$$\frac{n'}{l'} - \frac{n}{l} = \frac{n' - n}{r} = F$$

and apply it to the case of reflection at a spherical surface. It becomes, on simplification,

$$\frac{1}{l'} + \frac{1}{l} = \frac{2}{r}$$

Note, however, that the power F of the surface in the general formula is $-2n/r$.

We see, then, that the case of light passing from right to left is dealt with by assigning negative signs to the refractive indices. The general equation applied to the case right to left is now

$$\frac{(-n_1)}{l_1} - \frac{(-n_2)}{l_2} = \frac{(-n_1)-(-n_2)}{r} = \text{Power}$$

Thus, if the negative refractive indices are used to indicate reversal of the light, the power of a surface will be unchanged; this conclusion is also valid for a more complex system. This is practically

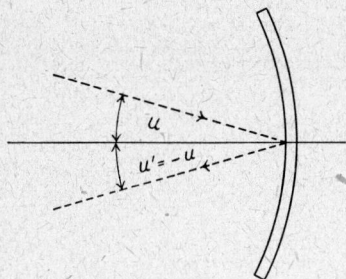

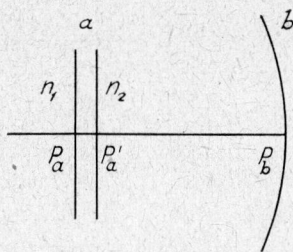

FIG. 208   FIG. 209

equivalent to applying the same formula for both cases, as above, p. 331.

In applying this method it must be carefully remembered that the formula for a system in air—

$$\frac{1}{l'} - \frac{1}{l} = F$$

is only a simplified form of the general formula

$$\frac{n'}{l'} - \frac{n}{l} = \frac{n'}{f'} = -\frac{n}{f} = F$$

(See p. 53.) If l_1 and l_2 are the conjugate quantities measured on the left and right of a system in a medium of refractive index n, the left to right equation is

$$\frac{n}{l_2} - \frac{n}{l_1} = F$$

while the right to left version is (interpreting the dash in the general formula to refer to the image space)

$$\frac{(-n)}{l_1} - \frac{(-n)}{l_2} = F;$$

again this is equivalent to applying the "left to right" formula to the "right to left" case.

We now see, however, that the general equations can be applied to any combination of refracting and reflecting surfaces. The separation $P_a'P_b$ of systems will be measured, as before, *from* P_a' to P_b, the order of meeting the systems by the light being *ab*.

Take the case of Fig. 209, in which a system *a* is mounted in front of a spherical mirror *b*. The light traverses *a*, is reflected by

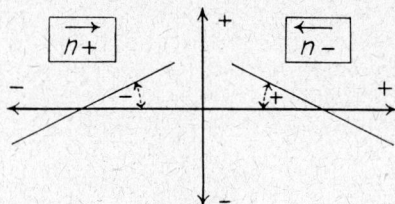

FIG. 210

b, and re-traverses *a*. The "separations" appearing in the Gaussian formulae are the *reduced* separations. Hence,

$$d_1 = \frac{P_a'P_b}{n_2} \qquad d_2 = \frac{P_bP_a'}{-n_2}$$

Since the light is reversed after reflection, the negative refractive index is used. Hence, $d'' = d'$ in this case, and $F_3 = F_1$, while

$$F_2 = -2n_2/r$$

The form of the resulting expression appears on p. 68.

Fig. 210 is a diagram intended to express the conventions explained above.

It may be noted that the reversal of the sign of the refractive index to denote reversal of the light gives consistent results with the Smith-Helmholtz formula, and the optical sine relation, also with equations for optical path, i.e. (refractive index) × (distance). In optical equations, both will change sign on reversal of the direction of the light.

APPENDIX II

REFRACTIVE INDEX DATA

Typical Optical Glasses and other Materials

Type	Refractive Index		Mean Dispersion	Partial and Relative Dispersions					
	N_d	V	$N_F - N_C$	$b - C$	$C - d$	$d - e$	$e - F$	$F - g$	$g - h$
Fluor crown	1·49429	67·9	0·00728	0·00130 / 0·179	0·00226 / 0·310	0·00173 / 0·238	0·00330 / 0·453	0·00388 / 0·533	0·00321 / 0·441
Boro-silicate crown	1·50970	64·4	0·00791	0·00142 / 0·180	0·00243 / 0·307	0·00190 / 0·240	0·00358 / 0·453	0·00420 / 0·531	0·00347 / 0·439
Hard crown	1·51899	60·4	0·00859	0·00150 / 0·175	0·00262 / 0·305	0·00205 / 0·239	0·00392 / 0·456	0·00467 / 0·544	0·00386 / 0·449
Light barium crown	1·54065	59·5	0·00908	0·00159 / 0·175	0·00277 / 0·305	0·00217 / 0·239	0·00414 / 0·456	0·00493 / 0·543	0·00407 / 0·448
Medium barium crown	1·56930	55·8	0·01021	0·00175 / 0·171	0·00310 / 0·304	0·00243 / 0·238	0·00468 / 0·458	0·00557 / 0·546	0·00465 / 0·455
Dense barium crown	1·61230	58·5	0·01046	0·00182 / 0·174	0·00319 / 0·305	0·00249 / 0·238	0·00478 / 0·457	0·00570 / 0·545	0·00472 / 0·451
Soft crown	1·51516	57·0	0·00904	0·00155 / 0·171	0·00274 / 0·303	0·00216 / 0·239	0·00414 / 0·458	0·00496 / 0·549	0·00416 / 0·460
Telescope flint	1·53042	52·0	0·01021	0·00175 / 0·171	0·00310 / 0·304	0·00242 / 0·237	0·00469 / 0·459	0·00561 / 0·549	0·00472 / 0·462
Barium light flint	1·56713	55·0	0·01032	0·00177 / 0·172	0·00312 / 0·302	0·00246 / 0·238	0·00474 / 0·459	0·00569 / 0·551	0·00475 / 0·460
E.K.2	1·74338	45·8	0·01624	0·00271 / 0·167	0·00487 / 0·300	0·00385 / 0·237	0·00752 / 0·463	0·00912 / 0·562	0·00767 / 0·472
Borate flint	1·61326	44·9	0·01365	0·00233 / 0·171	0·00411 / 0·301	0·00324 / 0·237	0·00630 / 0·461	0·00763 / 0·559	0·00647 / 0·474

Material									
Special barium flint	1·74416	44·7	0·01665	0·00279 / 0·168	0·00498 / 0·299	0·00396 / 0·238	0·00772 / 0·464	0·00936 / 0·562	0·00794 / 0·477
Extra light flint	1·54769	45·6	0·01201	0·00200 / 0·167	0·00360 / 0·300	0·00285 / 0·237	0·00556 / 0·463	0·00681 / 0·563	0·00579 / 0·482
Barium flint	1·60483	43·8	0·01380	0·00228 / 0·165	0·00410 / 0·297	0·00327 / 0·237	0·00643 / 0·466	0·00787 / 0·570	0·00673 / 0·488
Light flint	1·57838	40·7	0·01422	0·00235 / 0·165	0·00422 / 0·297	0·00337 / 0·237	0·00663 / 0·466	0·00816 / 0·574	0·00702 / 0·494
Dense flint	1·62258	36·0	0·01727	0·00281 / 0·163	0·00509 / 0·295	0·00409 / 0·237	0·00809 / 0·468	0·01005 / 0·582	0·00870 / 0·504
Extra dense flint	1·65108	33·6	0·01940	0·00310 / 0·160	0·00568 / 0·293	0·00460 / 0·237	0·00912 / 0·470	0·01141 / 0·588	0·00996 / 0·514
Double extra dense flint	1·80120	25·5	0·03142	0·00488 / 0·155	0·00904 / 0·288	0·00741 / 0·236	0·01497 / 0·476	0·01910 / 0·608	
Fused quartz	1·45887	67·9	0·00676		0·00210 / 0·311	0·00152 / 0·225	0·00313 / 0·463	0·00357 / 0·528	0·00293 / 0·433
Lithium fluoride	1·39225	99·1	0·00396	0·00074 / 0·187	0·00124 / 0·313	0·00095 / 0·240	0·00177 / 0·447	0·00202 / 0·510	0·00162 / 0·409
Potassium bromide	1·55998	33·4	0·01678	0·00258 / 0·154	0·00497 / 0·296	0·00395 / 0·235	0·00786 / 0·468	0·00986 / 0·587	0·00827 / 0·493
Sylvine(KCl)	1·49050	44·0	0·01114	0·00186 / 0·167	0·00332 / 0·298	0·00264 / 0·237	0·00518 / 0·465	0·00630 / 0·566	0·00539 / 0·484
Magnesium oxide	1·73764	53·5	0·01380	0·00229 / 0·166	0·00423 / 0·307	0·00326 / 0·236	0·00631 / 0·457	0·00764 / 0·554	0·00632 / 0·458
Perspex	1·49613	54·4	0·00912	0·00149 / 0·163	0·00269 / 0·295	0·00218 / 0·239	0·00425 / 0·466	0·00510 / 0·59	0·00432 / 0·474
Polystyrene	1·5929	30·7	0·0193		0·0056 / 0·290				
Fluorite	1·43390	95·4	0·00455	0·00081 / 0·178	0·00138 / 0·303	0·00109 / 0·240	0·00208 / 0·457	0·00244 / 0·536	0·00202 / 0·444

INDEX

339